South Asia

Selective studies of the essential geography of
India, Pakistan, Bangladesh, Sri Lanka and Nepal

KU-372-799

By the same author

Place, People and Work in Japan (with Phyllis Reiche)
Bangladesh
India: Resources and Development
Pakistan
Sri Lanka: Land, People and Economy (with M. Le M. Scrivenor)

South Asia

Selective Studies of the Essential Geography of
India, Pakistan, Bangladesh, Sri Lanka and Nepal

Second Edition

B.L.C. Johnson
Emeritus Professor of Geography
Australian National University

CHESTER COLLEGE

ACC. No.
830062

DEPT.

CLASS No.
915.4 JOH

LIBRARY

Heinemann Educational Books
London · Exeter (New Hampshire)

To my Wife

Heinemann Educational Books Ltd
22 Bedford Square, London WC1B 3HH

Heinemann Educational Books Inc.
4 Front Street, Exeter, New Hampshire 03833

© B. L. C. Johnson 1969, 1981
First published 1969
Second Edition 1981

British Library Cataloguing in Publication Data

Johnson, Basil Leonard Clyde
　　South Asia. – 2nd ed.
　　1. South Asia – Description and travel
　　I. Title
　　915.4　　DS337
ISBN 0–435–35488–4

Library of Congress Cataloging in Publication Data

Johnson, B. L. C. (Basil Leonard Clyde), 1919–
　　SOUTH ASIA.

　　Includes Index
　　1. SOUTH ASIA – DESCRIPTION AND
TRAVEL.　I. TITLE.
DS337.J63 1981　　954　　81–2955
ISBN 0–435–35488–4　　　　　　AACR2

Johnson, B. L. C. (Basil Leonard Clyde), 1919
　　SOUTH ASIA–

　　Includes Index
　　I. SOUTH ASIA – DESCRIPTION AND
TRAVEL　I. TITLE
DS337 J63 1981　　954　　81–2955
ISBN 0–435–35488–4

Printed by Interprint Limited, Malta

Preface

So much change has taken place in South Asia since the first edition of this book appeared in 1969 as to make it substantially necessary to write a revised edition. Quite apart from the major political reorganisation that resulted from Bangladesh emerging as an independent nation, there have been great economic and demographic changes in every country of the region.

Since writing the first edition I have been able to visit all the countries of South Asia with the exception of Bhutan, some of them several times and for prolonged periods, to write individual studies on Bangladesh, India, Pakistan and Sri Lanka.* The essence of these journeys and research is presented selectively in this present work, which while it follows the basic plan of its predecessor is largely new material.

The importance to the western world of a sound understanding of the countries of South Asia, their problems, potential and levels of development, needs no stressing. This book tries to provide such understanding with objectivity and at the same time sympathy for the peoples concerned, for whom I have over the years developed great affection.

For reasons of size the work is necessarily selective of what the writer considers the essential themes. Fuller treatment of these and other themes may be sought in the individual country studies. Although the countries of South Asia share many common characteristics in their past and in their developmental processes, differences in emphasis and their enormous range of scale makes inappropriate an overall approach to topics such as the 'green revolution', industrialisation or planning. Apart from the introductory chapters, mainly on the physical environment, and concluding chapter on the South Asian City, the countries are dealt with separately.

---

* *Bangladesh* (1975); *India: Resources and Development* (1979); *Pakistan* (1979); *Sri Lanka: Land, People and Economy* (1981), under co-authorship with Margaret Scrivenor; all published by Heinemann Educational Books, London.

Acknowledgements

In writing about South Asia, I am very conscious of the debt I owe to many people for inspiration, help, and friendship over close on forty years. Before World War II the late Sir Dudley Stamp stimulated my interest in the region where I was to soldier through the war years in the Indian Army. To those many friends, military and civilian, Hindu, Moslem, Sikh, Buddhist, and Christian, who in wartime sowed in me the seeds of a lasting affection for the region's people, I am deeply grateful. With the war's end Professor O. H. K. Spate helped discipline academically the demobilized soldier seeking to rehabilitate himself as an undergraduate, and I was among the fortunate number who heard as lectures chapters of his then embryonic masterpiece *India and Pakistan* (Methuen, London 1954; now in its third edition, 1967).

My thanks go to many colleagues among that most hospitable and friendly world-wide fraternity of geographers, in universities in many cities of the region; to countless administrators of every rank from Ministers to tea boys; to casual acquaintances of railway carriage, bus and plane; and to the very many courteous cultivators who shared with me their *chapatti* and *dhal*, the fruits of their trees, or cut me down green coconut for a refreshing drink in the heat of the day.

A particular word of thanks is due to two old friends and fellow South Asianists, Mr. B. H. Farmer, Director of the Centre of South Asian Studies in the University of Cambridge and Professor A. T. A. Learmonth of the Open University, who have been most generous in their help and in their constructive criticism of my efforts over the years.

B.L.C.J.

Australian National University,
Canberra

Contents

List of Figures

List of Tables

1 Hindu temples in Patan near Kathmandu, with women carrying loads of firewood.

2 The Taj Mahal, Agra, Uttar Pradesh, India, built in the 17th century by the Moghul Emperor Shah Jahan as a mausoleum for his wife Mumtaz Mahal, is an incomparable gem of Muslim architecture.

3 This statuary of the Graeco-Buddhist Gandhara culture (about 200 BC) in Swat, in northwest Pakistan is a reminder of the former almost ubiquitous extent of Buddhism in South Asia.
(courtesy Govt. of Pakistan).

Chapter 1

South Asia: Introduction

One-fifth of mankind occupies this region which forms the westernmost part, and so that closest to Europe, of the populous and humid marginal lands of Asia. South Asia has closer links to the Western world in its culture and its history than the other major divisions of the marginal lands – China and Southeast Asia. Its early civilisation, revealed in the cities of the Indus plains, Mohenjodaro and Harappa dating from 2500 BC, had contacts with the earlier Sumerian civilisation of Mesopotamia. The languages spoken by the majority of the region's inhabitants share a common ancestry with those of Europe. The people themselves could also claim that their genetic make-up owes a great deal to forbears common to peoples in the Mediterranean area.

In religion, South Asia developed its own distinctive and widely influential theocracies, and the size of the debt of Graeco–Judaeic–Christianity to Buddhist ideas is becoming better appreciated. From Hinduism, still the faith and way of life of about 600 million of the region's 900 or so million people, there sprang Buddhism as a reformed religion which, although claiming only some 22.5 million adherents today and now the majority faith only in Sri Lanka and the tiny Himalayan kingdom of Bhutan, spread vigorously through southeast and eastern Asia. The two other religions claiming sizeable numbers of followers are of foreign origin. Christianity, the faith of about 20 million, came to South India in the early centuries of its existence, and there persisted to be reinforced as the faith of the European mercantile nations from the fifteenth century. Islam, arriving later from the Middle East through both Arab trade and overland invasion, flourished more strongly to become the faith of almost 235 million, and the *raison d'etre* for the realisation of Pakistan as a separate nation, subsequently to become Pakistan and Bangladesh.

The history of South Asia over nearly four centuries has brought the region close to the West, and although the bonds of empire and political subservience have been shed in recent decades, the political and economic heritage in some measure remains.

India, and undivided Pakistan – comprising before their partition and independence the Empire of India – had experienced over 200 years of British rule, first under the East India Company and later the British government. As Ceylon, Sri Lanka had experienced Portuguese and Dutch suzerainty before becoming a British Colony. In the governments of these countries, which succeeded the British on attaining independence, the ideal of parliamentary democracy was a basic assumption.

Whether or not democracy as it is understood in the West can survive its transplantation to South

Fig. 1.1

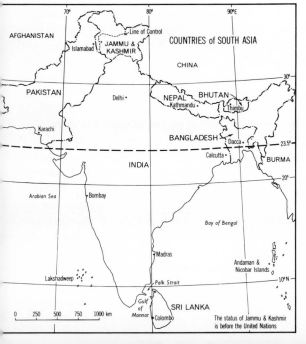

Fig. 1.2

Asia is an open question, but one of vital interest to the 'free nations' of the world. Some of South Asia's most sympathetic friends in the West may sometimes wonder whether its problems are of a kind and scale that require for their solution a measure of authoritarian leadership that universal suffrage seems unlikely to produce. India is attempting what some have called the greatest experiment in democracy, giving all adults the vote and making it possible for illiterate peasants to take a meaningful part in elections. Sri Lanka also has followed the democratic pattern of Britain, her one-time tutor. So too did undivided Pakistan, until irresponsibility in the democratic process so seriously threatened the country's unity and progress that a more authoritarian rule was imposed and a fresh approach was made towards creating responsible democratic government from the village level upwards. Both Pakistan and more recently Bangladesh have lapsed from the democratic ideal (temporarily perhaps) and authoritarian rule has followed military coups in both countries, without losing all vestiges of electoral tradition however.

Only Nepal remained independent of British rule, although closely linked by treaty ties. As a land-locked mountain state with its strongest cultural affinities with India, Nepal's freedom of manoeuvre in external matters is rather limited, though the arrival of the Chinese – as a political presence in what used to be the kingdom of Tibet – on the Himalayan frontier of Nepal, has introduced a new factor into the region's political scene, one which Nepal may find helpful in balancing the stronger pressures from the Indian side.

The countries of South Asia thus have much in common both in their past and in their present. Their pasts are closely interwoven although their futures seem likely, if anything, to diverge. Even though they are now separate sovereign states and despite the bitterness that taints their relationships – the issue of Kashmir between India and Pakistan that has three times flared into armed conflict, and the less violent but intractable issue of the large Tamil minority in Sri Lanka – the human bonds between them remain strong. The huge Muslim minority still living in India stands hostage to Pakistan's good behaviour towards India.

The State of Jammu and Kashmir remains a bone of contention between India and Pakistan. Without prejudicing the arguments on either side, this book accepts the *de facto* situation as the rational approach to regional study. Azad or 'Free' Kashmir, occupied by Pakistan is treated as a part of that country, while the larger area administered by India as an integral State of the Indian Union is similarly regarded as part of India.

All the countries of South Asia are badly in need of economic development if they are to raise living standards. Subsistence agriculture still supports the mass of their population. Although increasing decade by decade, the proportion of the people engaged in industry or living in towns is still very small in comparison with most of the developed world. Capital in the form of finance, materials, equipment and technological skill is desperately needed so that jobs can be created for the rapidly expanding population. High rates of population increase and low rates of capital accumulation are common problems. For the majority, standards of living are dismally low, and the spectre of local famine still stalks the land from time to time. In their levels of development and in the character and scale of their economic problems, the countries show considerable range, as the chapters which follow will demonstrate.

4 Sacred Hindu tank and temple at Sravanabelgola, Karnataka, S. India, with a granitic inselberg beyond. The view is taken from another inselberg upon which stands a colossal statue dating from 985 AD, the object of pilgrimage by Jains. (Courtesy Margaret Scrivenor).

To maintain unity within diversity is a common problem for all these countries in varying degree. India's problems stem from sheer size and linguistic diversity, so that most people have loyalties divided between the central government, their linguistic state, and possibly their caste or tribal affiliation. The original Pakistan proved incapable of holding together, and even in the separated parts there remain internal tensions linked to language and political tradition. In Sri Lanka the problems of uniting the nation are acute if on a smaller scale; namely, how to satisfy the nationalistic aspirations of the Sinhala-speaking Buddhist majority while preserving the rights of the Tamil-speaking Hindu minority, many of whom can claim that their ancestors have lived in the country continuously for over a millennium. These several issues are examined in their national context in the appropriate chapters following.

Chapter 2

The Natural Environment: Foundations and Form of the Land

In its rocks and their physiographic expression in the landscape, South Asia reveals great contrasts. South India contains some of the oldest rock formations known, and some of its landscapes have been exposed to sub-aerial erosion through scores – perhaps hundreds – of millions of years. On the other hand, parts of the Himalaya form one of the youngest mountain chains in the world, and a zone of instability is associated with the whole Himalayan system and its contact with the stable 'shield' of central and Peninsular India. The alluvial sediments that have filled the depression flanking the rising Himalaya to form the Indo-Gangetic Plains have themselves been involved in structural movements persisting into historic time.

Fig. 2.1

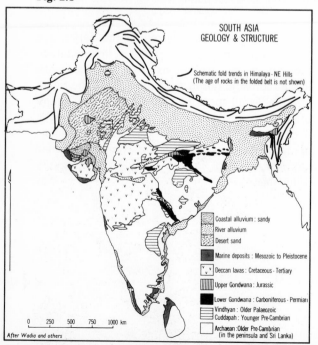

SOUTH ASIA
GEOLOGY & STRUCTURE

Schematic fold trends in Himalaya - NE Hills
(The age of rocks in the folded belt is not shown)

Coastal alluvium : sandy
River alluvium
Desert sand

Marine deposits : Mesozoic to Pleistocene
Deccan lavas : Cretaceous - Tertiary
Upper Gondwana : Jurassic
Lower Gondwana : Carboniferous - Permian
Vindhyan : Older Palaeozoic
Cuddapah : Younger Pre-Cambrian
Archaean :Older Pre-Cambrian
(in the peninsula and Sri Lanka)

0   250   500   750   1000 km

After Wadia and others

Structural and Physiographic Evolution

The principal events in the geological history of South Asia are reviewed here only in so far as they seem important to an understanding of the present geography of the region. Attention is focused on those aspects of geological structure and landscape morphology that affect man's ability to make a living: on gentle slopes and productive soils to cultivate, on economically useful minerals to work, on water resources to harness for irrigation or power.

Figure 2.1 shows the main features of the geology of South Asia. The structural relationships of the major formations in the subcontinent are shown diagrammatically in the sections in Figure 2.2.

The stable 'shield' of Peninsular India and Sri Lanka is considered to have formed part of an ancient land-mass referred to as Gondwanaland, which is thought to have broken up – through the process of 'continental drift' – to form parts of what are now South Africa, Brazil and Western Australia. In common with these areas, the Peninsular Shield is made up largely of very ancient formations. Granites and gneisses are widespread and are probably the oldest rocks. The *Dharwar–Aravalli* series include a great variety of metamorphosed sedimentary and igneous material, possibly as old as the granites and gneisses, and conveniently bracketed with them as of Archaean age, i.e. early Pre-Cambrian. These Archaean formations cover much of the Peninsula and occur also in the Meghalaya Plateau, which has been detached from the main mass by the foundering and alluviation of the Ganga–Brahmaputra Delta region. The Archaean rocks in places contain

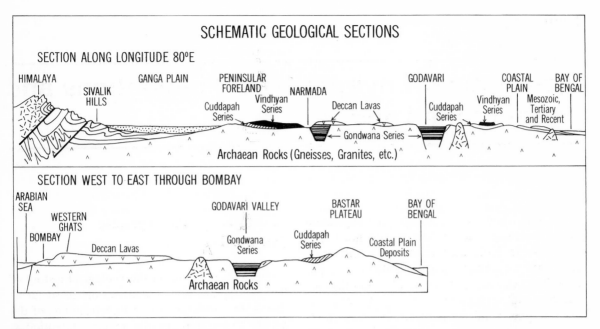

SCHEMATIC GEOLOGICAL SECTIONS

SECTION ALONG LONGITUDE 80°E

HIMALAYA   SIVALIK HILLS   GANGA PLAIN   PENINSULAR FORELAND   NARMADA   GODAVARI   COASTAL PLAIN   BAY OF BENGAL

Cuddapah Series   Vindhyan Series   Deccan Lavas   Cuddapah Series   Vindhyan Series   Mesozoic, Tertiary and Recent

←— Gondwana Series —→

^ Archaean Rocks (Gneisses, Granites, etc.) ^

SECTION WEST TO EAST THROUGH BOMBAY

ARABIAN SEA   WESTERN GHATS   GODAVARI VALLEY   BASTAR PLATEAU   BAY OF BENGAL

BOMBAY   Deccan Lavas   Gondwana Series   Cuddapah Series   Coastal Plain Deposits

Archaean Rocks

Fig. 2.2

valuable minerals: India's major iron ores of Bihar, Orissa and Karnataka, the manganese of Madhya Pradesh, gold, copper, asbestos, and mica.

The younger Pre-Cambrian (*Cuddapah*) series represent the sediments deposited in basins within the Archaean basement rocks and are found principally in Madhya Pradesh and Andhra Pradesh where they form impressive scarplands. In the latter area they are overlain by Vindhyan sedimentary rocks (Lower Palaeozoic, Cambrian–Ordovician) which are more extensively found in the north of the Peninsula. The Vindhyan Range along the line of the Narmada–Son rivers is the most impressive outcrop.

Of greater economic importance are the Gondwana Group, in geological age extending from Upper Carboniferous through Permian and Triassic time into the Lower Jurassic. The deposits of this group are preserved in rift-like troughs still followed in the main by major drainage lines, e.g. the Damodar and Godavari valleys. Coal seams, often of great thickness and little disturbed by folding, are found along the troughs and extend westward beneath the Deccan lavas and eastwards beneath the older alluvial deposits of the Ganga Plain in Bangladesh.

The Gondwana deposits are continental in origin and one has to turn to the coastal plains of the Peninsula to find appreciable areas of marine

5 Open cut mining of thick seam of coal. Damodar Valley, West Bengal. Note women carrying head baskets of coal. The coal is loaded into lorries to be taken for use in local factories or to be transhipped by basket loads into railway wagons to be sent all over India. The shelter by the pool covers a pump for keeping the workings dry.

formations of Mesozoic–Tertiary age. Apart from a small marine deposit in the watershed of the Narmada–Son rivers, evidence of marine transgression is lacking in the interior. It would seem that the Peninsula remained a relatively stable land-mass over long periods of geological time while the seas worked gently on the eastern coastlands to produce a narrow zone of plain built up of low cuestas of marine sediments.

Early in the Tertiary and beginning in late Cretaceous time, there occurred fissure eruptions of lava on an immense scale, which buried the northwestern part of the Peninsula beneath thousands of feet of basalt. Near Bombay the lava is 10,000 ft. (3,053 m) thick, and it is surmised that it must have extended some way westward and now lies deep beneath the Arabian Sea. Faulting along the line of the Western Ghats, and tilting of the lava plateau generally eastwards produced the main features of the present landscape.

It may well be that eruptions of the Deccan lavas were connected with the crustal instability associated with the Himalayan orogeny. To the north of the Peninsular 'Shield' of mainly ancient rocks (covered in places with younger continental, coastal, and extrusive igneous rocks) there lay a more or less broad depression, or geosyncline, into which the bordering continental land-masses of the Peninsula and Central Asia had long been discharging through their rivers the products of erosion. During Tertiary time the deposits in the geosyncline dating from Pre-Cambrian to Tertiary were folded and thrust upwards to form the Himalaya. The process was long-continued, and as the mountain chains grew erosion fast worked upon them, and great rivers carried vast quantities of material into the marine gulfs that separated the young ranges from the Peninsular 'Shield', then probably a large island. Continued uplift and fracturing raised more ranges, incorporating some of the recent deposits, which in turn were exposed to erosion. As the marine gulfs retreated conditions were locally favourable at various times to the formation of coal and petroleum and the accumulation of salt. Coal of Cretaceous and Tertiary age is found in workable quantity in Assam, Jammu, the Salt Ranges, and Baluchistan; oil-bearing structures are located in the Salt Ranges, the Assam Valley, and Gujarat, natural gas wells in Sind and Bangladesh, and the Salt Range has long been a source of rock salt. Vertical movement of the Himalaya may not yet have ceased, and certainly during the Pleistocene period displacements measured in thousands of feet took place. The mountain belt still suffers earthquakes; severe shocks have occurred at places as widely separated as Quetta, Kashmir, Himachal Pradesh, Bihar and Assam. On the geological map (Fig. 2.1) the various formations of the Himalaya have not been distinguished. The outer Himalayan belt, with the hills of the Assam–Burma border and the mountain belt of Baluchistan and the northwest, are largely of Mesozoic and Tertiary age. Rocks of almost all ages are found incorporated in the main Himalaya.

6   The Western Ghats south of Bombay, showing the horizontally bedded lava exposed along the deeply dissected edge of the Deccan Lava Plateau. In several locations similar to this the abrupt slope has been utilised to generate hydro-electric power.

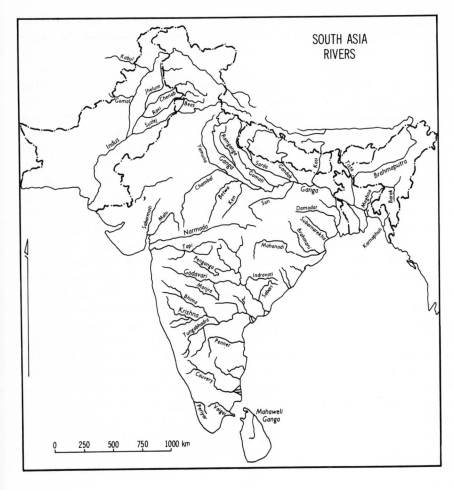

SOUTH ASIA
RIVERS

Fig. 2.3

The youngest element in South Asia's structure is the alluvium of the Indo-Gangetic Plains and the numerous smaller lowland areas. The major rivers are shown in Figure 2.3 which will be found useful for reference in subsequent chapters. It is important to realise the variety of materials that are generally termed 'alluvium' and the way in which differences in site in relation to present rivers affect their agricultural value. The term 'alluvium' includes fluvial deposits laid down at various times through the Pleistocene up to the present. The most recent floodplain deposits include some very fertile material, while the older alluvia – long exposed to the leaching effect of rainfall and standing often above the levels where present-day floods might introduce fresh plant nutrients in the form of soluble salts and silt – tend to give rise to poorer soils.

There is evidence, particularly in the Ganga Delta, that the alluvium has not been entirely stable even in recent historic time. The 'older' Pleistocene alluvial surfaces of the Ganga-Brahmaputra have been dislocated by faulting, with subsequent influence upon the local drainage pattern. Striking changes in course by some of the major distributaries and tributaries, such as the 'Old' Brahmaputra and the Tista, have had important repercussions on navigation and settlement over the past 200 years, a very short time in geomorphological terms.

A distinct type of deposit associated with the Pleistocene in northwest Pakistan is loess, which mantles parts of the Potwar Plateau between the Salt Range and the outer ramparts of the Himalaya. Disturbance of the vegetation cover through overgrazing has led to severe gullying in the loess.

Table 2.1   Physiographic regions (refer to Fig. 2.4)

1. *Baluchistan*
   1.1   Intermontane basins and ranges
   1.2   Sulaiman Range
   1.3   Kirthar Range

2. *Northwest Frontier Hills and Submontane Indus*
   2.1   Northwest Frontier Hills and high Valleys
   2.2   Submontane region

3. *Himalaya–Karakoram*
   3.1   Karakoram
   3.2   Kashmir Himalaya
   3.3   Central Himalaya
   3.4   Eastern Himalaya

4. *Hills and Plateaus of the Northeast*
   4.1   Northeastern Hills
   4.2   Meghalaya Plateau

5. *The Plains*
   5.1   Indus Plains
   5.2   Thar Desert
   5.3   Ganga Plains
   5.4   Ganga–Brahmaputra Delta
   5.5   Meghna Depression
   5.6   Assam Valley

6. *West Coastlands*
   6.1   Kathiawar and Kutch
   6.2   Gujarat Plains
   6.3   Konkan–Karnataka Coast
   6.4   Malabar (Kerala) Coast

7. *East Coastlands*
   7.1   East Bangladesh Coastlands
   7.2   Orissa Coast
   7.3   Andhra Coast
   7.4   Tamilnad Coast
   7.5   Sri Lanka Low Country

8. *Peninsular Foreland*
   8.1   Aravalli Hills
   8.2   Chambal Basin
   8.3   Bundelkhand
   8.4   Vindhyan Scarplands
   8.5   Baghelkhand
   8.6   Chotanagpur Plateau

9. *Peninsular Lava Country*
   9.1   Malwa Plateau
   9.2   Vindhyas
   9.3   Narmada Valley
   9.4   Satpura Ranges
   9.5   Deccan Lava Plateau

10. *Western Ghats*
    10.1   Western Ghats: Lava Section
    10.2   Western Chats: Archaean Section

11. *Plateaus and Basins on mainly Archaean Rocks*
    11.1   Chhatisghar Plain
    11.2   Dandakaranaya Plateau
    11.3   Telangana Plateau
    11.4   Karnataka Plateau

12. *Eastern Hills and Uplands*
    12.1   Orissa Hills
    12.2   Nallamallai Hills
    12.3   Balaghat
    12.4   Tamilnad Plateau

13. *Highland Blocks of South India and Sri Lanka*
    13.1   Nilgiri Hills
    13.2   Southern Ghats
    13.3   Sri Lanka Hill Country

14. *Lakshadweep and Maldives*

15. *Andaman and Nicobar Islands*

7   The Church of Bom Jesus in Goa, built in 1594 by the Portuguese, contains the remains of St. Francis Xavier who was a missionary in India in the 16th century.

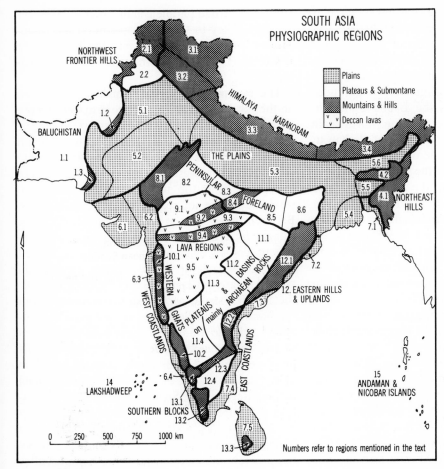

Fig. 2.4

Physiographic Regions

The end-product of South Asian structural and erosional history is summarised in the map of physiographic regions (Fig. 2.4) which leans heavily on Spate's work, and the accompanying key, Table 2.1. These regions provide a frame of reference for subsequent discussions. The numbers in parentheses in the text refer to Figure 2.4.

1. *Baluchistan.* In Baluchistan, the influence exerted on the alignment of the Tertiary fold mountains by the hidden northwesterly projection of the Peninsular Shield can be seen in the north–south trend of the Sulaiman (1.2) and Kirthar Ranges (1.3) north of Karachi, which break the generally east–west trend of the folds forming the Himalaya and the ranges of the Iranian complex. Fringed to the east by alluvial fans and pediments, the Sulaiman and Kirthar Ranges present to the traveller from the Indus Plains a forbiddingly bare and rugged front, rising in the vol-

canic Takht-i-Sulaiman to 3,374 m. Westward the east–west trend of the system is restored in the ranges of central Baluchistan and the Makran coast (1.1). Between the Chagai Hills and the Siahan Range are several basins of inland drainage, containing *playa* lakes, such as Hamun-i-Mashkel. In the Makran and the eastern half of Baluchistan the basins drain eventually to the sea.

2. *The Northwest Frontier Hills and Submontane Indus.* The Gomal River just north of Takht-i-Sulaiman effectively separates the Baluchistan region with its predominance of broad high upland features from the region to the north where valleys and mountainous spurs make up much of the terrain. Structurally, this is a most complicated corner, where the massive ranges of the Great Himalaya and Karakoram, trending from southeast to northwest, point across the Indus and Hunza valleys to the east–west and northeast–southwest trending systems of the Pamir and

Hindu Kush. The mountain and valley complex of the Northwest Frontier Hills and high valleys (2.1) is best described in terms of its rivers and their basins, several of which constituted the territories of former feudal states. Three basins constitute the submontane region west of the Indus (2.2): the Kurram waters the Bannu Plains; to its north is the smaller Kohat Plain; north again is the most important broad Vale of Peshawar, floored with alluvium brought down from the west by the R. Kabul, and from the north by the Swat and its parallel tributary, the Panjkora. These latter two valleys form the territory of the former States (now the Districts) of Swat and Dir respectively. The valley of the Upper Kunar which flows south to join the Kabul in Afghanistan constitutes Chitral District. Almost as isolated is the basin of the R. Gilgit in the western extension of the Indus furrow. Southwards from the bastion of Nanga Parbat, which forms the western extremity of the Great Himalaya, the Kagan and Kishen valleys drain to the Jhelum.

The Potwar Plateau is a distinctive submontane region enclosed between the Himalayan foothills in the north, the Indus to the west and flanked by the Salt Range which forms its abrupt scarp edge to the south. Basically, it is a bedrock plain characterised by close-textured low rocky ridges following the strike of the Siwalik (Sivalik) formations,* and masked in places by a cover of water-sorted loess, now extensively dissected by gullies.

3. *Himalaya–Karakoram.* This vast complex of mountain ranges with its numerous peaks reaching 6,000 m and more, sweeps in a 2,500 km arc from the gorge the Indus cuts through the flanks of Nanga Parbat (8,127 m) in western Kashmir, to the hairpin bend of the Tsangpo (Brahmaputra) as it enters northeastern India. The Karakoram (3.1) crowned by K2, the highest of 33 peaks exceeding 7,315 m, lies apart from the Himalaya proper, north of the Indus furrow. The latter extends southeastwards past the headwaters of the Indus to become the Tsangpo furrow which runs west–east, the whole trench, at around 3,660–4,270 m, marking the edge of the Tibetan Plateau which rises to its north. The Indus–Tsangpo furrow can be regarded as the innermost element of the

Himalaya. Broad parallelism of structural features provides a key to the landscape, but a more convenient regional division is into the Kashmir (or Western) Himalaya, Central and Eastern Himalaya.

The ranges of the Great Himalaya are flanked on the south by a 110 km wide zone of spurs whose accordant summit–levels at about 4,600 m suggest a former erosion surface. This in turn is flanked by the Lesser or Outer Himalaya ranges more developed in the western half of the system, where the Dhaoladhar (up to 4,570 m) and Pir Panjal (to 4,725 m) are impressive ranges in themselves. Between these and the plains lie the Sivalik Hills. Carved by erosion out of the fractured and distorted deposits of mainly coarse detritus, derived from the Himalayan ranges as they grew to full stature in late Tertiary and early Pleistocene times, the Sivaliks strike parallel to the mountain front for hundreds of kilometres, presenting a formidable barrier to transverse movement on account of the ruggedness of the terrain rather than its absolute relief which is rarely as much as 900 m above sea level (*cf.* the 300 m of the adjoining plains). Between the Sivaliks and the Lesser Himalaya there are occasional breaks in the close succession of rocky scarp and jungly vale, and the landscape opens out into a submontane alluvial basin a few kilometres wide – the Kangra Valley east of Pathankot, Dehra Dun, the Kathmandu Valley and other 'duns' of lesser note.

In the Kashmir Himalaya (3.2) the fairly regular progression of steps upwards from the Sivaliks to the Great Himalaya is interrupted by the Vale of Kashmir – 30–40 km wide and more than 130 km along its axis parallel to the Pir Panjal. The Vale is a synclinal basin floored with a variety of alluvial deposits (lacustrine, fluvial and fluvio-glacial) through which the R. Jhelum meanders at 1,600 m above sea level before entering its deep gorge through the Pir Panjal.

In the Central Himalaya (3.3) from Himachal Pradesh through to Eastern Nepal the parallel elements are more compact. Some major rivers rise on the southern slopes of the Great Himalaya – the Chenab, Beas and the Ganga – while the Sutlej and Gogra rise in the high plateau of Tibet and carve courses across the mountain belt.

The Eastern Himalaya (3.4) extend from the Arun–Kosi basin in eastern Nepal, through Sikkim

* India now favours the transliteration Sivalik

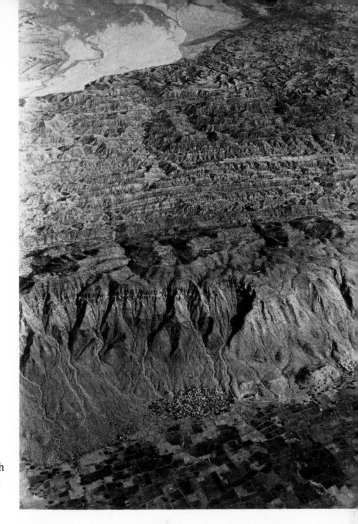

8 A section of the Salt Range scarp in Pakistan, with the plain of the Jhelum in the foreground and villages at its foot. The extreme dissection of the Potwar Plateau above the scarp is clearly seen.

and Bhutan and into Arunachal Pradesh. The Sivalik belt is lacking here or at best a very minor feature. Transverse rivers such as the Arun, draining the Everest massif (8,840 m), and the Tista, break the Lesser Himalayan belt into numerous spurs projecting from the main chain of mountains and consequently prevent the structural strike from dominating the landforms. East of Kanchenjunga (8,579 m) high peaks become fewer, and the Tibetan peak Namcha Barwa (7,756 m) overlooking the bend of the Tsangpo (Brahmaputra) is the last of the great summits west of the river, beyond which the crest line falls progressively along the water parting between tributaries of the Brahmaputra and the Salween in Burma.

4. *Hills and Plateaus of the Northeast.* Differing markedly from the Himalaya in the scale of their relief and in their morphology, the ranges (4.1) which sweep southwest and south from the eastern extremity of Assam, none the less stem from the same orogeny. For the most part the Cretaceous and Tertiary strata of the region are relatively unresistant shales and sandstones arranged in simple anticlines and synclines. The trend of the close folds is clearly indicated in the parallelism of the elongated trellised drainage pattern, particularly well seen in the Chittagong Hill Tracts of Bangladesh, and in the adjacent hill-country of India. In the north where the Patkai and Naga Hills form the border with Burma, the system reaches its highest elevation of 3,825 m in the Saramati peak. Generally, however, heights over 2,100 m are exceptional and the level of ridges declines southwards to average 600 – 900 m between the Chittagong coast and the Burma border.

Of a quite different morphological character is the Meghalaya Plateau (4.2) which is a detached eastern extension of the Chotanagpur Plateau, the connecting section now lying 600 m below the alluvium of the North Bengal Plain in Bangladesh. The Meghalaya Plateau presents a particularly steep 1,500 m wall southwards above the Meghna Depression of Bangladesh.

INDUS PLAINS MORPHOLOGY

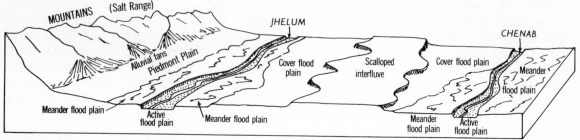

Fig. 2.5

5. *The Plains.*   Representing the present surface of the more or less deep alluvial fill of the trough that marks the contact zone between the stable Peninsular Shield and the Himalayan fold system, the Plains may be treated as a single physiographic unit despite the variation in detail that exists within them. Subdivision of the plains in Figure 2.4 is on the basis of drainage basins, with the extensive delta of the Ganga–Brahmaputra as a separate region. While alluviation in the floodplains of rivers great and small have been the common genesis of the regions' features, differences in age and scale are significant in characterising sub-regional divisions.

In the main, the Plains are the product of the larger rivers rising in the Himalaya – the Indus and its Punjab tributaries, the Ganga and its tributaries, and the Brahmaputra. Relatively speaking, the tributaries from the Peninsular foreland, principal among them the Son and the Chambal, have contributed little by reason of their smaller scale, gentler gradient and the lesser precipitation in their catchments. The alluvial deposits of the great river systems may conveniently be differentiated on the basis of age and the consequent degree of obliteration of the features which distinguish an actively developing floodplain – levees, backswamp depressions, abandoned meander ox-bows, etc.

The *active floodplains* contain the usually braided and changing channels of the river separated by more or less temporary islands of young alluvium which are sandy or clayey depending on distance from the channel responsible for their deposition. Low bluffs or levees mark the limits of the active floodplains. In the deltas particularly, the active floodplains are areas of frequent change which can affect a considerable breadth of country tens of miles in extent. Elsewhere, as in the Middle Ganga Plain and Punjab, the active floodplains are more permanently fixed between bluffs.

Meander floodplain and *cover floodplain* are terms used to describe the still relatively young alluvium no longer subject to periodical reworking by the rivers (see Fig. 2.5). In the case of the meander floodplains, the levees, meander belts, and backswamp features of the past active stage may still be discerned, while in the cover floodplain such features have been obscured by the levelling effect of sheet flooding which has gradually reduced the raised elements of the landscape and filled in the depressions.

A still older element of the alluvial landscape is the *scalloped interfluve* or 'old alluvial' surface. The term 'scalloped interfluve' is expressive of the way in which the flanks of the older alluvial interfluve areas have been cut into by the meandering of the active rivers. These older surfaces, in some cases dated as Pleistocene, are most widespread in the higher parts of the Punjab and Ganga Plains, and in the latter are found in quite extensive remnants on the flanks of the delta proper in West Bengal and Bangladesh. Benches of similar age and material fringe the Tertiary hill-country of Bangladesh where they are valued as relatively level but drainable land for tea plantations (Fig. 16.2). From the Upper Ganga Plain westwards into the Punjab the interfluves may carry patches of sandy soil, sometimes windblown and hummocky, while their edges may be extensively fretted by gullies cut back from the present river.

Independent of the great rivers, the plains increase in slope as the mountain belt is approached. Here is a zone of confluent alluvial fans constituting a continuous piedmont plain into which the short, generally intermittent streams from the hills lose themselves. In Uttar Pradesh and along its borders with Nepal, this belt of often gravelly porous alluvium is known as the *bhabar* and is succeeded down slope by the *terai*, a marshy zone where the water table reappears at the surface in a spring-line of headward-sapping gullies. *Bhabar* and *terai* are not found in this form throughout the piedmont belt, although comparable features with variations according to rainfall regime and local conditions are widespread. In the Piedmont of West Bengal and the Assam Valley the *terai* is well developed in a marshy zone known as the *duars*.

The physiographic subregions within the plains are identified only briefly here; in view of their importance in supporting the bulk of South Asia's population they are discussed in more detail in later chapters. The Indus Plains (5.1) include the great triangle of plains built up by that river's Punjab tributaries, the 'five rivers' which give the region its name: Jhelum, Chenab, Ravi, Beas and Sutlej. The wealth of Pakistan and of the Indian state of Punjab lies in the Indus Plains. East and southeast of the Indus and Sutlej rivers the intensively irrigated alluvial plain gives place abruptly to the Thar Desert (5.2). Much of the surface is sand, arranged into dune formations in many areas 'fixed' by scanty vegetation, but in places may be traced the dry courses of former river systems like the Ghaggar. Clay bands beneath the sand give rise to saline lakes towards the Indus in Khairpur. Peninsular Shield rocks similar to those forming the Aravalli Hills underlie the whole area, outcrop-

ping in places as rocky inliers in the sandy wastes. Similar scattered inliers occur in the Pakistan Punjab near Sargodha, forming the Kirana Hills (512 m) between the Jhelum and Chenab rivers, and providing the most northerly surface evidence of the projecting shield around which the Himalayan folds have been wrapped. On its eastern margins the Thar becomes less arid, and its rolling sand plains fade away in the gently sloping pediments of the Aravallis.

Unlike the Indus Plains which become progressively more arid downstream towards Sind, the Ganga Plains (5.3) extend from semi-arid Haryana to the humid plain of North Bengal. The latter is the most easterly of the series of broad alluvial fans that press the Ganga and its Himalayan tributaries towards the Peninsular Foreland. The head of the Ganga–Brahmaputra Delta (5.4) lies near where the Ganga enters Bangladesh, and is mainly south of that river and its continuation as the Padma beyond the confluence of the Jamuna (Brahmaputra). The Meghna Depression (5.5) in northeastern Bangladesh is in part an immense backswamp to the 'Old' Brahmaputra, and partly a seasonal natural reservoir for the floods of the Surma entering it from Assam. Plains of varying degrees of swampiness surround the depression. Chapter 15 discusses the finer details of Bangladesh's lowland morphology which enter so significantly into its economic development. In the Assam Valley (5.6) the Plains find their eastern extremity, with the braided course of the turbulent sandy Brahmaputra discouraging settlement along its axis.

9   The Himalaya in Nepal. The peak of Mt. Everest is just obscured by cloud in the right centre. Ice falls and valley glaciers with surface moraines flow to the right.

6. *The West Coastland.* From Kutch to Kanya Kumari (Cape Cormorin) the coastal lowlands may be seen as the product of marine erosion sawing into the steep western edge of the Peninsular plateaux, lava in the north, Archaean rocks in the south. The whole coast seems hinged about Goa, the shoreline to the north often showing features of submergence while that to the south is emergent. The latter, the Malabar (Kerala) section of the coastal belt (6.4), comprises three elements:

(a) a benchland with old leached soils often cut in Tertiary sediments along the foot of the plateau;
(b) a belt of alluvium along the larger transverse valleys and tending to fill in the lagoons, cut off from
(c) a line of multiple sandy beach ridges.

The Konkan–Karnataka Coast (6.3) as far as Bombay is so cut up by spurs from the Western Ghats enclosing the basins of short rivers terminating in drowned valleys as to deter longitudinal communications by land. The lateritic benchland element is present, but alluvium is restricted to the valley bottoms. North of Bombay a coastal plain becomes more evident in the Gujarat Plains (6.2) and although the rivers enter the sea through short estuaries, drowning has not been so severe as to prevent the active accumulation of silt and mud to form tidal marshes. The Western Ghats stand back from the coast in Gujarat extending northwards till the Tapi and Narmada valleys finally break their continuity.

Across the Gulf of Cambay the Kathiawar Peninsula (6.1) is a low plateau of Deccan lava fringed with a benchland above a coast no longer predominantly submergent. Kutch, which separates it from the Indus delta, consists of a number of Mesozoic sedimentary and lava 'islands' in a 'sea' of mudflats, perhaps the estuaries of bygone rivers which used to traverse the now arid Thar Desert.

7. *The East Coastlands.* These are more heterogeneous than their West Coast counterparts, and include several deltas as well as elements of marine erosion and deposition. In the East Bangladesh coastlands (7.1), the Tippera Surface east of the Meghna Estuary and merging with the Chittagong coastal plain has features distinct from those of the delta proper (5.4 above). On the other side of the Bay of Bengal the coastlands may be divided conveniently into three. The Orissa Coast (7.2) includes the Mahanadi Delta and the true coastal plain flanking it to north and south. The Andhra Coast (7.3) continues south from it to become dominated by the Godavari–Krishna Delta. Low benchlands back the delta and continue south into Nellore. In the Tamilnad Coastal Plain (7.4) low cuestas of Tertiary and Mesozoic marine deposits form a lower transitional step to the Tamilnad Plateau (11.4 below) and often carry a capping of red soil reminiscent of the similar benchlands of Kerala and the 'old alluvium' of West Bengal and Bangladesh. The Cauvery Delta is a major young alluvial element. Across Palk Strait, the Sri Lanka Low Country (7.5) has many features in common with both the Tamilnad and Kerala coastlands. The coastlines of all of them show ample evidence of progradation, consisting frequently of actively silting lagoons behind offshore beach ridges built up by longshore drifting.

10 The River Meghna near its confluence with the Padma (Ganga) in Bangladesh. This view, taken in August with the river in flood, shows waterlogged fields of paddy and jute. The dark linear features are settlements, built on river levees, their houses hidden beneath trees. The numerous village sites of this kind are an indication of the changeable course of the river within the Ganga Delta.

8. *The Peninsular Foreland.* Under this term may be grouped the areas made up of the geologically 'solid' structures which flank the Indo–Gangetic plains on the south.

In the west, the Aravalli Hills (8.1) consist of rugged ridges of Pre-Cambrian rocks decreasing northwards from about 1,700 m to disappear beneath the alluvium of the plains around Delhi. A region of lower relief developed on Vindhyan sandstones and Archaean gneiss extends from the Aravallis through the Chambal Basin (8.2) and Bundelkhand (8.3) to the Vindhyan Scarplands (8.4) which overlook the Valley of the Son. Eastwards Baghelkhand (8.5) merges into the gentle rolling plateaux of Chotanagpur (8.6) where occasional isolated hills stand out abruptly as much as 1,000 m above the general surface.

The Chotanagpur Plateau slopes away to the northeast, beneath the Ganga alluvium, but its structures persist to form a foundered link to the Meghalaya Plateau.

The Peninsular interior consists of a series of plateaux and basins, the principal distinguishing factor being the underlying rock, either Deccan Lava or largely Archaean formations.

9. *The Peninsular Lava Country.* This covers about a third of the interior, and is differentiated by the structural lines of the trough of the Narmada Valley (9.3), flanked by the higher hill features of the Vindhyas (9.2) to the north and the Satpura Ranges (9.4) to the south. The area physiographically most distinctive in this broad region is the Deccan Lava Plateau (9.5), a country characterised by great expanses of nearly level plateau formed by the lava flows into which the rivers have cut a landscape of wide gently stepped valleys. From its high western edge extensively over 750 m above sea level, the plateau slopes eastwards with a low gradient, its main area being drained by the Godavari, Bhima and Krishna rivers. North of the Ajanta Hills the drainage is westwards by the Narmada and Tapi, while beyond the Vindhyas the Malwa Plateau (9.1) drains north to the Chambal. The lavas weather to a moisture-retentive black clayey soil, *regur*.

10. *The Western Ghats.* These are the steep westward facing scarp of the eastward tilted block of Peninsular India. In their northern section the Ghats are cut out of the lava flows piled one on top of another to give a stratified appearance (10.1). From Goa southwards the Ghats are in Archaean formations (10.2), but present an equally formidable barrier to communications despite a deceptively softer aspect due to the more continuous cover of rain-forest.

11. *The Plateaus and Basins on mainly Archaean Rocks.* Stretching northeastwards from the Archaean section of the Western Ghats (10.2) in a broad belt parallel to the east coast and separated from it by the steep zone of the Eastern Hills and Uplands (12) are a series of upland plateaux and basins which may conveniently be resolved into four sub-regions. The most northerly, the Chhatisgarh Plain (11.1), a basin in Cuddapah sedimentary rocks, rises gradually southwards to include the Bastar Plateau. Beyond it the Dandakaranaya Plateau (11.2) extends to the Godavari Valley, here a structural trough containing Gondwana coal measures. In the Telangana Plateau (11.3) to the south, with Hyderabad at its heart, the general level reaches 600 m, somewhat lower than the Karnataka Plateau (11.4) that succeeds it southwards, often over 900 m. Both are extensively planated surfaces, mainly in gneisses, studded with granitic inselbergs, alone or in clusters, that tower steep-sided 300 m and more above the surrounding plateau.

12. *The Eastern Hills and Uplands.* These are a rather mixed group of regions necessarily distinguished however from the major divisions that flank them on either side. The Orissa Hills (12.1), largely in Pre-Cambian gneisses, schists and Charnockites, reach 1,525 m. Ruggedly dissected, they present a steep fretted slope to the coastal plain. In the Nallamallai Hills (12.2) parallel arcuate ranges in Cuddapah metamorphosed sedimentaries form an impressive series of escarpments to the central group of which the name properly belongs. Remarkably fine flagstones are quarried here. Trending southwest from the southern extremity of the Nallamallai, a more or less steeply sloping zone, Balaghat (12.3), separates the Karanataka Plateau (11.4) from the lower Tamilnad Plateau (12.4). The latter is particularly well developed around Coimbatore. Outlying dissected fragments of the higher plateau, such as

the Javadi and the Shevaroy Hills, distinguish this region from the simpler structures of the Tamilnad Coastal Plain (7.4).

13 *The Highland Blocks of South India and Sri Lanka.* The abruptness with which these Archaean blocks rise above the adjacent plateau surfaces sets them apart physiographically. The Nilgiri Hills (13.1) rise to 2,670 m and extensive areas lie over 1,800 m, below which the block slopes steeply away on all sides; to the 1,000 m Karnataka Plateau to the north, most sharply towards the Tamilnadu Plateau at about 400 m to the southeast, and to the west in a sinuous much fretted edge, characteristic of the Western Ghats, tumbling 230 m per kilometre over a bare 8 kilometres to the Malabar coastal lowlands.

South of the Palghat Gap, the first clear break in the high western edge of the Peninsular plateaus south of the Tapi valley, the highland blocks reappear in the Southern Ghats (13.2). Unlike the Nilgiris the blocks here present their steepest face either to the north, where the Anaimalai and Palni Hills overlook the Palghat Gap, or to the southeast, towards Madurai and Tirunelveli, as the scarps of the Palni and Cardamom Hills. The highest summit is at 2,694 m in the Anaimalais but the proportion of the upland exceeding 1,800 m is less than in the Nilgiris. From the Cardamom Hills southwards the plateau belt narrows, losing height somewhat and culminating in a peak of about 1,645 m within 30 km of Kanya Kumari, the southernmost point of the mainland.

The Sri Lanka Hill Country (13.3) is essentially similar to these mainland blocks, though its limits, especially to the southwest, are not so distinct. A peak 2,524 m high crowns the highest platform surface of the plateau. The relief of Sri Lanka is treated in more detail below (Chapter 18).

14. *Lakshadweep and Maldives.* These constitute a group of coral atolls in the Arabian Sea off the west coast of South India.

15. *The Andaman and Nicobar Islands.* These lie closer to Sumatra than to India, are structurally the continuation of the Arakan Yoma of Burma, and represent the visible portions of a Tertiary mountain chain, mainly submerged beneath the Bay of Bengal.

Chapter 3

The Natural Environment: Climates of South Asia

Most of us living in the urbanised industrial societies of 'highly developed' countries or in the westernised sectors of 'less developed' countries, are accustomed to the fact that excessive heat or cold or humidity in the environment in which we live can be effectively and inexpensively controlled indoors. Air-conditioning, space heating, and less extravagantly activating the air with fans to increase our comfort by assisting the body's natural evaporative cooling system, all require the output of some generally inanimate energy. The vast majority of the population of South Asia are still a long way from that stage of economic and technological advance when they can escape the actualities of weather and climate by taking refuge in an air-conditioned living-room or office. As farmers and farm labourers, most of the rural dwellers have to work in the outdoor climate anyway, and as often as not in the blazing sunshine. For them and their families conditions have changed little, if at all, from those described by Blanford, quoting from a resident in the Punjab in the 1880s. Although these comments are not applicable in detail throughout South Asia, particularly as far as the coldness of the cold season is concerned, they may help the 'denizen of the temperate zone' to conceive of the very different march of the seasons of the monsoon climate and the intensity of its discomfort at its hottest.

'Like the rest of India, the Punjab has really but three seasons: the summer or hot season, the rains, and the winter ... the cold season. The hot season begins in April ... The west wind holds sway and ... is a veritable hot wind. A denizen of the temperate zone can hardly realise to himself the dessicated, truly scorching heat of this wind. When exposed to it one may imagine one is facing an open furnace.

In order to enjoy fresh air at this season one must take exercise in the early dawn, between 4 and 5 in the morning; for no sooner has the sun risen than the heat sets in again ... At sunrise ... houses must be closed, only a small door being left open for communication with the outside ... Man and beast languish and gasp for air ... Vegetation suffers equally: almost all green things wither; the grass seems burnt up to the roots; bushes and trees seem moribund; the earth is as hard as a paved highway; the ground is seamed with cracks; and the whole landscape wears an aspect of bareness and sadness. At length, in June, the hot winds cease to blow, and are followed by a calm; and now indeed the heat is truly fearful; all things pine for the rain ...

'The southerly and easterly winds bring first clouds and violent storms with heavy rain showers, which are repeated daily, or at all events every two or three days; and finally the rains ... In July the trees begin a second time to burst into leaf; grass springs up once more, and soon a vegetation is developed, that, fostered by warmth and moisture is scarce to be kept within due bounds ... After from four to six weeks of heavy rain, often falling uninterruptedly for 2 or 3 days in succession, it clears up, and sometimes some weeks pass without further rain; after which a week or two more of rainy weather brings the season to a close. Grateful as is the coolness brought by these showers, the more oppressively hot and sultry is it, when the rain ceases and holds off, if only for half a day. The atmosphere weighs on one like a heavy coverlet; and then comes the daily and the nightly plague of mosquitoes. Insect and reptilian life is now active; of evenings it hums and buzzes and croaks all around ... Woodwork swells, and doors and windows can be fastened only with much difficulty. Shoes and all articles of leather become quickly coated with fungus, books become mouldy and worm-eaten, paper perishes, linen becomes damp ...

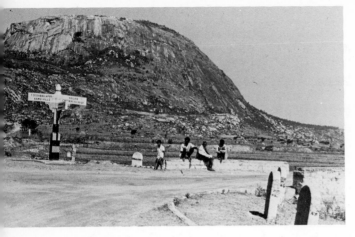

11 Nandi (1,600 m), north of Bangalore, Karnataka, is a granitic inselberg standing 600 m above the plateau surface. Tippu Sahib, among the last of the indigenous leaders to resist the British at the end of the 18th century had his fortress on top of this mountain. The local gneiss is used in the culvert and roadside markets.

'The period which immediately follows the rains up to October is the most unhealthy season in the year. Decaying vegetation under an ardent sun generates miasma (pollution) the consequences being fever, dysentery, and not infrequently cholera. Towards the end of the rains one rejoices indeed to see the heavy dark clouds disappear, but the heat soon becomes once more so great that one longs for the cold season ... watching for some sign of the cool westerly and northerly winds. With the beginning of October these winds set in steadily, clearing the skies, and now the blue firmament appears in all its splendour ... From October to Christmas, as a rule, the weather is clear and fine, the air is pure and most delicious ... In December and January ... the nights are positively cold ... During the second half of the cold season we have in the Punjab a good deal of rain ... In February we have a short spring; many trees unfold their leaves ... But this spring is of short duration, and in March it is already warm on the plains and the hot summer is at hand; an occasional dust storm, however, for a while keeps off the summer heat ...'*

The Monsoon

Although the word has been applied to the climate of one-third of Asia, and has also been borrowed for use in other parts of the world, 'monsoon' rightly belongs to the Indian Ocean. It is derived from the Arabic (and thence Urdu) word *mausim* denoting 'season', but was originally applied to the distinct seasonal winds blowing between Arabia and the East Indies, the winds which Arab traders used to drive their ships to and fro on their annual

voyages in quest of spices, ivory, and fine fabrics. Through Portuguese and Dutch the word entered the vocabulary of the British merchants and rulers in India, and for these land-lubbers it came to mean the seasonal rhythm of wet and dry rather than the changing wind systems familiar to sailors. In fact the monsoon in common parlance tended to refer specifically to the wet-hot season, heralded by a fanfare of violent storms and torrential rain – the 'breaking of the monsoon'. However the word was used, its application to the climate of the area carried the sense of marked seasonality.

Two basic factors are strongly influential in the climate of South Asia: the mountain girt high plateaux which separate it from the rest of Asia on the north, and the great expanse of ocean washing the Indian Peninsula and Sri Lanka and extending and widening southwards beyond the Equator. Only in Baluchistan and Kashmir does the region with which we are concerned extend appreciably beyond the mountain wall. The Himalaya are backed beyond the Brahmaputra (Tsangpo) and Indus valleys by the Kailas and Karakoram ranges. The latter, with the Hindu Kush branching southwest to continue the rampart into Afghanistan, tower continuously over 4,000 m and for great distances over 5,500 m. These ranges effectively bar the movement of airstreams at surface level between south and 'inner' Asia and vice versa. By contrast, to the south no relief feature stands high enough to prevent the free flow inland of airstreams from the surrounding seas. Not only does the relief of the land play a major part in the dynamics of climate, but it also has a strong influence on cloudiness and rainfall. Air passing across abrupt changes of slope is caused to rise to elevations at which temperatures may fall below

*Blanford, Henry F., *A Practical Guide to the Climates and Weather of India, Ceylon and Burmah*(London, 1889), pp. 127–29

dew point, so provoking condensation and perhaps precipitation. The *orographic lifting* of air induced by the Himalaya, the Western Ghats, and the hills of Sri Lanka and Assam has a marked effect on rainfall on those areas. The other main process inducing air to rise in quantity is the *convergence* of streams of air leading to the increase in 'thickness' of airstream which finds an outlet in ascent from which cloudiness and precipitation can often result through cooling. Occasionally two streams of monsoon air, one moving up the Ganga Valley from the Bay of Bengal, the other across Rajasthan from the Arabian Sea, converge over the Punjab Himalayan foothills to produce abnormally heavy rainfall and floods. Conversely, *subsiding* air is warming, and so becomes clearer as it descends, bringing dry weather. Such subsidence is generally associated with *divergence* of airstreams at the surface, but also takes place where airflow is down−slope as happens when westerly airstreams descend from Baluchistan and Afghanistan and spread onto the Indus Plains.

Meteorologically there are basically two seasons in South Asia. In the season of the Northern hemisphere's winter the northern circumpolar circulation dominates the scene dynamically. A major branch of the jet-stream located at the equatorward edge of the circumpolar whirl helps maintain stable anticyclonic conditions over South Asia. Light northeasterly winds, the normal 'trades' in these latitudes but very much weaker than their oceanic counterparts in the Pacific, exert some influence over northern and eastern Sri Lanka, bringing rain, while the latitude of Colombo remains within range of the influence of the intertropical convergence and so rarely has a really dry month. Under the path of the jet-stream along the southern flank of the Himalaya, generally shallow low pressure systems move along the eastern Mediterranean and into Pakistan and northwestern India bringing some useful but relatively slight rainfall in late winter, but no further east than Patna.

The 'wet monsoon' season occurs after the north polar influences (and the jet-stream) have withdrawn beyond the mountain wall, leaving the way clear ultimately for equatorial maritime air to invade the region bringing with it more or less heavy precipitation. The influence of the southern circumpolar circulation, now in its winter strength, is felt in the strong surges of air of the southern 'trade winds' sweeping north of the equator to become the southwest monsoon.

A distinctive characteristic of the climate of most of the South Asian mainland, sensibly if not meteorologically, is its threefold division into (1) the cool and mainly dry winter, agriculturally the *rabi* season, (2) the hot and mainly dry season from about March or April into June, and (3) the wet monsoon 'bursting' in June and lasting into September or later. A transitional autumnal period of variable duration and weather, depending on latitude, links the 'wet' and 'cool' seasons, but hardly ranks as a separate season.

12 A yam leaf serves as umbrella for this Bangladeshi farmer sheltering from the rain.

Temperature

With agriculture the mainstay of the economies of South Asia, by far the most important climatic factor is rainfall. By comparison the other major climatic element, temperature, is of small significance. Low winter temperature is a limiting factor to plant growth only in the north, particularly in the mountains. Figure 3.1 shows some significant winter isotherms.

Effectively, low temperature causes a serious hiatus to plant life only at high elevations in the Himalaya and its intermontane plateaux and valleys, and in the Northwest Frontier Hills. Even here temperatures permit the cultivation of autumn

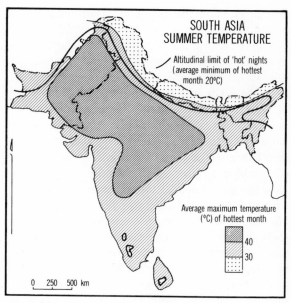

Fig. 3.2

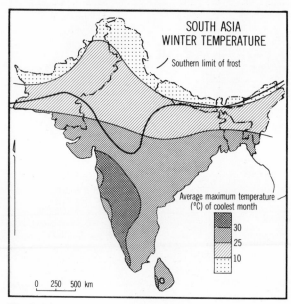

Fig. 3.1

being exceeded only in the Peninsular west interior, furthest from the moderating northeasterly breezes. (See also the tabulated climatic data in Table 3.1.)

Summer isotherms (Fig. 3.2) suggest more homogeneous conditions than in winter. Setting aside the mountains where elevation reduces shade temperatures appreciably (note the maxima for Leh in Table 3.1, overleaf) it is only in the

Fig. 3.3(a)

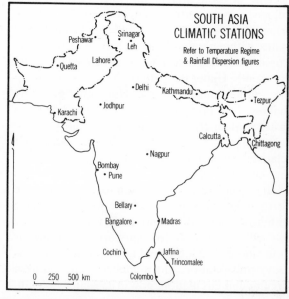

sown wheat. The plains of Northern Pakistan and Northwest India have occasional ground frost, but in lowland India generally the only major constraint exerted on agriculture by low winter temperatures is on some rice varieties which may not mature in December and January north of the tropics. As the map shows, most of South Asia enjoys a pleasantly warm winter marked by day after day of clear sunny weather, comparable to the ideal summer of many a temperate land.

Figure 3.3 shows temperature regimes for representative stations. Average daily maxima lie generally within the comfortable 20s (°C), this level

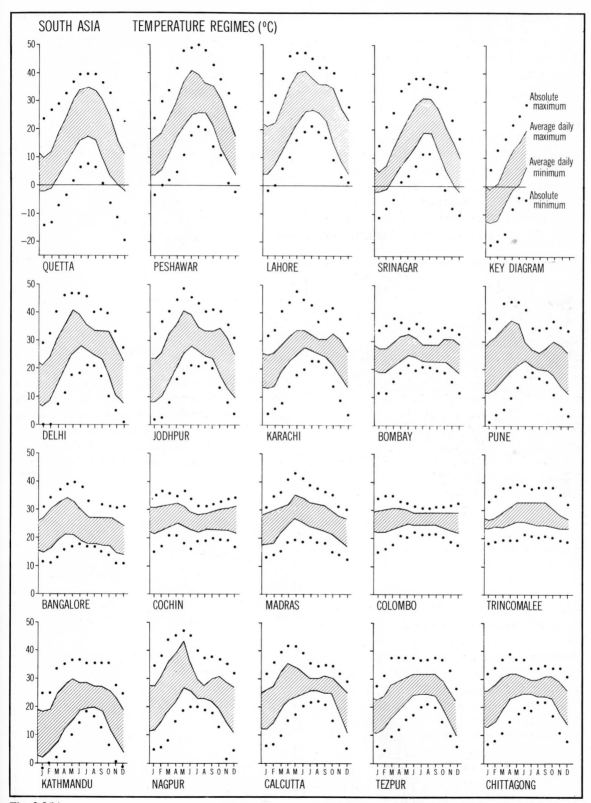

Fig. 3.3(b)

Table 3.1 Climatic data (temperatures °C, rainfall in mm)

Region Station (Altitude in metres)	No. of years recorded	Jan	Feb	Mar	Apr	May	June	July	Aug	Sept	Oct	Nov	Dec	Year
Cold Dry														
1. Leh (3,514)														
Av. daily max.	23	−1	1	7	13	16	20	25	24	21	15	8	2	
Av. daily min.	23	−13	−12	−6	−1	1	7	10	10	6	0	−7	−11	
Av. temperature	23	−7	−6	0	6	9	14	18	17	14	8	1	−4	
Av. rainfall	clino	12	9	12	7	7	4	16	19	12	7	3	8	116
Arid (Monsoonal)														
2. Karachi (4)														
Av. daily max.	43	25	26	29	32	34	34	33	31	31	33	31	27	
Av. daily min.	43	13	14	19	23	26	28	27	26	25	22	18	14	
Av. temperature	43	19	21	24	27	29	30	29	28	27	27	25	21	
Av. rainfall	clino	7	11	6	2	0	7	96	50	15	2	2	6	204
Arid (Mediterranean)														
3. Quetta (1,587)														
Av. daily max.	30	10	12	18	23	29	34	35	34	31	25	18	13	
Av. daily min.	30	−2	−1	3	7	11	15	18	17	10	14	0	−2	
Av. temperature	clino	4	6	11	16	21	24	27	25	21	14	9	5	
Av. rainfall	clino	37	43	42	12	7	1	18	4	1	1	6	23	195
Semi-arid														
4. Jodhpur (224)														
Av. daily max.	23	24	27	32	37	41	40	36	34	34	35	31	26	
Av. daily min.	23	9	11	16	21	26	28	27	25	24	18	13	10	
Av. temperature	23	17	19	24	29	34	34	32	30	29	27	22	18	
Av. rainfall	clino	8	5	2	2	6	31	122	146	47	7	3	1	380
Monsoon – Mediterranean overlap														
5. Peshawar (359)														
Av. daily max.	33	17	19	24	29	37	41	40	37	36	31	25	19	
Av. daily min.	33	4	6	11	16	21	25	26	26	22	14	8	4	
Av. temperature	clino	11	13	17	23	29	33	33	31	29	24	18	13	
Av. rainfall	clino	39	41	65	42	40	7	39	41	14	10	10	15	363
6. Srinagar (1,587)														
Av. daily max.	30	5	7	14	19	24	29	31	31	28	22	16	9	
Av. daily min.	30	−2	−1	3	7	11	14	18	18	12	5	−1	−2	
Av. temperature	30	1	4	9	13	18	22	25	24	21	14	8	4	
Av. rainfall	60	73	72	104	78	63	36	61	63	31	28	20	36	665
Sub-humid: maximum rainfall in summer monsoon														
7. Lahore (214)														
Av. daily max.	23	21	22	28	35	40	41	38	36	36	35	28	23	
Av. daily min.	23	4	7	12	17	22	26	27	26	23	15	8	4	
Av. temperature	clino	12	15	21	27	32	34	32	31	30	25	19	14	
Av. rainfall	clino	31	23	24	16	12	38	122	123	80	9	3	11	492
8. New Delhi (216)														
Av. daily max.	10	21	24	31	36	41	39	36	34	34	34	29	23	
Av. daily min.	10	7	9	14	20	26	28	27	26	24	18	11	8	
Av. temperature	10	14	17	23	28	34	34	32	30	29	26	29	16	
Av. rainfall	clino	25	22	17	7	8	65	211	173	150	31	1	5	715
9. Pune (559)														
Av. daily max.	24	31	33	36	38	37	32	28	28	29	32	31	29	
Av. daily min.	24	12	13	17	20	22	23	22	22	21	19	15	12	
Av. temperature	24	22	23	27	29	30	28	25	25	25	26	23	21	
Av. rainfall	clino	2	t	3	18	35	103	187	106	127	92	37	5	715
10 Bangalore (921)														
Av. daily max.	32	27	30	33	34	33	29	28	28	28	28	27	26	
Av. daily min.	33	14	16	18	21	21	19	19	19	18	18	17	15	
Av. temperature	33	21	23	26	28	27	24	24	24	23	23	22	21	
Av. rainfall	clino	3	10	6	46	117	80	117	147	143	185	54	16	924
Sub-humid: tendency to summer drought														
11. Bellary (449)														
Av. daily max.	30	31	34	37	39	39	34	32	32	32	32	31	29	
Av. daily min.	30	17	19	23	26	26	24	24	23	23	22	19	17	
Av. temperature	30	24	27	30	33	33	29	28	28	28	27	25	23	
Av. rainfall	60	3	5	5	20	48	43	41	61	125	107	51	3	512

Table 3.1 *continued*

Region Station (Altitude in metres)	No. of years recorded	Jan	Feb	Mar	Apr	May	June	July	Aug	Sept	Oct	Nov	Dec	Year
Humid: tendency to summer drought: 4 – 7 wet months														
12. Madras (16)														
Av. daily max.	60	29	31	33	35	38	38	36	35	34	32	29	29	
Av. daily min.	60	19	20	22	26	28	27	26	26	25	24	22	21	
Av. temperature	60	24	25	28	31	33	33	31	31	30	28	26	25	
Av. rainfall	clino	24	7	15	25	52	53	83	124	118	267	308	157	1,233
13. Trincomalee (7)														
Av. daily max.	25	27	28	29	32	33	33	33	33	33	31	29	27	
Av. daily min.	25	24	24	24	26	26	26	26	25	25	24	24	24	
Av. temperature	clino	26	26	27	29	30	30	30	29	29	28	26	26	
Av. rainfall	clino	211	95	48	77	68	18	54	103	89	235	355	374	1,727
Humid: maximum rainfall in summer monsoon: 4 – 5 wet months														
14. Bombay (11)														
Av. daily max.	60	28	28	30	32	33	32	29	29	29	32	32	31	
Av. daily min.	60	19	19	22	24	27	26	25	24	24	24	23	21	
Av. temperature	60	24	24	26	28	30	29	27	27	27	28	28	26	
Av. rainfall	clino	2	1	0	3	16	520	709	419	297	88	21	2	2,078
15. Nagpur (310)														
Av. daily max.	28	28	32	37	41	43	37	31	31	32	32	29	27	
Av. daily min.	28	13	16	20	24	28	16	24	24	23	20	16	12	
Av. temperature	28	21	24	29	33	36	32	28	28	28	26	23	20	
Av. rainfall	clino	14	19	22	20	13	210	407	288	173	65	17	3	1,251
6 – 7 wet months														
16. Calcutta (6)														
Av. daily max.	60	27	29	34	36	36	33	32	32	32	32	29	26	
Av. daily min.	60	13	15	21	24	25	26	26	26	26	23	18	13	
Av. temperature	60	20	22	28	30	30	30	29	29	29	28	24	20	
Av. rainfall	clino	13	24	27	43	121	259	301	306	290	160	35	3	1,582
17. Kathmandu (1,324)														
Av. daily max.	10	18	19	25	28	30	29	29	28	28	27	23	19	
Av. daily min.	10	2	4	7	12	16	19	20	20	19	13	7	3	
Av. temperature	10	10	13	17	20	23	24	24	24	23	20	15	11	
Av. rainfall	10	19	9	36	32	99	198	378	346	168	37	4	2	1,328
8 – 9 wet months														
18. Chittagong (14)														
Av. daily max.	60	26	28	31	32	32	31	30	30	31	31	29	26	
Av. daily min.	60	13	15	19	23	24	25	25	24	24	23	18	14	
Av. temperature	clino	20	24	26	28	28	28	28	28	28	27	24	21	
Av. rainfall	clino	10	23	58	116	285	507	642	572	344	228	56	17	2,858
19. Tezpur (79)														
Av. daily max.	20	23	24	28	28	31	32	32	32	32	30	27	24	
Av. daily min.	19	11	13	17	19	22	25	26	26	25	22	16	12	
Av. temperature	19	17	19	23	24	27	29	29	29	29	26	22	18	
Av. rainfall	20	13	28	58	158	252	305	366	366	208	107	18	5	1,884
20. Cochin (3)														
Av. daily max.	43	32	32	33	33	32	29	29	29	29	31	31	32	
Av. daily min.	43	22	23	25	26	26	24	23	24	24	24	24	23	
Av. temperature	43	27	28	29	30	29	27	26	27	27	28	28	28	
Av. rainfall	60	23	20	51	125	297	724	592	353	196	340	171	41	2,933
21. Colombo (7)														
Av. daily max.	25	30	31	31	31	31	29	29	29	29	29	29	29	
Av. daily min.	25	22	22	23	24	26	25	25	25	25	24	23	22	
Av. temperature	clino	26	26	27	28	28	27	27	27	27	27	26	26	
Av. rainfall	clino	88	96	118	260	353	212	140	124	153	354	324	175	2,397
10 wet months														
22. Simla (2,202)														
Av. daily max.	30	8	9	14	18	22	23	21	19	19	17	14	11	
Av. daily min.	30	2	3	7	11	14	16	16	15	14	11	7	4	
Av. temperature	30	5	6	11	15	18	20	19	17	17	14	11	8	
Av. rainfall	75	61	69	61	53	66	175	424	434	160	33	13	28	1,577

Sources: US Dept. of Commerce, *World Weather Records*, 1951 – 60 Vol. 4 Asia 1967
Great Britain, Meteorological Office, *Tables of Temperature, Relative Humidity and Precipitation for the World*, Part V: Asia, 1966

Notes: Clino means climatic normal, the average over a long period, t = trace

near-equatorial south, along the west coast, and around the head of the Bay of Bengal that average daily maxima fail to top 38°C (100°F). The effect of continentality is clear. Absolute maxima at stations well inland, like New Delhi, Jodhpur and in the plains of Pakistan lie in the 40s (°C) for five or six months.

For Jacobabad in the Kachhi Plain of Sind, one of the world's notorious 'hot spots', the June maximum averages 45°C and the absolute maximum soars to 53°C; the average minimum is 29°C. Intolerable as such heat may be thought to be, it must not be overlooked that at these temperatures low humidity may give some amelioration. In fact, Jacobabad's June nights at 29°C may be pleasant compared with those at Karachi at 28°C, where the higher humidity on the coast makes both night and day almost unbearably oppressive.

From an examination of the temperature regimes of characteristic stations in Figure 3.3 the following salient features emerge.

The characteristic regime shows a relatively steep climb in temperature from a midwinter minimum (December or January) to a maximum in May or June, the peak of the hot dry weather. With the break of the monsoon, bringing fairly general cloud if not rain, the temperature drops less abruptly through July–August–September. In some cases this falling-off takes the form of a trough on the graph, as temperatures rise again to a secondary maximum in September–October, reflecting the reduction in frequency of rainfall and in cloud cover.

Generally, temperatures fall more steeply again from October to December, marking the change in meteorological conditions following the re-establishment of the jet-stream south of the Himalaya. In winter the diurnal range of temperature is greater than in summer at most stations, a consequence of lower minima resulting from night radiation in clear weather.

Diurnal and seasonal range tend to increase with latitude and with continentality of position: compare Bombay with Pune and Nagpur, and Karachi with Lahore.

Several progressions may be noted. Colombo's near equatorial equability is modified in Trincomalee where rainfall is mainly in winter, the associated cloudiness reducing daytime temperatures. In summer the positions are reversed, Trincomalee suffering higher temperatures while Colombo benefits from greater cloud cover.

Calcutta, basically similar to Nagpur but with a slightly smaller diurnal range on account of its position nearer to the sea, may be contrasted with Tezpur further east, where early pre-monsoon rainy weather moderates temperatures in March–April–May while they are rising month by month in the metropolis. Simla, typical of the Himalayan hill stations to which the British used to flee to escape the stifling heat of the plains, illustrates the effect of altitude. Its regime is, in general, closely parallel to that of New Delhi. Although at 2,202 m (cf. New Delhi, 216 m) Simla's average minima in winter are only two to three degrees below those of the plains city, its absolute minima are much lower. More importantly, its average summer maxima lie 15–19°C below the maxima at New Delhi.

13 Houses in Karachi present a blank windowless wall to the street and are capped by ventilators which catch the southwest monsoon winds and sea breezes in the hottest period of the year. Only males are visible in the street.

Rainfall

It is appropriate to introduce this discussion of rainfall regimes with the cool season which begins over much of South Asia with one or two months of absolute drought. November, and more assuredly December, are months when rain is extremely rare except in the southeast of Tamilnadu and the adjacent northern part of Sri Lanka. The rains here are due in part to the 'retreating monsoon' – of which more below – and to the onset of the so-called northeast monsoon, the trade winds setting directly on-shore from the Jaffna Peninsula southeast past Trincomalee.

From January to March passing depressions bring some precipitation to the northwest of the subcontinent and along the length of the Himalaya, but most of the mainland remains dry as the cool season turns to hot. The first inklings of pre-monsoon rain reach the extreme northeast in March.

With the passing of the March equinox it becomes evident that the cool season is over. Temperatures rise day by day, and one looks forward to afternoon cloud to reduce the build-up of heat in buildings and so moderate the evening temperature. In April, thunder showers bring temporary respite. By May the Intertropical Convergence Zone, the ITC, with which is associated heavy equatorial convectional rainfall, begins to move gradually northwards across India, bringing with it the 'break' of the monsoon.

Fig. 3.4

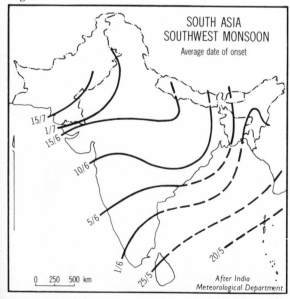

SOUTH ASIA
SOUTHWEST MONSOON
Average date of onset

15/7
1/7
15/6
10/6
5/6
1/6
25/5
20/5

0   250   500 km

After India
Meteorological Department

The southwest winds which give the summer monsoon its prefix, are the resultant of cyclonic airflows within the monsoon air mass. This, as the dates of its first burst indicate, is moving more directly northward (Fig. 3.4). The southwest monsoon winds sweep across the Western Ghats bringing torrential orographic rain to the steep scarp and the coast at its foot. The airstream recovers stability as it descends across the Deccan, which thus lies in typical rainshadow relationship to the Ghats. In eastern India the monsoon drives from the south towards Bengal, one part swinging up the Ganga Valley, as a southeast stream under the deflective influence of the Himalaya. Another part moves as a converging and ascending airstream between the Northeastern Hills and the Meghalaya Plateau, dousing in its wake the hill town of Cherrapunji, whose sole claim to fame is as holder of the world's average rainfall record of 11,437 mm. A daily downpour of as much as 924 mm has occurred in June, when the normal total for the month is almost 2,700 mm. The other airstream, travelling up the Ganga Valley, spreads heavy rain along the Himalayan ranges. It loses moisture and thickness as it goes, arriving over the Thar Desert only 500 metres thick and inhibited from releasing its remaining load of moisture by an overriding 'lid' of warmer westerly air originating in the mid-latitude subtropical high pressure cell that stands semi-permanently over the Sahara and extends a ridge across Iran, Afghanistan and the Indus Valley. When on occasion this lid retreats westward, the desert receives one of its rare soakings, and the possibility exists for the convergence of two humid airstreams, that from the Ganga Valley, and that flowing directly from the Arabian Sea.

Throughout the monsoon, dynamic waves in the ITC cause the characteristic pulsations in the weather, bringing periods of heavy rain interspersed with brief respites of clear but unpleasantly sticky conditions, which increase in length during August to become the dominant feature of September's weather. Thereafter settled conditions return in the north, and the ITC retreats southwards, continuing to allow a measure of convergence and precipitation over a diminishing area of southern India. In the Bay of Bengal the effect of this 'retreating monsoon' in bringing an autumnal maximum to the Tamilnadu coast is reinforced by the occasional occurrence of tropical cyclones, which move westwards across the Bay to trace arcuate clockwise courses along India's east coast and the delta fringe of Bangladesh. Tropical cyclones are responsible for heavy rainfall in October – November, and sometimes for considerable devastation and loss of life particularly in Orissa, West Bengal and Bangladesh. Storm surges associated with cyclones heading into the shallowing and narrowing waters at the head of the Bay of Bengal can sweep sea water inland, as in Bangladesh in 1970.

The amount of rainfall and its seasonal incidence are the most significant facts influencing agriculture. Figure 3.5 shows annual average rainfall. The influence of the Western Ghats and the Himalaya, Meghalaya Plateau, Northeastern and Sri Lankan Hills in stimulating precipitation is clear, as are also the rainshadow in the Deccan, and the diminution of total rainfall up the Ganga Valley. It may be noted that the 1,000 mm isohyet divides South Asia into two roughly equal parts, a division that carries into agricultural regionalisation as the boundary between rain-fed rice cultivation and that of wheat or millets. Different aspects of rainfall incidence are depicted in Figure 3.6 showing the length of wet and dry seasons, Figure 3.7 of rainfall incidence and the rainfall dispersion diagrams for individual stations (Figure 3.8).

The rains arrive earliest and last longest in Sri Lanka, Kerala and coastal Karnataka in the southwest, and in the northeast from Orissa to Bangladesh and Assam. The highest parts of these regions, and the Central and Kashmir Himalaya, have no true dry season, though the regime of their rainfall is clearly monsoonal. The Central and Kashmir Himalaya, the Karakoram and the Northwest Frontier Hills have a substantial winter precipitation from depressions arriving from the west. Central India, with four to five wet months from June to October embodies the average characteristic of the monsoon. To the northwest the wet season is reduced to two or three months starting in July. The Thar Desert and Sind with notoriously erratic rainfall, tend to receive whatever comes in July at the time the monsoon breaks. In the southeast, Tamilnadu and adjacent parts of Andhra, although in the path of the monsoon as it passes over the Peninsula from the southwest, are in a rainshadow due to the subsidence of the dyna-

14   A Wakhi farmer rides his yak in the high valley semi arid grazing lands of upper Baroghil, in inner Gilgit. Lack of moisture in the rain shadow of the Himalaya and very low winter temperatures restrict vegetation to herbs and grasses.
(Courtesy Elizabeth Staley).

Fig. 3.5

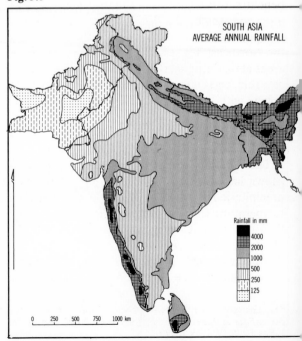

SOUTH ASIA
AVERAGE ANNUAL RAINFALL

Rainfall in mm

4000
2000
1000
500
250
125

0   250   500   750   1000 km

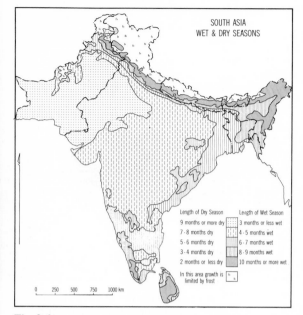

SOUTH ASIA
WET & DRY SEASONS

Length of Dry Season	Length of Wet Season
9 months or more dry	3 months or less wet
7 - 8 months dry	4 - 5 months wet
5 - 6 months dry	6 - 7 months wet
3 - 4 months dry	8 - 9 months wet
2 months or less dry	10 months or more wet

In this area growth is limited by frost

0   250   500   750   1000 km

Fig. 3.6

mic southwesterly airstream. They have some rain, but their major falls come from August onwards into November when the doldrum conditions of the retreating monsoon settle over this region and Kerala. A small coastal strip around Palk Bay on the mainland has four wet months starting in October. Only this area of India can be said to benefit substantially from the so-called northeast monsoon which, as a flow of air across the Bay of Bengal, is for four of five months the assertion of the Northeast Trades, the typical wind in oceanic areas at this latitude. It does not set in until January as a rule, and cannot be credited (despite common belief) with the rainfall more properly assigned to the earlier retreating monsoon. Trincomalee (Table 3.1) with the rest of north and east Sri Lanka benefits most from the northeast monsoon.

The durations of both wet and dry seasons are shown in Figure 3.6. A wet month is one in which precipitation (in mm) exceeds twice the average temperature (in °C). Where precipitation is less than this value it has been shown that conditions of stress appear in vegetation in South Asia.* Although a small proportion of annual rainfall comes outside the monsoon period, the latter

*H. Gaussen, 'The vegetation maps', *Travaux de la Section Scientifique et Technique*, Inst. Francais de Pondichery, Tome 1, Fasciscule IV, 1959, p. 170

accounts for around 80 per cent of the total. Exceptions to this are the Indus Plains and the areas to the west (where the monsoon's share falls away from 50 per cent to less than ten on the Iranian border) and parts of Sri Lanka. The length of the dry season gives a fair indication of the need for irrigation if agriculture is to be carried on outside the rainy season.

Figure 3.9 brings together the essential climatic elements of concern to the cultivator: temperature and the amount, duration and incidence of rainfall. Cold climates, where average temperatures below freezing for a month or more are a severe constraint on agriculture, are limited to the Himalaya and higher parts of the northwest. The inner regions of Kashmir, the upper Indus Valley and the Karakoram, are distinguished by their aridity. (Note Leh in Fig. 3.8.)

Fig. 3.7

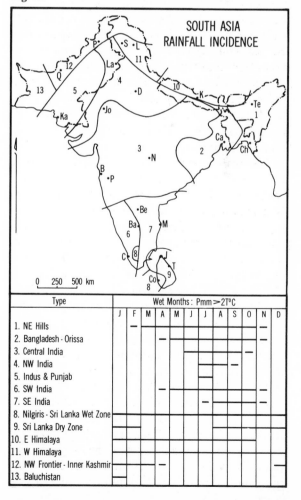

SOUTH ASIA
RAINFALL INCIDENCE

0   250   500 km

Type	Wet Months: Pmm > 2T°C											
	J	F	M	A	M	J	J	A	S	O	N	D
1. NE Hills		—										
2. Bangladesh - Orissa					—							
3. Central India									—			
4. NW India								—				
5. Indus & Punjab								—				
6. SW India					—							
7. SE India								—				
8. Nilgiris - Sri Lanka Wet Zone												
9. Sri Lanka Dry Zone												
10. E Himalaya												
11. W Himalaya												
12. NW Frontier - Inner Kashmir		—										
13. Baluchistan												

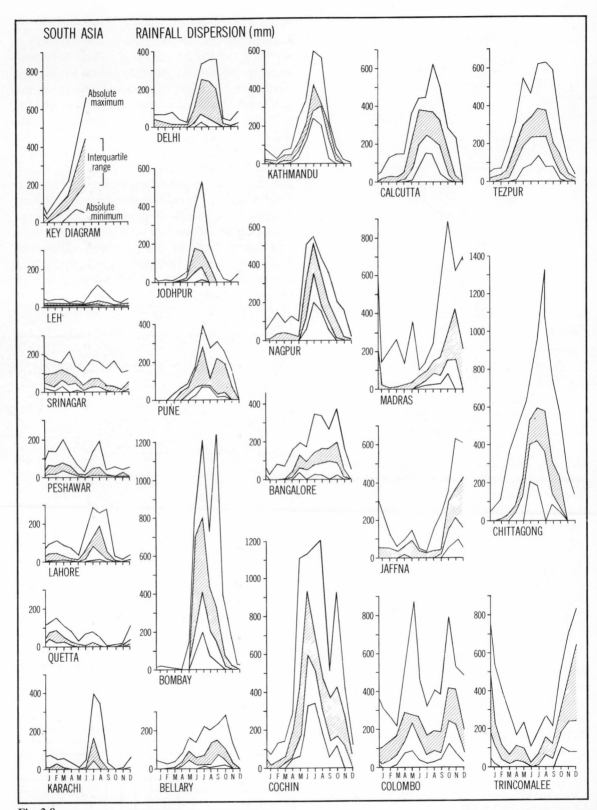

Fig. 3.8

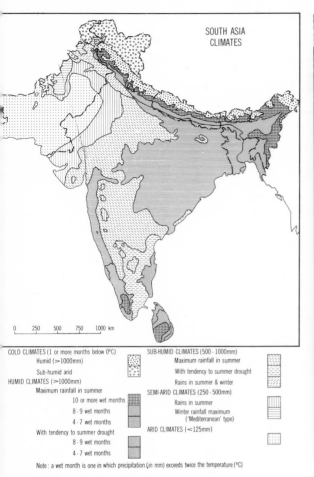

SOUTH ASIA
CLIMATES

0   250   500   750   1000 km

COLD CLIMATES (1 or more months below 0°C)
    Humid (>1000mm)
    Sub-humid arid
HUMID CLIMATES (>1000mm)
    Maximum rainfall in summer
        10 or more wet months
        8 - 9 wet months
        4 - 7 wet months
    With tendency to summer drought
        8 - 9 wet months
        4 - 7 wet months

SUB-HUMID CLIMATES (500 - 1000mm)
    Maximum rainfall in summer
    With tendency to summer drought
    Rains in summer & winter
SEMI-ARID CLIMATES (250 - 500mm)
    Rains in summer
    Winter rainfall maximum
        ('Mediterranean' type)
ARID CLIMATES (<125mm)

Note : a wet month is one in which precipitation (in mm) exceeds twice the temperature (°C)

Fig. 3.9

15 Around the outside of the walls of Jodhpur Fort is packed the city with its flat roofs appropriate to the arid climate. In the distance are barren rocky hills.

For the rest, rainfall rather than temperature is the basis for division. Relative terms are used to distinguish four climatic types: *humid* for those with more than 1,000 mm of rainfall per year: *sub-humid* for those with between 500 and 1,000 mm, *semi-arid* between 250 and 500 mm, and *arid* with below 250 mm. The length of the rainy season (as already defined) within the two relevant regimes, the one with summer rains and the other tending to summer drought, gives five regional types which are agriculturally distinctive. The sub-humid climates may be separated on the basis of regime (or its absence in areas of equable distribution). The semi-arid and arid climates are not subdivided.

Chapter 4

India: The Political Map

Constitutionally, India is a federation of 22 States together with a number of Union Territories administered by the central government. The States and Territories (as in 1978) are shown in Figure 4.1. The pattern of India's political geography reflects a number of different forces at work.

At the time of gaining independence from British rule India still contained within its territory a number of French and Portuguese enclaves dating from the early days of European mercantile contact with the country. The French retired gracefully and promptly from the scene, handing over to India the sovereignty of Pondicherry (where they now maintain a valuable research institute) and

the associated enclaves shown in Figure 4.1. The Portuguese held on to their possessions until 1961 when India forced the issue by the military occupation of the principal area, Goa, so ending European suzerainty in South Asia. The former enclaves still retain, however, a measure of separate identity as Union Territories, and have so far not been absorbed by the contiguous States.

As to the internal boundaries of the Indian State, two factors have been uppermost. The British, in the course of 200 years of political domination, had divided up the subcontinent into 11 provinces (in which the process of introducing self-government had progressed with varying degrees of success) and a patchwork of 'Native' Indian or princely states in which a form of indirect rule through hereditary Maharajas, Rajas etc., obtained. Until the East India Company handed over political control to the British government after the Indian Mutiny of 1857 (now termed the First War of Independence), the Company had been gradually extending the area of its direct rule. The British Government put a stop to this process and effectively froze the pattern of princely states as of 1857, each becoming a protectorate of the British Crown (Fig. 4.1).

The coming of independence in 1947 enabled this pattern to be unfrozen, and indeed threw the whole political system into the melting pot from which was cast, after several modifications, the present situation. In this most recent phase of state-making a powerful new factor, that of language, has operated. A comparison of the map of States with that of the distribution of major languages (Figs. 4.1 and 4.2) shows several significant correlations. Where language is not a differentiating factor, the boundaries of the former British Indian provinces can often be traced, but substantial alterations have been made to the pattern of the former princely states. Democratic, usually linguistically determined, States have re-

Fig. 4.1

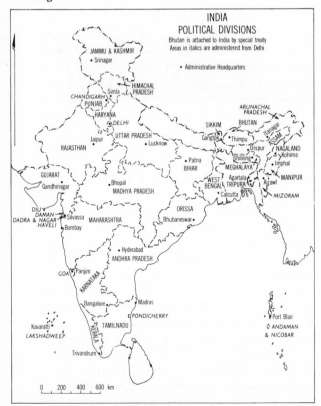

INDIA
POLITICAL DIVISIONS
Bhutan is attached to India by special treaty
Areas in italics are administered from Delhi

• Administrative Headquarters

placed the latter, some of which – like Hyderabad – leave scarcely a trace on the map today. Others like Mysore (now Karnataka) live on with altered boundaries as well as new constitutions.

Several hundred languages and dialects are spoken in India. The 1961 Census enumerated 1,653 'mother-tongues' of which 82 were spoken by more than 100,000 people in 1971. The 23 major languages with the number claiming them as their mother-tongue are listed in Table 4.1 which covers 96 per cent of the population. The vast majority of the population speak a language belonging to one of two families, Indo-Aryan and Dravidian. Speakers of several of the Indo-Aryan languages find it relatively easy to communicate across language barriers in 'bazar Hindi' which serves as a *lingua franca* for much of northern India. Hindi is the official national language and is widely used in the north in education and administration. In the south, the four major Dravidian languages domi-

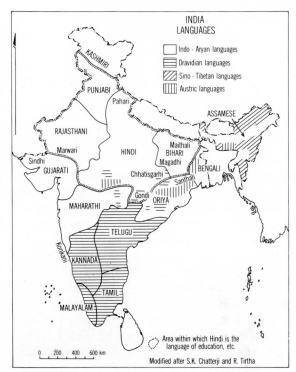

Fig. 4.2

Table 4.1 Principal languages, 1971
(millions and per cent of total population)

Language	No.	%
1. Hindi	163	30
2. Bengali	45	8
3. *Telugu*	45	8
4. Marathi	42	8
5. *Tamil*	38	7
6. Urdu	29	5
7. Gujarati	26	5
8. *Malayalam*	22	4
9. *Kannada*	22	4
10. Oriya	20	4
11. Punjabi	16	3
12. Bhojpuri (Bihari)	14	2.6
13. Assamese	9	1.6
14. *Chhatisgarhi*	7	1.3
15. Magahi/Magadhi	7	1.3
16. Maithili	6	1.1
17. Marwari	5	0.9
18. Santhali*	4	0.7
19. Kashmiri	2	0.4
20. Rajasthani	2	0.4
21. Sindhi	1.7	0.3
22. *Gondi*	1.5	0.3
23. Konkani	1.5	0.3

*Santhali belongs to the Austro-Asiatic branch of the Austic group of languages. With the exception of Santhali the languages shown in Roman script belong to the Aryan family: those in italics are Dravidian languages

nate and their speakers may find English an easier means of communicating when outside their own State, though Hindi, now being taught as the second language in schools, may well be displacing English. In central government, while Hindi is the language established by the constitution, English is legally acceptable. The speakers of Tamil, Telugu, Kannada and Malayalam in the Dravidian States tend still to resent any threat to force upon them Hindi, the language of what they see as a dominating north.

The close fit of the pattern of States with that of languages is clear from the maps. The four largest Dravidian languages have their own States: Tamilnadu, Andhra Pradesh (Telugu), Karnataka (Kannada) and Kerala (Malayalam).

In the Indo-Aryan areas the truly linguistic States are Maharashtra (Maharathi) and Gujarat (Gujarati), essentially carved out of old Bombay Province, Punjab (Punjabi), West Bengal (Bengali) and Orissa (Oriya). Hindi is the language of Rajasthan, Haryana, Himachal Pradesh, Uttar Pradesh, Madhya Pradesh and Bihar, though in the latter there are pressures for the recognition of Bhojpuri. In Assam, while the majority speak Assamese, there is strong rivalry from Bengali spoken by a vigorous minority. In the hills of the northeast, former hill states and tribal areas have achieved statehood on the basis of tribal affiliations rather than on strictly linguistic grounds. Thus Tripura, Manipur, Nagaland and Meghalaya have become fully fledged if abnormally small States. Most of Jammu and Kashmir in the western Himalaya is administered by India as an integral State of the Union with Urdu as its official language reflecting the Muslim majority of its people, who would however claim Kashmiri as their mother-tongue. Its western margins are under Pakistan control as 'Azad Kashmir'.

16   A porter pulls his heavy load in the wholesale market, Bangalore. Human labour is still cheap in India.

Apart from Delhi with over four million people, the Union Territories are the relatively small former colonial enclaves: Goa, Daman and Diu, and Dadra and Nagar Haveli (once Portuguese), Pondicherry (French); the backward and strategically sensitive areas on the northeast frontier; Arunachal Pradesh and Mizoram; the island groups of the Andaman and Nicobar Islands in the bay of Bengal and Lakshadweep in the Arabian Sea; and Chandigarh, the joint shared capital of the original Punjab State later partitioned to make Punjab and Haryana.

Table 4.2 sets out the administrative divisions of India, and their populations at the last census and the principal languages spoken.

The creation of linguistic States has met the demand for regional identity but carries with it the risk that local loyalties may outweigh the sense of national unity. Bangladesh's example of national self-determination is unlikely to be followed by any of the Indian states; central government holds the purse strings and in its planning seems to work to prevent the development in any State of excessive feelings of injustice that might encourage serious thoughts of secession from the Union. This is not to say that there are no language problems. The non-Hindi speaking States may unwittingly perhaps inhibit intercourse between States by insisting on the use of the State language in schools and

Table 4.2   Administrative division of India

States	Population (millions)	Main languages
Uttar Pradesh	88	Hindi, Urdu
Bihar	56	Hindi, Bihari
Maharashtra	50	Marathi
Andhra Pradesh	44	Telugu
West Bengal	44	Bengali
Madhya Pradesh	41	Hindi, Gondi, etc.
Tamilnadu	41	Tamil
Karnataka	29	Kannada
Gujarat	27	Gujarati
Rajasthan	26	Rajasthani, Hindi
Orissa	22	Oriya
Kerala	21	Malayalam
Assam	15	Assamese, Bengali
Punjab	14	Punjabi
Haryana	10	Hindi
Jammu & Kashmir	5	Kashmiri
Himachal Pradesh	3	Hindi, Pahari
Tripura	1.6	Bengali, Tripuri, Manipuri
Manipur	1.1	Manipuri, Bengali
Meghalaya	1.0	Khasi, Jaintia, Garo
Nagaland	0.5	Various tribal
Sikkim	0.2	Bhutia, Nepali

Union territories	Population (thousands)	
Delhi	4,066	Hindi, Urdu, Punjabi
Goa, Daman, Diu	858	Marathi, Kannada
Pondicherry	472	Tamil
Arunachal Pradesh	468	Various tribal
Mizoram	332	Various tribal
Chandigarh	257	Punjabi, Hindi
Andaman & Nicobar Islands	115	Andamanese, Nicobarese
Dadra and Nagar Haveli	74	Gujarati, Marathi
Lakshadweep	32	Malayalam

universities. Barriers are thus erected to the free flow of educated job-seekers from one State to another. Speakers of a minority mother-tongue, like Gondi in Maharashtra, for example, really face the prospect of becoming tri- or even quad-ralingual if they are to aspire to the highest offices in the land. In addition to Gondi, they need Marathi (the State language) in the local schools, the national language Hindi, to gain access to central government employment, and English for higher, university education. Variation of scripts adds to the difficulties of interstate travel; the literate Hindi speaker driving into neighbouring Punjab cannot read the sign posts written in Gurmukhi script, and similar problems face the traveller from Karnataka into Maharashtra. With only 29 per cent of the population recorded as literate in 1971 (39 per cent of the males, 19 per cent of the females) the situation is not yet as acute as its parallel in Europe would be were English, French, German and Italian each to use different scripts, but the potential of linguistic differentiation for political divisiveness seems likely to increase rather than otherwise as the country develops.

Government

As a Union of States, India is governed by the President elected by an electoral college of the Houses of Parliament of the central government and the Legislative Assemblies of the States. The President is advised by a Council of Ministers, led by the Prime Minister, who are responsible to the House of the People, the Lok Sabha, which is elected by universal adult franchise, its membership being approximately proportionate to the population of the State. There is an Upper House, the Rajya Sabha or Council of the States, which has a 'rotating' membership mostly elected by the members of the State Legislative Assembly of each State, which body is directly elected by the people. In turn each State has a Legislative Council composed partly of elected members of the Assembly and partly of non-members representative of local government, educational and cultural interests. The Lok Sabha holds final control of money matters, and may in times of emergency intervene in areas normally reserved to the States.

Most revenue is collected by the Centre which distributes funds to the States. Within the plans

17 A village market preparing for business at Seringapatam, near Mysore in Karnataka. Earthern ware pots and woven baskets are essential domestic utensils. Small stalls sell the vegetable produce of individual farmers. The umbrellas are shelter from the high sun.

approved by the Centre these are responsible for executing schemes for development and for the day-to-day running of their administrations. The Centre is directly responsible for administering the Union Territories in most of which there are Legislative Assemblies with powers, however, less wide than those of the State Legislatures.

India's system of government is, then, a federal one, similar in many respects to that of Canada or Australia. The States are very dependent on the Centre and tend to be dominated by it. Although subjects, such as agriculture, education, cooperatives, industry and health are State responsibilities under the constitution, the policies the States should adopt are dictated by the Centre which holds the purse strings. The dominance of a single party at the Centre from Independence to 1977 is seen as contributory to this situation in which the Planning Commission has become very powerful and 'ubiquitous' in its role.*

The strength of the system lies in its broadly democratic basis. Among its weaknesses is the risk that States may receive development finance for political reasons rather than to meet purely economic and social ends, and the real difficulty of compelling a reluctant State legislature – which probably draws its power from the landed and wealthier classes – to implement effectively legislation such as land reforms which strike at their own power base.

Intermediate between the Centre and the States are five Zonal Councils, Northern, Eastern,

*W. H. Morris-Jones, in M. Venkatarangaiya and M. Shiviah (Eds), *Indian Federalism*, New Delhi, 1976

18   A village Panchayat in Tamil Nadu. The women members stand to one side.

Western, Southern and Northeastern, whose function is to discuss matters of common interest among the States and Union Territories within the Zone. The Northeastern Council covers Assam and the smaller States of Manipur, Meghalaya, Nagaland and Tripura, plus the Union Territories of Arunachal Pradesh and Mizoram. These are grouped together for the coordination and unification (where appropriate) of planning. With these responsibilities and powers of review of security measures within the Zone, the Northeast Council has the character of a decentralized executive body of the Centre.

Within the States there is generally 'grass-roots' democratic government exercised by elected local bodies. Village assemblies or Gram Sabhas elect Panchayats which have wide responsibilities for the economic and social welfare of the community. They derive funds from house and land taxes, levies on markets and fairs, sales taxes, etc. While broadly democratic, they are required to ensure that the scheduled caste and tribal population of the village are directly represented, and also the women. A

group of Panchayats constitute a Block and above this is the District, with democratic representative committees at each level. Members of State Civil Services provide full-time expertise and executive responsibility.

Urban areas are administered by Corporations, Municipal Committees or Councils, depending on their size, and these embody principles similar to those underlying Panchayat Raj or rule.

While the constitutional legal framework of a free democracy exists, – and in law all men are equal – the facts of social and economic life often belie these ideals. Inequalities of wealth and opportunity based on caste are rife.

Caste is probably the strongest element in the Hindu way of life, and despite some weakening of its former rigidity and strength, particularly in the cities, it still permeates rural society and inhibits its weaker, lower-caste members from asserting their constitutional rights and raising their socioeconomic status. Caste is basically a system of functional stratification of the society, maintained by religious sanctions. It seems to have its origins in the domination of tribal populations by immigrant groups, and so had some genetic basis, though despite theoretical prohibitions on inter-caste marriage, the racial identity of caste or tribe has long since disappeared.

There are basically three groups of castes. At the apex of the system are the Brahmins, the priestly caste of the Hindu religion, themselves divided into three main exogamous sub-castes: the highest are scholars of the Hindu religious books, while ranking below them are the temple priests and the priests who perform religious rites for the non-Brahmins. In practice, Brahmins may be land-owners, or belong to a variety of professions. As a general rule they are well educated and seldom poor. The second and largest group are the non-Brahmin caste Hindus, including landowning castes, cultivators, traders, moneylenders, artisans like potters, goldsmiths and carpenters, and castes rendering services to Brahmins and caste non-Brahmins, such as barbers and washermen. Below these are the group of 'untouchable' castes, the Harijans, who nevertheless live in association with the higher caste groups as labourers and menials, sweepers, disposers of dead animals, human excreta and so forth. They were formerly (and in practice still sometimes feel themselves) debarred from temples and from streets occupied by Brahmins.

Under the village *jajmani* system the rights, responsibilities and obligations of each caste group towards the others are clearly established in practice by tradition, and caste committees may extract penalties from those who fail to observe the rules.

The tribal Adivasis have generally remained outside the congeries of castes described above, but when they do come into socio-economic association it is at a very low rank in the hierarchy.

Of recent years the five-year plans have stressed as objectives the dissemination throughout the nation of social justice, and the improvements of the lot of the 'backward classes', a term now used to include the scheduled castes (the 'Untouchables' or Harijans), the scheduled and other tribes, and others in the population constituting the lowest 20 – 30 per cent in economic terms. There are 80 million in the scheduled castes (almost 15 per cent of the total population) and 38 million (almost 7 per cent) in scheduled tribes. If the pressures for self-determination of States on the basis of language have now largely been met, there remains the possibility of similar pressures developing from the tribal population of Central India where there is talk of a movement for a State to collect together the scheduled tribes of Madhya Pradesh, Bihar, Orissa and West Bengal.

19 Vidhan Sondha – Government House of Karnataka State, Bangalore. (Courtesy Nina Johnson).

Chapter 5

India: Food for the People

How many people?

India, already with over 625 million people, appears poised on the brink of demographic change. While mortality rates have been declining over many decades under the impact of modernisation in public health and protective medicine, the maintenance of a very high birth rate has resulted in a rise in the rate of population growth from one census to the next. After a decade or so of vigorous propaganda it seems that family planning is beginning to influence the population equation. It is essential for the success of national economic planning, for food self-sufficiency and for better standards of living that this should come about as soon as possible.

Poverty is endemic throughout India, and with it both qualitative and quantitative deficiencies in the diet. Adequate food properly distributed throughout the society is an essential prerequisite for the creation of a population physically and mentally energetic enough to tackle the problems of development. Since Independence there has been a continuous struggle at the national level to grow enough food to meet demand and so to become independent of food imports. In years of drought, imports have exceeded 10 million tonnes; in good years less than half a million tonnes has been needed, and current hopes are that 1975–76 marked the beginning of an era in which the government controlled sufficient stocks of grain to meet year-to-year fluctuations and so keep prices stable and imports to a minimum.

At the 1971 Census the population totalled 548 million, an increase of nearly 25 per cent over 1961. A total of 700 million is expected in 1986 according to the planners, or in 1982 if the intercensal rate of increase were maintained. Figure 5.1 summarises

Fig. 5.1

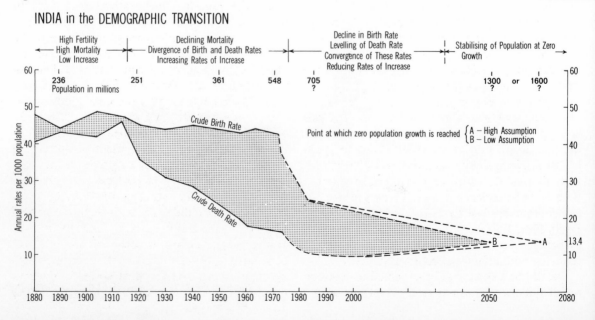

INDIA in the DEMOGRAPHIC TRANSITION

20 Transplanting paddy seedlings into irrigated fields for a dry season crop, near Goa. Some of the cultivators probably find employment in the iron mines lying beyond the ridge in the background.

the vital statistics for India over the past 100 years and projects forward to a time when numbers are stabilised.

In terms of the theory of the demographic transition the first turning point in India's population history came after World War I. Up to that time India had experienced high birth rates and equally high death rates; the former fairly constant, the latter fluctuating with the incidence of epidemic disease, with or without accompanying famine. The total population increased only slowly, some decades registering near static or even slightly falling numbers. From the 1920s, public health measures including mass inoculation against small-pox and the increasing application of preventive and curative medicine had a dramatic impact on the death rate which, as the graph shows, plummeted through the inter-war years and continued falling after Independence. The immediate effect of this is vividly demonstrated in the lengthening of the lifespan. In 1921 an Indian could expect to live to be 20 (on average); by 1941 this expectation at birth had risen to 32, which remained the span at the time of Independence. Subsequently the increase has continued, to 41 by 1961 and 47 by 1971. The Draft Fifth Five-Year Plan projects the increase to 54 by 1978 and 56 by 1983. All this is due to reducing both infant and adult mortality.

Death rates, then, can be expected to continue to fall, but at a diminishing rate, to reach an annual rate of perhaps 10 per thousand in the middle 1980s and thereafter inevitably to rise a little as the population as a whole begins to have a larger proportion of ageing people.

The birth rate on the other hand has not yet changed appreciably. It had fallen from its traditional levels in the high 40s to the low 40s per thousand by about the time of Independence. Effectively it has remained static since then, at between 40 to 42 per thousand. Apparent falls in the past have been reflections of the larger total population (due to falling death rates) rather than to any real change in reproductive habits. The planners see some glimmerings of change in the sample surveys of 1972 which gave an overall rate of 36.6 compounded of a rural rate of 38.4 and an urban rate of 30.5. Grasping at these straws, they are bold enough to forecast a continuing downward trend to less than 30 by 1978 and to about 25 by 1983.

There has been much propaganda to encourage family planning; indeed, an excess of enthusiasm for sterilisation was partly to blame for the Congress Party's first fall from power in 1977. Ultimately however, it is likely that parents and not government will decide the issue. India is still a very long way from being a welfare state. A man looks to his family and particularly his sons as his only prospect of security in old age or ill health. There is no old-age pension, not even the 'work house' for the aged destitute. For the lowest labouring classes, children are potential breadwinners even if for eight or nine years they are additional mouths to be fed. To their parents the case for family planning cannot be argued in the unanswerable logic that convinces politicians. There is a high probability that some of their children will die before becoming economically useful, and their concern to ensure there will be sons to maintain them justifies their large families. While this social pattern persists, and until the health and survival of the children of the poor can be assured, the authoritarian imposition of family limitation might be seen by them–at least–as a grievous injustice.

India's demographic experience is summarised in the population pyramid (Fig. 5.2). It is a broad-based pyramid characteristic of the less developed countries (LDCs). In the highly developed countries (HDCs), where infant mortality rates are low and life expectancy is high, there is little tapering in the pyramid until middle age, where mortality begins to thin out the age groups. The age – sex pyramid for Sweden (Fig. 5.2) is characteristic of a mature HDC.

A consequence of India's demographic structure is its high dependency ratio. In 1973 it was 77, that is 100 people aged 15 – 64 supported 77 aged 0–14 and over 65. This represents a heavy burden on the economically active population and compares with ratios of between 58 and 62 in northern and western Europe, Australia and North America.

How large India's population will become before it stabilises is entirely conjectural. Two estimates are shown in Figure 5.1. On a 'low' assumption, 1,300 million could be the peak reached in the year 2051; on a 'high' assumption, 1,600 million in 2071. What technological innovations and institutional changes will have to occur to make it possible to support populations of this order can only be surmised, and the fundamental question will be whether they can be fed, clothed, housed and educated better than at subsistence or survival level.

The Draft Fifth Five-Year Plan opened with these words: 'Removal of poverty and attainment of economic self-reliance are the two strategic goals that the country has set for itself'. The primary task is to become self-sufficient in food, but equally important is to ensure that work is available to make it possible for every breadwinner to earn the means to purchase it.

Fig. 5.2

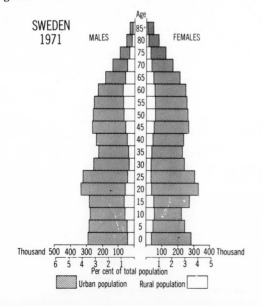

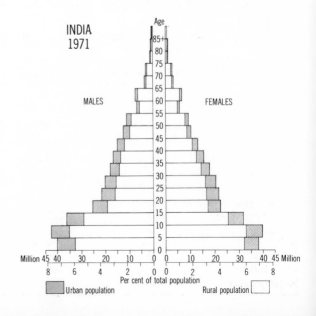

21 Sugar cane is being hauled by tractor to the mill at Kolhapur, Maharashtra.

Food Needs

There are two kinds of food needs to be met to ensure a healthy population: There is a quantitative need, which if not met results in undernourishment and, in extreme circumstances, starvation. There is also a qualitative need, which if not met produces malnutrition and deficiency diseases. Malnutrition is the more insidious since its sufferers may be unaware of the cause of the debility or of the disease to which they are prone. However, malnutrition is rare when quantitative needs are met. The National Institute of Nutrition at Hyderabad, in its *Diet Atlas of India* (1971) sets out separate balanced dietary scales fulfilling the basic needs for calories and protein for strict vegetarians, who make up some 28 per cent of the population, and for non-vegetarians (Table 5.1). The 'average' diet available provided 1,945 calories against an estimated

need of 2,357, and 49 grams of protein against a need of 44.3. Too much of the protein is second class vegetable protein however. In only three States in the 1960s did the average calorie intake exceed the estimated need: Punjab, Haryana and Madhya Pradesh – all predominantly rural.

Cereals play a much larger part in the diet than they do in the more developed countries, and the overall provision of calories and proteins is much lower. Indians by and large need more and better protein than they get, and more calories in total.

The overall extent of undernourishment in the Indian population is difficult to gauge, but P. V. Sukhatme (writing in 1965) considered that between a third and a quarter had too little food. Malnutrition, he thought, was more widespread and affected half the people. The lack of a properly balanced diet is a major factor reducing resistance to disease, and several specific maladies may be

Table 5.1 Daily dietary needs in India (in grammes)

	Vegetarian diet		Non-vegetarian diet		Average per capita need	Average per capita availability (1970)
Cereals	369.5		369.5		369.5	395
Pulses	68.9	78.4	52.2	64.7	68.6	51
Groundnuts	9.5		9.5			
Leafy vegetables	107		107		107	10
Other vegetables	125		125		125	53
Fruits	37		37		37	44
Milk	241		154		178	108
Oils, fats	35		39		38	10
Flesh foods	—		49		35	12
Sugar/jaggery	40		40		40	46

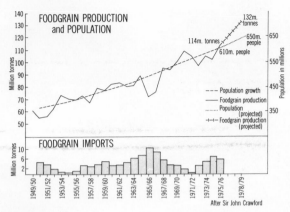

Fig. 5.3

traced to the lack of some mineral or vitamin in the diet. Retarded growth in children is often due to protein deficiency, and Indian diets are notoriously lacking in first class animal protein. Pulses provide second class protein, and it is thought that children in particular need to be able to take in their protein requirements without having to consume an excessive quantity of calories in pulses and cereals in order to do so. The outstanding deficiencies in the average diet are of vegetables and milk, both important sources of protective vitamins and minerals, and both relatively easy to supply from Indian agricultural resources if properly developed. The problem of balancing food production and demand even in years of good rainfall has been ever present since Independence, varying only in the degree to which it has been necessary to spend foreign exchange on imported food grains. Production has increased overall but, as Figure 5.3 shows, it has fluctuated with an inevitable but varying impact on imports. Persistent population increase makes it difficult to close the gap, let alone improve the quantity of foodgrains available per head, and hard to build up the buffer stocks essential to insure against seasonal scarcity due to weather and economic scarcity due to rising prices engineered by hoarders.

Chapter 6

India: Planning and Economic Development

The problems facing Indian planners are formidable. In summary, they have to activate the human resources to produce what the nation needs in the way of food and other raw materials from the soil, and to produce a surplus of such commodities as can profitably be exported. They have to establish and expand industries upon which future economic growth can be erected; to create employment opportunities for the millions of unemployed and underemployed; to raise the general level of economic activity so that people have the means and the opportunity to buy more of the necessities for a better standard of living. At the same time they have to bring about agricultural, industrial, and demographic revolutions as quickly as possible so that the population explosion does not devour the whole substance of whatever increases in production can be achieved. No other country of comparable size has attempted so much within a society committed to parliamentary democracy.

The Five-Year Plans

The policy for development and the broad strategy to be followed by central government ministries and the States in carrying out the policy are laid down in the five plans. To paraphrase the terms of reference of the Planning Commission, derived from the constitution, the aim is to bring about a socialist pattern of society in which both public and private enterprise have a place, but in which the concentration of wealth or power in the hands of a few is to be avoided, and the lot of the more backward and underprivileged in the community is to be raised.

In the First Plan (1951 – 56), agriculture and irrigation received most attention. The necessity to import food had already appeared, caused partly by the loss, following Partition, of the food surplus regions of the Pakistan Punjab and Sind. Transport and communications also had to be rehabilitated in the aftermath of the run-down during the war years followed by the disruption to the system occasioned by Partition.

In the Second Plan (1956 – 61), the ultimate shape of the economy became clearer. Heavy industry and power dominated thinking, rather as they had in the planning of development in the USSR. The establishment of iron and steel industries, heavy chemicals (including fertilisers), and heavy machinery and engineering industries was meant to lay the foundations for future industrial growth.

An interesting aspect of the Third Plan (1961 – 66) and one which persists in subsequent plans, was the emphasis given to power development urgently needed for agriculture (for irrigation pumps) and for industry alike, not to mention the demands of the urban public now enjoying some degree of modernisation of their traditional lifestyle. Self-sufficiency in foodgrains is an objective that has recurred in every plan thereafter, but proves difficult to achieve while the number of mouths to feed persists in increasing at a greater pace. Similarly the need to increase jobs and to reduce disparities in wealth are recurrent themes.

The war with Pakistan in 1965 was an expensive diversion of effort and resources, and was followed by severe droughts which compelled the expenditure of scarce foreign exchange on food imports.

Such was the economic crisis provoked by these events that the Fourth Plan could not be introduced, there being insufficient funds for investment. In the three years that followed, from 1966

22 Coal-fired thermal electric power station. Durgapur, Damodar Valley, West Bengal. The British-built Durgapur Steel Works are visible on the right horizon.

to 1969, *ad hoc* annual plans were implemented with whatever funds could be made available, and a fresh Fourth Five-Year Plan period began in 1969.

Outlays under the Fourth Plan were more in balance than previously, allowing that the investment in power was to benefit both rural agricultural and urban industrial sectors. There was much stress placed on the need to uplift the condition of the backward groups and to ensure them social justice, a campaign that gained ground in the Fifth Plan (1974–79).

In the Fifth Five-Year Plan the mixture of outlays was much as before; with the prosecution of the green revolution, fertilisers and pumps, in increasing demand, were to be supplied substantially from domestic production. Overall economic self-reliance at long last appeared to be an achievable goal, *if* the birth rate really had taken a downward trend. Taking up the call made in earlier plans, the needs of the more backward 30 per cent in the population were singled out for special attention, implying not only investment but a vigorous pursuit of programmes to implement land reforms and to broaden the availability of rural credit.

The Fifth Plan was terminated prematurely after four years and a new Five-Year Plan was initiated for 1978–83. The following extract from the Draft Five-Year Plan 1978–83 demonstrates a change in emphasis in planning:

'What matters is not the precise rate of increase in the national product that is to be achieved in five or ten years, but whether we can ensure within a specified time frame a measurable increase in the welfare of the millions of the poor.

'It is proposed, therefore, that the principal objectives of planning should now be defined as achieving within a period of ten years:

(i) the removal of unemployment and significant underemployment;
(ii) an appreciable rise in the standard of living of the poorest sections of the population;
(iii) provision by the State of some of the basic needs of the people in these income groups, like clean drinking water, adult literacy, elementary education, health care, rural roads, rural housing for the landless, and minimum services for the urban slums.'

Structure of the Economy

Poverty is the outstanding economic characteristic of the Indian population. In terms of per capita share of Gross National Product as calculated by the World Bank, India in 1973 ranked close to the bottom of the table in the company of Pakistan and Sri Lanka. A selection from that table is given in Table 6.1 to show the enormous disparity between India and the highly developed countries.

Measurement of GNP is a much less certain undertaking in a country like India where the subsistence element in agriculture remains so high, than in more economically sophisticated countries with totally monetised economies. Furthermore it

Table 6.1 Gross National Product per capita (1975) and annual average growth rate (1970–75) for selected countries (US dollars)

USA	7,120	1.6	Spain	2,750	5.1	Indonesia	220	3.5
W. Germany	6,670	1.9	USSR	2,550	3.1	Sri Lanka	190	1.1
Australia	5,700	2.4	China	930	5.7	Pakistan	160	0.8
Japan	4,400	4.0	Malaysia	760	5.3	India	140	0.5
UK	3,780	2.0	Egypt	260	1.3	Bangladesh	90	− 2.3

Source: World Bank *Atlas*, 1977.

must be remembered that the per capita figure is a gross average. The disposable income of the poorest tenth of the population is barely a fifth of the average.

India's Domestic Product is still predominantly from the primary sector, though the secondary and particularly the tertiary sectors have been making substantial gains in the last decades. This is an

Table 6.2 Structure of Gross Domestic Product by Sectors and per cent of total (Rs 782,440 million)

	1977–78
Agriculture	38.3
Forestry and fishing	2.1
Mining	1.4
TOTAL PRIMARY SECTOR	**41.8**
Manufacturing	16.4
Construction	5.9
Public utilities	1.5
TOTAL SECONDARY SECTOR	**23.8**
Transport, storage, communications	5.6
Trade, hotels	12.7
Banking, insurance	2.9
Real estate, etc.	3.8
Public administration and defence	4.8
Other services	4.7
TOTAL TERTIARY SECTOR	**34.5**

Table 6.3 Distribution of working population by occupation, 1971 (percentage of each item represented by females in parentheses, numbers in millions)

Total population	548 (48.2)
Total workers	180 (17.4)
Total workers as percentage of total population	32.9

Workers by occupation	Number	Per cent of total workers	Females as per cent of group
Primary sector	**130**	**72.0**	**27.2**
Cultivators	78.2	43.3	11.8
Agricultural labourers	47.5	26.3	42.1
Livestock, forestry, fishing, plantations, etc.	4.3	2.4	18.2
Secondary sector	**20.2**	**11.1**	**12.4**
Mining, etc.	0.9	0.5	13.4
Cottage industry	6.4	3.5	20.9
Manufacturing industry	10.7	5.9	8.1
Construction	2.2	1.2	9.2
Tertiary sector	**30.2**	**16.7**	**9.7**
Commerce	10.0	5.6	5.5
Transport, communications	4.4	2.4	3.3
Other services	15.8	8.7	14.1

Fig. 6.1

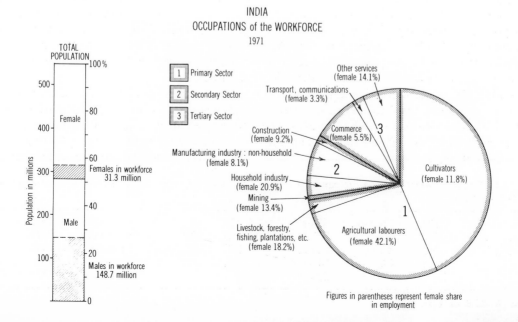

INDIA
OCCUPATIONS of the WORKFORCE
1971

Figures in parentheses represent female share in employment

indication of modernisation in the economy as a whole. The position is summarised in Table 6.2.

Table 6.3 (and Fig. 6.1) show the distribution of the working population by occupation as recorded in the 1971 Census. Of the working population thus enumerated only one-tenth is employed in the 'organized sector', meaning the more or less modernised part of the economy in which employment is generally full time. The distribution of this section of the workforce is as in Table 6.4.

Table 6.4 Distribution of the workforce in the organised sector 1975

Occupation	Number (million)	Per cent of total	Per cent in public sector
Forestry, plantations	1.222	5.7	28.2
Mining	0.8	4.1	84.4
Coal mining*	(0.513)		
Manufacturing	5.203	26.7	21.1
cotton textiles	(0.859)		
Construction	1.074	5.5	89.2
Electricity	0.593	3.0	93.1
Commerce	0.804	4.1	58.3
Transport, communications	2.448	12.5	96.8
Other services	7.464	38.3	84.8
TOTAL	**19.506**	**99.9**	**65.1**

* January 1975
† July 1975

The very high percentage of employment in the public sector outside manufacturing and plantations reflects the policies of the government in the direction of public ownership and socialisation. While planners can apply to the organised sector the conventional yardsticks used in developed economies, these must be used with caution in appraising the capacity of the 'informal' or traditional sector of the economy, in the rural areas particularly, to create employment or to absorb the surplus of man-hours available. For example, the 43.3 per cent of the working population described as cultivators are self-employed family groups as a rule, whose labour is fully utilised for very long hours during planting and harvesting seasons, when extra hands will generally be hired from the pool of agricultural labour. The capacity of the cultivator to absorb more labour depends on how much land he utilises, and the intensity with which he is able to farm it, which depends in turn on his access to credit for the necessary inputs. For the present at any rate, it will fall to this group more than any other to provide employment both for its own increase in numbers, and for the increase in the traditionally landless labourers. Any rural – urban flow that might result from the development of less labour-intensive agricultural technology would add to the urban unemployed. For the foreseeable future, rurally based small-scale and cottage industries will have to be encouraged and continue to receive protection from the

23 Raising water to irrigate crops by driving cattle down an incline. The cow in the foreground is chewing crushed sugarcane waste. Scene on the Deccan Lava Plateau near Bijapur, Karnataka.

'organised' industrial sector, and ways need to be found for the self-employment of the large proportion of the agricultural labour force who are seasonally unemployed.

Table 6.5 Exports (per cent of totals: 1974–75 Rs 32,986 million, 1977–78 Rs 53,736 million)

Item	1974–75 %	1977–78 %
Jute manufactures	8.8	4.6
Cotton and other textiles	6.5	4.6
Clothing	4.1	4.4
Fish and products	2.0	3.2
Tea	6.8	10.3
Coffee	1.6	3.6
Leather	4.1	5.1
Oil cake, etc.	3.1	2.5
Vegetable oils	1.0	0.5
Sugar	10.3	0.3
Cashew kernels	3.6	2.8
TOTAL PROCESSED AGRICULTURAL AND FISHERY PRODUCTS	**51.9**	**41.9**
Raw cotton	0.5	0.01*
Fruit and nuts	4.1	3.1*
Crude animal and vegetable materials	3.5	3.2*
Tobacco	2.4	2.2
Hides and skins	0.1	0.2*
TOTAL AGRICULTURAL RAW MATERIALS	**10.6**	**8.7**
Iron and steel	2.6	3.5
Petroleum products	0.4	0.5
Machinery and transport equipment	10.7	11.5
Pearls, gemstones etc.	3.0	10.1
TOTAL MINERAL BASED MANUFACTURED GOODS	**16.7**	**25.6**
Iron ore	4.9	4.5
Manganese ore	0.5	0.2
TOTAL MINERAL RAW MATERIALS	**5.4**	**4.7**
TOTAL OF ITEMS LISTED	**84.6**	**80.9**

*Estimated
Source: Government of India *Economic Survey 1978–79,* New Delhi 1979.

Exports, Imports and the Balance of Payments

However India decides to apportion wealth and power among its citizens, in so far as it lives within an international economic community, it must pay due regard to maintaining sound financial relationships with the rest of the world. Payment for imports must be balanced by earnings from exports, or the shortfall met from reserves or from loans and grants in aid from friendly nations.

Tables 6.5 and 6.6 list the principal exports and imports in 1974–75/1977–78.

Table 6.6 Imports (per cent of total)

Item	1974–75 Rs 44,681 million %	1977–78 Rs 60,664 million %
Wheat and rice	17.1	2.0
Fruits and nuts	1.4	1.1*
Oilseeds	0.2	0.1
Vegetable oils	0.3	11.7
Milk Products	0.6	0.8*
TOTAL FOODSTUFFS	**19.6**	**15.7**
Petroleum and products	25.9	25.7
Non-ferrous metals	3.4	3.2
Raw cotton	0.6	3.3
Wool	0.6	0.5
Jute	t	t
TOTAL INDUSTRIAL RAW MATERIALS AND FUELS	**30.5**	**32.7**
Iron and steel	9.3	4.3
Metals, manufactured	0.6	0.6
Chemicals	4.0	3.2
Fertilisers	10.1	5.6
Pharmaceuticals	0.8	1.1
Coal tar, dyestuffs	0.3	0.3
Paper and pulp	1.5	1.7
TOTAL MANUFACTURED MATERIALS	**26.6**	**16.8**
Machinery	8.9	11.8
Electrical machinery	3.4	2.9
Transport equipment	2.8	3.8
TOTAL MACHINERY, ETC.	**15.1**	**18.5**
TOTAL OF ITEMS LISTED	**91.8**	**83.7**

*Estimated
Source: as Table 6.5
Note: t = trace

24 Tata Oil Mills, Cochin, Kerala, processing vegetable oils into 'vanspati' cooking oil, using a variety of raw materials including coconut oil, groundnuts and other oilseeds.

The very broad base of India's export trade is apparent, and it is a healthy indication of development that processed and manufactured goods far outweigh raw materials. The latter are still important, however, especially the iron ore exports (mainly to Japan) as a source of foreign exchange, even though not creating many jobs locally. India has become a significant exporter of metal manufactures, machinery and transport equipment, much of which goes to other countries in the Third World, and is clearly the most industrialised nation in South Asia.

In its import trade India has been severely hit by the escalation in oil prices since 1974. Petroleum imports now far exceed in total expenditure any other item, though the anticipated expansion in domestic oil production should ease the situation somewhat in the near future. Except for highly sophisticated manufactured goods, India has the capacity to satisfy an increasing proportion of its needs, and the same is hopefully true of foodgrains and foodstuffs generally.

The lists of trading partners in Tables 6.7 and 6.8 show not only that India has escaped from its colonial past but also that it is clearly a 'nonaligned' country, trading with the 'Free World' and the 'Communist Bloc'. Japan, the USA and the USSR appear among the top four in both lists.

In common with its South Asian neighbours, India suffers from a chronically adverse balance of payments and relies heavily on loans and grants to balance the account. But for the oil crisis, India would have been in credit following the bumper harvests of 1976 – 77.

Table 6.7 Countries receiving India's exports 1977–78 (per cent of total)

Country	%
USA	12.5
USSR	12.2
UK	9.7
Japan	9.4
West Germany	4.5
Belgium	3.8
France	2.7
United Arab Emirates	2.6
Netherlands	2.5
Saudi Arabia	2.3
Iran	2.2
Kuwait	2.1
Italy	1.9
Hong Kong	1.6
Australia	1.5
TOTAL listed here	71.5

Table 6.8 Countries providing India's imports 1977–78 (per cent of total)

Country	%
USA	12.5
West Germany	9.2
Iran	9.1
UK	7.7
USSR	7.3
Japan	7.1
Saudi Arabia	4.1
Canada	3.0
Belgium	2.6
United Arab Emirates	1.5
Italy	1.4
Netherlands	1.3
Australia	1.2
Kuwait	1.1
Switzerland	1.1
Poland	1.0
TOTAL (listed here)	71.2

Chapter 7

India: Agriculture

Introduction

The Indian farmer still cultivates to a degree for the direct subsistence of himself and his family. While the larger farmers sell about two-thirds of their production, the smaller ones retain a similar proportion for subsistence. Which crops the farmer decides to grow within the physical constraints of soil, climate and the availability of irrigation to supplement rainfall, are in part a reflection of these subsistence requirements and in part a response to market opportunities. The crops grown, the methods of tilling the soil and of tending the plants, the nice adjustment of farming activity to the climatic and hydrological calendars, and the manner of adaptation to local variations in site such as floodplains, slopes and upland interfluves, all owe much to tradition, built up over millennia of trial and error.

For many centuries man has interfered in the hydrological cycle in order to overcome the deficiencies he found in the natural environment, notably the regular alternation of wet and dry seasons and the extreme variability of rainfall in many areas. Water is a limited resource the efficient use of which is of increasing importance as the demand expands from agriculture, industry and a water and power-using population with rising living standards. India cannot afford to allow water to run to waste and must strive to bring under control as much of its water resources as possible. As their development proceeds the options remaining to India within her own borders diminish and the long-term future for utilising effectively the flow in many of the Himalayan rivers will depend on international cooperation between India, Nepal and China, the countries in whose territories are located sites for storage reservoirs. In the Peninsula the major rivers have been harnessed to the extent that few opportunities remain for future development of surface water.

Meanwhile, the main prospects for improving the efficiency of water use lie in the continued development of groundwater through sinking traditional open wells and modern tube wells.

Granted cultivable soil, an adequate water supply is the farmer's major need. In order to play his full part in the economy today, however, the farmer has to adopt a much more modern approach to his enterprise than did his forebears.

Modernisation in the context of agriculture implies change both in the infrastructure and the technology of farming. The traditional system of agriculture while it embodies much common sense built up over centuries of trial and error, also contains some elements of archaic folklore, religious belief, superstition and prejudice which collectively can only be labelled as irrational by modern scientific man. In abstract terms, modernisation aims to create for the cultivator within a given physical environment a framework of socio-economic conditions which will enable him, acting rationally and using factors and methods of production in a scientifically appropriate way, to achieve an optimum level of efficiency.

The relationship of the farmer to the land he tills is an important factor influencing his willingness to invest money and energy in its productivity. For whom does he labour and risk his wealth? For a landlord who takes half his crop and makes no contribution to the costs of production other than the land? For the moneylender into whose clutches he has fallen in bad years or to meet social obligations involving ostentatious expenditure? For himself? Reform of the land-holding system is proceeding fitfully in the Indian States since it involves probably the strongest challenge to tradition within the whole area of development.

25 Crushing sugar cane (seen growing in the background) using bullock power to turn the rollers. Juice trickles into a drum let into the ground. Crushed waste litters the surface behind: near Hissar Haryana.

How much land a farmer, whether owner or tenant, operates is another matter bearing on his efficiency as does also the question of its consolidation from a number of traditionally scattered parcels into a contiguous holding. Ceilings for land ownership are set for each State in a move towards a more equitable distribution of resources, but a proprietary holding is not necessarily an operational holding, and it is the latter which is of more fundamental economic importance. A basic problem for government is to balance the political demand for equity against the more pragmatic necessity to maximise agricultural productivity in the national interest; the two are at times in conflict.

After land the farmer's most urgent need is generally for credit to enable him to finance his operations. Modern methods require investment in better seed, in fertilisers, in pesticides, in irrigation equipment, in wells, storehouses, etc. Easier access to credit at a fair rate of interest for farmers with little or nothing to offer by way of collateral has become an important instrument of modernisation policy.

The term 'green revolution' can loosely be assigned to the use of modern technology. It covers essentially the adoption of high yielding varieties (HYV) of seed, the use of artificial fertilisers in quantity, and the chemical protection of plants against pests and diseases. A prerequisite for the green revolution has been an assured and controllable irrigation supply. Modernisation is now spreading to non-irrigated farming, and new HYV are being evolved for semi-arid as well as for flood lands. To achieve the close water control demanded by the dwarf varieties which formed the thrust of the HYV programme initially, farmers, whether or not they live within canal commanded areas, often invest in their own wells and in pumps energised by electricity or oil. They may also apply inanimate forms of energy in tractor ploughing, to free themselves further from the limitations of traditional village labour relationships.

Crops

The principal annual field crops grown in India are shown in Table 7.1. These totalled over 160 million hectares in 1977–78. In addition somewhat over 5 million ha were under perennial tree crops.

The annual crops may be divided into two groups, according to their growing season. Roughly two-thirds of the crop area is in *kharif* crops, which rely on the monsoon rains and are harvested in early winter or towards the end of the rainy season. Most of the rice is grown in *kharif*, mainly as a winter crop (Fig. 7.1); in Assam and West Bengal where the rainy season starts earlier, there are two *kharif* crops, autumn harvested (*aus*) and winter harvested (*aman*). The greater part of the millets area is under *kharif* varieties; bajra (Fig. 7.2), jowar (Fig. 7.3), and ragi (Fig. 7.4). Maize (Fig. 7.5), cotton (Fig. 7.6), jute, groundnuts and some other oilseeds and some pulses are *kharif* crops.

The complementary season is known as *rabi* and is dominated by wheat (Fig. 7.7), gram and oilseeds like mustard and rapeseed and rabi jowar (Fig. 7.8). *Rabi* crops are sown at the start of the cool, dry season to be harvested in the early summer, in March and April. Only a small proportion of the rice area is *rabi* (Fig. 7.9): the north is too cool for the so-called 'summer' rice (*boro* in West Bengal) and its demands for irrigation water make its cultivation difficult in many areas during the dry season.

Figure 7.10 shows the ratio of *kharif* to *rabi* cropping. The area of strong dominance of *kharif* cropping covers the Assam Valley and the Northeastern Hills, much of the plateau country in South Bihar and Orissa, most of Tamilnadu, Kerala, coastal and southern Karnataka, Gujarat and the coast of Maharashtra. Inland of these is a block of districts in the lava region of Maharashtra–Madhya Pradesh, and northwards two areas in Rajasthan and the Vale of Kashmir. Several reasons may be adduced for this pattern.

High rainfall supports *kharif* rice as the major crop in the eastern areas mentioned, along the west coast from Kerala to Maharashtra, and in Kashmir.

Late *kharif* rainfall supplemented by canal and short-term tank irrigation explains the area in lowland Tamilnadu. On the Karnataka Plateau thin soils and a modest rainfall support *kharif* cropping but allow only a small amount of tank-fed *rabi* cropping.

On the lava soils of Maharashtra–Madhya Pradesh and the adjoining part of Gujarat, non-irrigated cotton, bajra and jowar are profitable rain-fed crops, while towards Kutch there is no question of *rabi* cropping on account of the very low rainfall and sandy soils. The same can be said

26 After sugar cane juice has been reduced by boiling in a pan over a fire of crushed cane, the gur is poured into a mould to cool. Lumps of gur in the right foreground. Near Hissar, Haryana. Gur is the form in which most of the rural population of South Asia take sugar. It is whole sugar, unrefined, tasting like fudge with a light syrupy flavour.

Table 7.1 Area under principal crops, 1977–78 (thousand ha and per cent of total)

Crop	Thousand ha	%
Rice	40,002	24.9
autumn rice	17,642	11.0
winter rice	20,607	12.8
summer rice	1,753	1.1
Millets	29,960	18.6
kharif jowar	10,325	6.4
rabi jowar	5,948	3.7
bajra	11,035	6.9
ragi	2,652	1.6
Wheat	21,203	13.2
Barley	1,992	1.2
Maize	5,700	3.5
Other cereals	4,740	2.9
TOTAL CEREALS	**103,597**	**64.4**
Gram	8,253	5.1
Arhar	2,623	1.6
Other pulses, kharif	7,393	4.6
Other pulses, rabi	5,268	3.3
TOTAL PULSES	**23,537**	**14.6**
Groundnut	7,175	4.5
Other oilseeds	8,921	5.5
TOTAL OILSEEDS	**16,096**	**10.0**
Cotton	7,815	4.9
Jute and mesta	1,156	0.7
Sugar cane	3,220	2.0
Condiments and spices	1,491	0.8
TOTAL CROPS*	**160,911**	**100.0**

*Total includes other crops totalling 3,999,000 ha (2.5%) viz. guar seed, potato, tobacco, tapioca, sunn hemp
Source: Agricultural Situation, January 1979

for much of Rajasthan. In Kashmir winter cold tends to inhibit *rabi* cropping.

At the other extreme, in another third of the districts more than half the total sown area (TSA) is in *rabi* crops. These districts are more concentrated in area, in a broad belt dominated by wheat, stretching from Punjab into Madhya Pradesh, and through southern Uttar Pradesh to Patna in Bihar. A much smaller belt where *rabi* jowar is favoured, runs southeast in the Deccan behind Bombay. These are all areas of relatively low rainfall. The northern plains benefit considerably from irrigation and from the small amount of winter rainfall which may occasionally reach as far east as Patna. Southwards into the plateau country these advantages are largely lacking. The slight predominance of *rabi* wheat over the alternative *kharif* jowar probably reflects dietary preference in an area where *kharif* rainfall is inadequate for rice. On the Deccan between Pune and Bijapur, *rabi* jowar does well on moisture retained from monsoon rainfall by the black soils. The preference here for a *rabi* crop shows a nice adaption by the farmers to the need to conserve the light rainfall in this rainshadow belt to be used in the cool season when evaporation is at a minimum.

The mildness of the Indian winter in the lowlands enables farmers who have access to irrigation water to grow both *kharif* and *rabi* crops on some of their land. There is thus a fair corres-

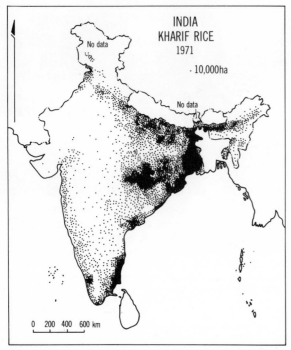

Fig. 7.1

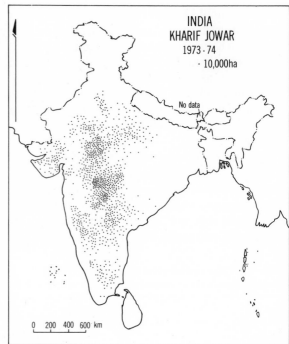

Fig. 7.3

Fig. 7.2

Fig. 7.4

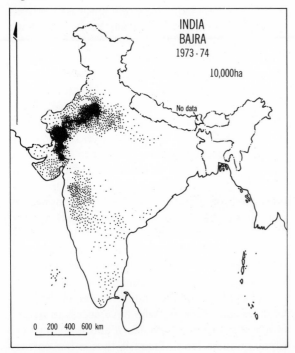

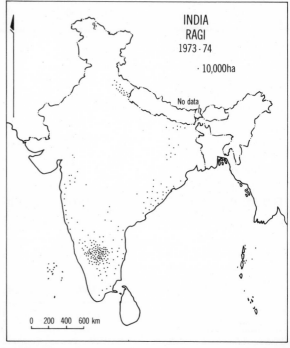

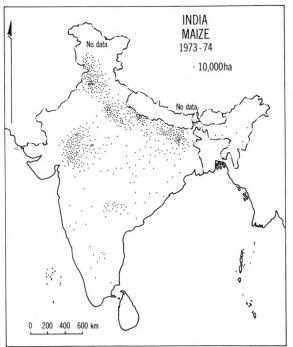

Fig. 7.5

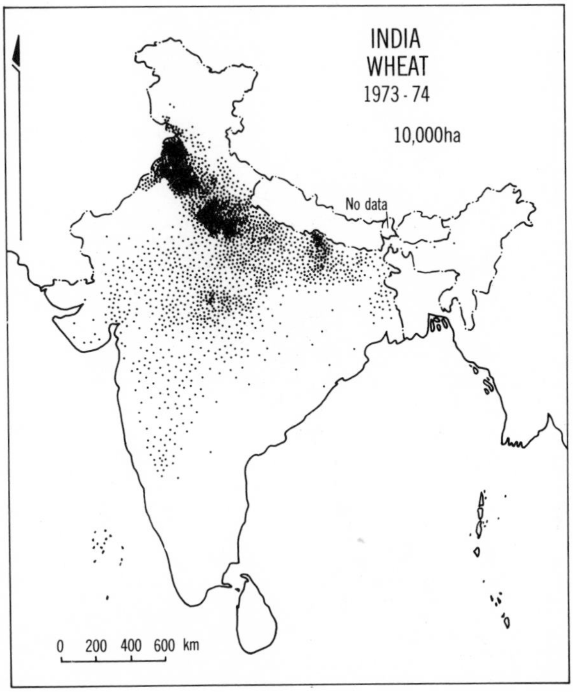

Fig. 7.6

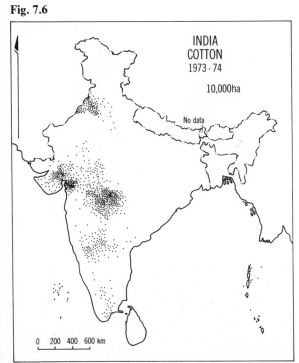

Fig. 7.7

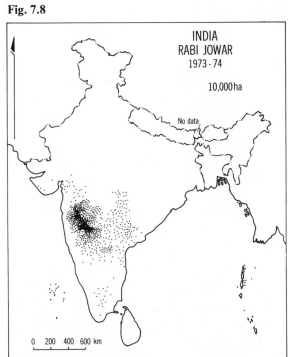

Fig. 7.8

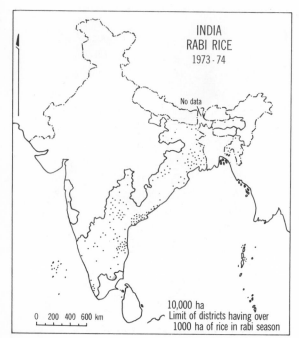

Fig. 7.9

pondence between the areas most irrigated and those showing the highest intensities of land-use, i.e. of multiple cropping. (Figs. 7.11 and 7.12). Irrigation in general guarantees the farmer a *kharif* crop by assuring him of water in the periods of uncertain rains perhaps at the commencement and more certainly towards the end of the monsoon, enabling him to maximise the use of this season. It may also allow him to pre-water the fields in which he later sows a non-irrigated *rabi* crop.

The Indian farmer generally grows a variety of crops on his land, traditionally in order to protect himself against failure of any one crop for whatever environmental reason, and in more recent times to avoid putting all his eggs into one economic basket. The complexity of cropping patterns may be comprehended from a study of the three maps in Figures 7.13, 7.14, and 7.15.

Figure 7.13 shows the leading cereal or tuber crop by districts, and may be taken as pointing fairly accurately at the staple source of starch food. Rice, mainly *kharif*, leads in all the eastern areas where rainfall exceeds 1,000 mm, along the west coast of the Peninsula, and in the irrigated coastal lowlands of Andhra Pradesh and Tamil-

Fig. 7.10

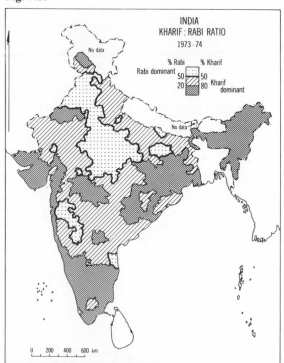

Fig. 7.11

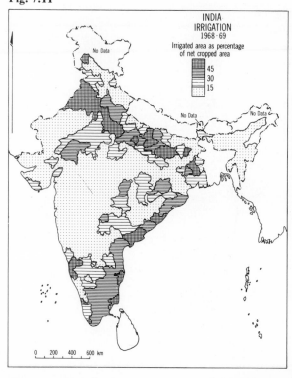

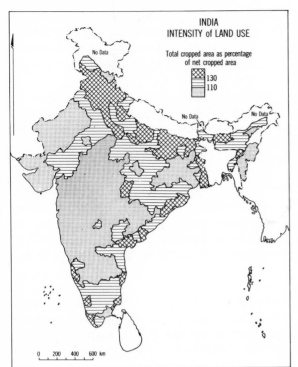

Fig. 7.12

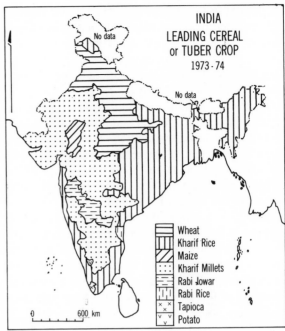

Fig. 7.14

Fig. 7.13

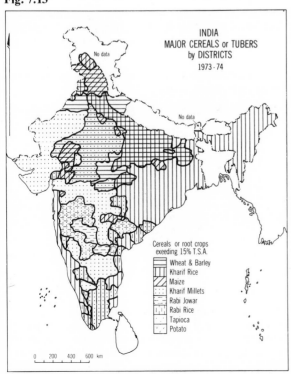

Fig. 7.15

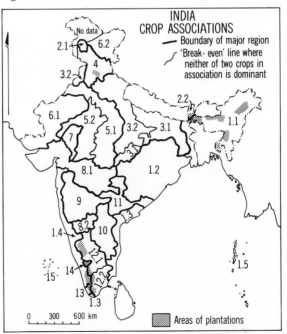

nadu, and in the Vale of Kashmir. Wheat rules in the irrigated plains of the north, maize in a small area of the Aravalli Hills, while one or other of the millets leads in the drier uplands of the Deccan and the west. Potatoes dominate only in the Nilgiri Hills, and as a cash crop rather than as a staple food for local consumption. Tapioca in the far southwest is both a staple and an industrial crop.

In Figure 7.14 are shown the areas where more than 15 per cent of the total sown area is taken up with a particular cereal or tuber crop. There is clearly a considerable overlap between rice and wheat in the Ganga Plain, and between rice and millets in the south. Wheat overlaps with *kharif* millets in Rajasthan–Madhya Pradesh, and there is an interesting combination of *kharif* and *rabi* millets (the latter jowar) in parts of the Deccan lava country. The potato and tapioca dominated districts in the south are seen to have rice as a secondary staple.

In Figure 7.15 a system of crop associations is mapped, each district being categorised on the basis of its primary crops (those exceeding 15 per cent of total sown area) and secondary crops (5–15 per cent TSA).

Although they have been excluded from consideration as major staples the importance of pulses and oilseeds in Indian agriculture and traditional diet cannot be overemphasised. For the large mass of the population pulses are the major source of protein. Religious beliefs prohibit some from eating meat, but even for the others meat is a comparatively rare luxury. Oilseeds provide cooking oil, a less expensive substitute for traditional *ghi*, clarified butter. Together with coconut oil, also used in cooking in the south, the oilseeds are in demand as industrial raw materials, notably for soap making and food industries at home and abroad.

Pulses are widely grown as *rabi* and *kharif* crops. Gram (chick pea) is the main *rabi* pulse, arhar or tur (pigeon pea) the main *kharif* pulse. *Rabi* pulses are often complementary to *kharif* rice cultivation in which role they are important in the Ganga Plain in UP, Bihar and West Bengal, and in the Mahanadi Delta in Orissa. In a belt through central Rajasthan the crop alternates with *kharif* bajra, not necessarily in the same year unless rainfall has been abundant. In both cases the fertilising propensities of pulses as nitrogen fixers seem a significant factor.

Kharif pulses, like their *rabi* counterparts, tend to be relatively neglected and low-yielding. Some, like arhar, have a long growing season and are harvested in mid-winter. They are of little importance towards the wetter northeast and southwest where land is too valuable to use on such low-yielding crops unless they can be taken casually after an early rice harvest. In Rajasthan they are used to make use of feeble monsoon rainfall on light soils and to provide food for man and fodder for his flocks and herds in an inhospitable environment. For the rest, *kharif* pulses are fairly evenly spread throughout the Peninsula with some tendency to be preferred to *rabi* pulses in the black soil regions, where they fit in as a fertilising crop alternating with cotton.

The oilseeds also divide into *kharif* and *rabi*

27 A small tank, near Madras, Tamilnadu, irrigates fields to the right of its bund. As the water recedes grass may be cut in the tank bed. Another tank to the left of the picture irrigates the fields upstream of this tank.

groups. *Kharif* oilseeds include the larger part of the groundnut crop, and all castorseed and sesamum. There is a marked concentration of *kharif* oilseeds, mainly of groundnuts, in Kathiawar and to a lesser extent on light soils in Andhra and Tamilnadu. These crops favour sub-humid conditions and are largely absent where rainfall exceeds 1,000 mm. *Rabi* oilseeds show a more diffuse pattern. A minor concentration occurs in Punjab–Haryana where rape and mustard are popular, and spreads into Rajasthan UP and Madhya Pradesh; mustard is the staple source of cooking oil in Bengal and Assam. They are absent from the west coast, where the coconut palm provides an alternative source of vegetable oil.

It must be remembered that it is only rarely that a regional boundary is other than a zone of transition. There may be a sharp line demarcating irrigated and non-irrigated land in arid areas, or alluvial plain and mountain slope, but gradational changes are more usual. Furthermore, a district may exceed 10,000 km² in area, and its consolidated agricultural data can obscure variation in cropping pattern. In three major regions the ratio between the two principal elements in the crop association pattern is used to establish a 'break-even' line where an approximate balance is reached. The system of crop association regions is as follows; the numbering refers to Figure 7.15.

Crop Association Regions

1. *Regions tending to dominance of rice,* even to its monoculture in places. No other food grain reaches the level of 15 per cent TSA, and rarely do other crops, since very few of them are able to share the agricultural environment created by the farmer to suit the rice crop: bunded fields holding water on the land for weeks at a time. Furthermore, in eastern India the paddy fields are often called upon to carry an autumn (in Bengal the *aus*) crop of rice before the main winter (*aman*) crop, and some may even continue in cultivation under a *rabi* rice (*boro*) crop. The growing of crops other than rice is thus inhibited at least in some degree by that plant's specialised requirements. To the extent that minor crops lend distinctiveness to parts of the rice-dominated area, they are mentioned below.

1.1 In northeastern India the monotony of the paddy landscape is relieved in winter by *rabi* oilseeds along the Assam Valley, to which is added *kharif* jute in a continuous zone from mid-valley west and south around the Bangladesh border. Within West Bengal, a little wheat indicates the eastern limit of a crop combination that extends as far as the Pakistan border in Punjab. Tea plantations are an important element in the economy of the valley, but are completely divorced from field cropping. Within the hill country of Arunachal Pradesh, Nagaland, Manipur, Mizoram and to some extent Tripura, the cultivation of rice and maize in permanent fields is supplemented and in places supplanted by shifting agriculture. Data for the latter are not collected however. Usually a mixture of seeds is planted at the beginning of the rains on slopes whose bamboo and scrub jungle of three or more years' growth has been slashed and burned. Typically, hill rice, maize, various millets, beans, cotton, cucumbers and bananas are dibbled in together to be harvested piecemeal through the year. The Meghalaya plateau is rather more developed than the border hill country, producing some jute and potatoes as a speciality.

1.2 The plateau country of south Bihar, Orissa and the eastern districts of Madhya Pradesh remains one of the least developed regions of India. *Kharif* rice, seldom insured by irrigation, is very dominant and cropping intensity is extremely low. On the northern flank of the region in plateau Bihar, maize is a subsidiary crop, while in the Mahanadi delta and towards Madhya Pradesh *rabi* pulses rise in places to over 15 per cent TSA.

1.3 The Andhra deltas and the east coast generally south to the Cauvery delta have well developed irrigation to supplement rainfall which, though moderate, extends over a longer period due to the effect of the retreating monsoon in the south. The cropping pattern lacks diversity except at a minor level. *Rabi* rice reaches 15 per cent TSA in the Godavari–Krishna deltas and Nellore. Kanyakumari in the uttermost south is an outlier of this crop association type, having 94 per cent TSA under rice.

1.4 With the exception of the two southernmost districts of Kerala, the whole west coast as far north as Valsad in Gujarat is a region dominated by *kharif* rice, relieved in Kerala by subsidiary tapioca, and by *kharif* pulses and jowar northwards, the latter exceeding 15 per cent TSA on sloping lands unsuited to paddy. Tree crops decline in importance northwards: coconuts and arecanuts on the coastlands, and the more tolerant cashew on the coastal platforms. Plantation crops are confined to the southern part of the region, extending little further north than Coorg.

1.5 Rice reaches near monocultural status in the Andaman and Nicobar Islands, strung in the Bay of Bengal between southeastern Burma and Sumatra. Coconuts and arecanuts are important, and rubber, coffee, oil palm and various spice trees are also grown.

2. *Rice is in combination with maize* as a substantial *kharif* crop in two widely separated and topographically dissimilar areas.

2.1 In the Vale of Kashmir, maize reaches 31 per cent TSA occupying the slopes and gravel terraces, with rice (49 per cent) on the better alluvium of the Jhelum floodplain. Brilliant yellow *rabi* mustard and deep-green wheat watered by winter rains add colour to this naturally beautiful landscape in the springtime.

2.2 Near the other end of the Himalaya in Darjiling maize (28 per cent TSA) with ragi on the poorer terrain are in association with rice (53 per cent). The area is more renowned, however, for its high level tea. A similar crop association extends into Sikkim.

3. *Rice and wheat* are in combination almost the full length of the plains from the Pakistan border to West Bengal, and there are extensions from this belt into the Himalaya and south onto the Peninsular foreland in Madhya Pradesh. In the western part of the region wheat is more important than rice and the converse is true in the east.

3.1 The western limit of the area of rice – wheat association corresponds closely to the 1,000 mm isohyet, reaching furthest west on the Nepalese border and in the Bagelkhand region of the plateau in Madhya Pradesh. In a few districts close to the Nepalese border maize is added to the combination, an indication of coarser soils in the *barbar-terai*.

3.2 The area in central UP and northern Madhya Pradesh where wheat leads rice in combination shows a great deal more variety among the minor crops than do the rice–wheat regions. The reason probably lies in the fact that when the land is under wet rice little unflooded space is available for pulses and oilseeds, *rabi* varieties of which can stand alongside wheat without difficulty. The submontane plain in western UP has a higher rainfall (close to 1,000 mm) than the more southerly part of the Ganga plain this far west. This together with abundant groundwater for tube well irrigation allows sugar cane to assume a major role in the crop association with wheat–rice in many districts. This crop is increasingly popular under the impetus of high prices for factory-refined sugar for export to earn foreign exchange, and a strong domestic demand. Much of the latter is for the simpler product of the gur or jaggery producing plants, often set up seasonally to crush cane and boil up the juice over fires fuelled with waste cane. Sugar is planted during the dry season to be harvested up to a year or more later, during most of which time an assured supply of water is essential.

28 Wallardie Tea Estate, Kerala, a British-owned garden. Picking is in progress (top left); the manager's bungalow is top right. Shade trees also provide leaf mulch. On the skyline is a plantation of eucalyptus trees for fuel.

Manures and fertilisers are liberally applied to achieve high yields.

Further west in northern Haryana, and again in Amritsar and Gurdaspur on the Pakistan border, maize reaches primary level after wheat-rice. The patch in Haryana lies astride the Yamuna–Ghaggar interfluve – the Indo-Gangetic divide, and both areas are relatively close to the gravelly Sivalik foothills, conditions likely to give rise to environmental niches more favourable to maize than to the other crops in the association. On the finer soils of Firozpur, canal irrigation supports the intensive cultivation of wheat–rice with *kharif* cotton and *rabi* pulses as minor crops. Man's efforts as a traditional engineer have produced in the UP Himalaya remarkable feats of terracing to provide irrigated fields for rice and wheat, with ragi as a hardy *kharif* millet grown on the marginal land. Locally important, but insignificant in the gross pattern are temperate vegetables and potatoes grown for urban centres in the plains where these are scarce during the hot season.

4. *A wheat–maize region* can be distinguished in the western outer Himalayan foothills of Jammu–Kashmir and Himachal Pradesh. Compared with the Vale of Kashmir to the north and the UP Himalaya discussed immediately above, rice slips into a secondary and even a negligible position in some areas where the establishment of a paddy soil is too difficult in coarse alluvium and colluvium. Steep hill slopes are roughly levelled into stone-faced terraces to support rain-fed crops, but the ground created is too porous for paddy.

5. Merging into the wheat–rice region (3.2) to the east, and into the area of bajra dominance to the west, the *wheat–kharif millets region* forms part of an east–west continuum across northern India.

5.1 In a great arc extending from Ganganagar at the northern tip of Rajasthan, eastwards through southern Haryana and southeast from Delhi in a broad stretch reaching to the Maharashtra border, wheat is the more important crop in association with jowar and bajra. Irrigation compensates for semi-aridity in the northern part, while southwards rainfall becomes *relatively* more reliable. *Rabi* oilseeds and pulses are commonly found in secondary roles.

5.2 Within and west of the arc just described, *kharif* millets, increasingly bajra, assume first place as rainfall and its reliability decreases, and as soils become sandier and stonier in the Aravalli belt. The pockets of better agriculture have the support of local irrigation, but for the most part the farmers follow moisture-conserving dry-farming practices involving long fallow periods.

29 Terraced paddy fields in the Vale of Kashmir have sinuous bunds following the contour. The poplar trees indicate the temperate nature of the climate here. (Courtesy R. Hancock).

Subsidiary crops are similar to those in the preceding area, with *kharif* oilseeds, pulses and sometimes maize in evidence.

6. *Regions dominated by kharif millets*

6.1   Ultimately with diminishing rainfall, a region is reached where bajra's dominance as the primary foodgrain is uncontested. Pulses, sown extensively though thinly for food and fodder, are associated crops at primary or secondary level, particularly important in a region where livestock, camels, sheep and cattle play a vital role in the economy.

6.2   The remote high valleys and plateau of Ladakh in inner Kashmir are a dry land of a different sort, an agricultural environment of even more extreme difficulty than Rajasthan on account of cold winters and very intense insolation during summer. Ragi dominates as the *kharif* crop with winter wheat, hardy barley, and oilseeds in support but the economy leans heavily on transhumance of sheep and yaks.

7. *Maize* associated with wheat and barley in the north, or with rice in the south characterises the agriculture of the south–central Aravalli Hills from southern Rajasthan into western Gujarat. A variety of secondary crops include *kharif* millets, cotton and oilseeds, and *rabi* pulses and oilseeds indicating the diversity of crop environments available within the small compass of this sometimes rugged region.

8. Southwards through the Peninsular interior the millets take the place of wheat as the leading foodgrain wherever rice cannot be grown. Cotton and *kharif* oilseeds play important roles.

Cotton and the kharif millets jowar and bajra form a dominant association on the *regur* soils of the Deccan lavas of northern Maharashtra and Kathiawar, and on the intervening alluvial area around the head of the Gulf of Cambay, and again on the southern edge of the lava country in Karnataka.

8.1   The main cotton belt of Maharashtra–Gujarat is a region of low cropping intensity where *kharif* crops dominate to a high degree. Rabi jowar sometimes reaches primary level, but other *rabi* crops such as pulses, oilseeds and wheat achieve only secondary level though they are widely grown

except in Kathiawar. Here an important, sometimes dominant role is assumed by groundnuts as a *kharif* crop.

8.2   The 'little' cotton belt of Karnataka is in a region of deep regur. Cotton and kharif jowar, in one district rabi jowar also, stand in primary position in the crop association, with as many as five crops at secondary level, including *kharif* pulses and oilseeds, rice and wheat.

9. Separating the two cotton belts on the Maharashtra–Karnataka Deccan lava plateau is the *jowar region* par excellence. Through its centre runs a belt where rabi jowar predominates (see also Fig. 7.13) but kharif jowar shares primary status at either end of this belt, and dominates throughout the rest of the region. The role and types of secondary crops vary a good deal. Where water is available for irrigation, rice and sugar cane appear. Normally however, the minor crops depend on rainfall or remanent moisture. *Rabi* wheat, pulses and oilseeds, *kharif* cotton, pulses and oilseeds variously join the association with jowar.

10. *Kharif jowar* combines with *kharif oilseeds*, particularly groundnuts, in this region, comprising most of the Andhra Deccan south of Hyderabad. From the Krishna southwards, granites and gneisses give place to slates and quartzites making for considerable variety in soil quality. Where irrigation is available rice enters the combination, but this is only important in the south and for the most part rain-fed agriculture prevails. *Kharif* pulses are widely grown, with chillies and tobacco important.

11. Kharif (sometimes rabi) jowar and rice reach a balance in what may best be described as a *zone of transition* between the last three regions and those to the east dominated by rice alone. The zone follows the Wainganga valley and the middle Godavari to above its delta, and incorporates the low hilly country through Khammam to the sea at Vishakhapatnam corresponding to a narrow belt with less than 1,000 mm rainfall (see Fig. 3.5). Appropriately in a transition zone, there are generally three crops exceeding 15 per cent TSA and up to five above 5 per cent.

12. In the remaining large region from central Karnataka to the dry coast of southern Tamilnadu, *kharif millets and rice* are in association, the ratio favouring millets in the north, rice in the south. Ragi is the millet preferred in the north, jowar and bajra in the south. The ability to grow rice depends largely on the availability of tank irrigation, though canals and wells, now operated commonly by electric pumps, are present in some parts. Cotton is an additional ingredient in the south. The accent is on *kharif* cropping and intensity is at best only moderate, at worst very low. Coconuts and arecanuts are locally quite important, and the numerous toddy palms are reminders of the times before Tamilnadu introduced prohibition and the brewing of alcoholic beverages for sale was forbidden.

13. Trivandrum and Quilon in southern Kerala have a crop association of *tapioca with rice*, both at primary level. No other field crop reaches even 3 per cent TSA. Perennial crops are present in abundance: coconuts, arecanuts, and rubber in the lowlands, and at higher levels, coffee, cardamoms and tea.

14. One district, the Nilgiri Hills, constitutes a *potato–rice region*. Potatoes, occupying 56 per cent TSA mainly on slopes, are grown for sale in the plains while rice, on 25 per cent TSA, is cultivated on terrace fields for local subsistence. Temperate vegetables do well in this hill country, much of it over 2,000 m. Spices, ragi and tapioca add to the variegated pattern of field crops in a landscape interspersed with tea, coffee, cinchona and eucalyptus plantations.

15. For the sake of completeness it may be noted that the economy of Lakshadweep, the group of coral islands in the Arabian Sea, is based on coconuts and tuna fishing. Field cropping is practically non-existent. Marine resources have for centuries attracted the population neatly described by Schwartzberg as 'oceanic Muslim'.

Tree Crops

Perennial tree crops are an important element in the pattern of land-use in the moister and milder parts of India. In terms of entrepreneurial scale, production ranges from the small homestead orchard planted for domestic use, to the large plantation.

Fruit trees of which mangoes are the most popular, are widely grown, and often cover an area equivalent to 1 per cent of the area under field crops. Most homestead gardens include one or two fruit trees, and where conditions are appropriate, coconut and arecanut trees, all primarily for domestic use. There are however areas of commercial specialisation.

Coconuts, a major source of vegetable oil and of the fibre which is the basis of the coir industry are particularly important along the west coast, southwards from Goa.

Traditionally the ground beneath the palm trees was used at most for grazing, but now it is common to till and fertilise the plantation, and growers are encouraged to cultivate tapioca, bananas, vegetables, spices etc. within the groves. The coconut is not exclusively a coastal crop, and grows extensively in the tank-watered valleys of the southern Karnataka plateau, and in the adjacent Tamilnadu uplands. The coasts of Tamilnadu and Andhra Pradesh are important for coconut and it is also common in Orissa and West Bengal. Overall, the pattern reflects tropical conditions with mild

30 This man at Alleppy, Kerala, is poling a raft of coconut husks held in a net. They will be retted to obtain the coir fibre for making mats etc.

winters, moderate to high rainfall or alternative access to moisture.

Frequently found in association with coconuts is the arecanut palm, the fruit of which is the so-called 'betel nut' much in demand for chewing with lime and leaf of the *Betel piper* vine. Arecanuts are an important cash crop in Kerala, the moister parts of Karnataka, and in Assam.

A third nut tree, the cashew (*Anacardium occidentale*), is exotic both in its antecedents and its principal markets. A native of South America, introduced by the Portuguese as a fruit tree, the cashew thrives on the sometimes lateritic dissected platform-like coastal plateaux of the Peninsula, on the west coast from Ratnagiri southwards to its major area of production in Kerala, and on similar country in coastal Andhra and Tamilnadu, as well as on sandy beach ridges in the latter state. While the fresh fruit is used in preserves, the nut has a dual use. It contains an inner kernel which when separated constitutes the cashew nut of commerce. In addition, the oil extracted from the nut-shell has heat and acid-resistant qualities and serves a number of industrial purposes in plastics and paints.

The tree crops discussed so far did not generally attract capital investment from abroad as did the traditionally 'plantation' crops–tea, coffee, rubber and cardamoms. Foreign, always mainly British, interest in the cultivation and processing of these crops is dwindling year by year, though two British plantation companies rank among the top nine expatriate enterprises remitting profits overseas.

Tea

In tea India leads the world, producing 34 per cent of the total. Its export accounts for 10 per cent of foreign earnings. The industry employs three-quarters of a million labourers to pick 360,662 ha organised in some 13,000 gardens.

Tea produces best in a warm, humid climate without too marked a dry season and requires well-drained land. Indian production is mainly from Assam which has more than half the total area in four districts at the head of the Brahmaputra Valley. There is a smaller area in Cachar, adjacent to the tea garden belt of Sylhet in Bangladesh; south of the latter are the tea estates of the Indian State of Tripura. All this tea is grown at a relatively low altitude, as is that in the Duar belt

which fringes the Himalayan foothills in western Assam and north Bengal. At higher levels are grown the fine teas of Darjiling. Further west there are small areas of tea grown in the Himalayan foothills of Bihar, UP and Himachal Pradesh. In South India the main producing regions are in the Southern Ghats astride the Kerala–Tamilnadu border, and in the Nilgiri Hills north of the Palghat Gap. An area of lesser importance for tea, but well known for coffee, lies in and northwest of Coorg.

Tea production in the principal districts is shown in Table 7.2.

Coffee

Coffee is generally cultivated on small estates and its production is largely confined to the three southern States. Out of a total of 146,458 ha, Karnataka has 89,990, Kerala 31,852 and Tamilnadu 23,410. Annual output reaches over 100,000 tonnes in a good year (as in 1977–78).

Rubber

Most of the world's natural rubber comes from equatorial regions where seasonal fluctuations in production are minimal. In India, the area most closely approximating to equatorial conditions is Kerala, where 92 per cent of the total area under rubber is located. Tamilnadu and Karnataka account for most of the rest. Output runs at over 147,000 tonnes which, with the product of a synthetic rubber factory in UP with a capacity of 26,000 tonnes (using alcohol derived from the byproducts of sugar refining as a base), makes India self-sufficient.

Cardamoms

The cultivation of cardamoms occupies a relatively small area, sometimes being in lightly opened

Table 7.2   Tea production, 1977 (thousand kg)

Assam	291,411
West Bengal	131,206
Others in North India	6,895
Tamilnadu, including Nilgiri Hills	73,320
Kerala	53,450
Karnataka	3,430
INDIA TOTAL	**559.810**

Source: Times of India *Directory and Year Book, 1979*

forest, sometimes as an undercrop to rubber or in association with coffee. In Kerala, Karnataka and Tamilnadu 98,000 ha produced 4,600 tonnes, most of which were exported (1977–78). Sikkim contributes a further 200 tonnes. Production is being expanded to meet increased demand from the Arab world, whose purchasing power has risen dramatically in recent years, and where cardamom is an essential ingredient of mutton pilau and coffee.

Irrigation

In a country of such a markedly seasonal rainfall regime and having many areas of only moderate or even low rainfall suffering from high variability of total received, it is not surprising that man's ingenuity has long been exercised to reduce his dependency on capricious nature. As Table 7.3 shows, a quarter of the area sown is irrigated.

Table 7.3 Irrigation (thousand hectares)

	1975–76*	Per cent of total
Net area irrigated from		
canals	13,775	40
tanks	3,986	12
tube-wells	6,715	19
other wells	7,577	22
other sources	2,438	7
TOTAL	**34,491**	**100**
Irrigated more than once	8,385	22
Gross area irrigated	42,876	
Net area irrigated as per cent of net area sown		24
Gross area irrigated as per cent of gross area sown		25
Net area sown	142,224	
Gross area sown	170,995	
Area sown more than once	28,771	17

* Indian Agriculture in Brief, 1978

Table 7.4 Net area irrigated by source and by States, 1975–76

Thousand ha and percentage of State total

Region	Canal	%	Tank	%	Tube well	%	Other wells	%	Other sources	%	Total	% of India total	Gross area irrigated as % of TSA
1. *Northwest*													
Haryana	1,036	59	1	t	682	39	31	2	4	0.2	1,754	5.1	50
Himachal Pradesh	—	—	t	t	2	2	1	1	87	97	90	0.3	17
Jammu & Kashmir	288	93	—	—	2	1	1	t	11	4	302	0.9	40
Punjab	1,383	44	—	—	1,559	50	172	6	7	t	3,121	9.0	74
Rajasthan	887	35	253	10	58	2	1,319	52	30	1	2,547	7.4	17
2. *North Centre*													
Bihar	896	32	118	4	846	31	225	8	675	24	2,760	8.0	30
Uttar Pradesh	2,743	35	338	4	3,189	40	1,314	17	349	4	7,933	23.0	40
3. *Northeast*													
Assam, etc.*	362	48	2	0.3	—	—	5	0.7	378	51	747	2.2	19
West Bengal	960	64	303	20	—	—	17	1	209	14	1,489	4.3	19
4. *West Centre*													
Gujarat	245	17	25	2	130	9	999	71	15	1	1,414	4.1	15
Madhya Pradesh	801	44	132	7	26	1	700	39	145	8	1,804	5.2	9
Maharashtra	379	21	260	14	—	—	1,046	58	117	6	1,802	5.2	11
5. *Southeast*													
Andhra Pradesh	1,627	47	1,100	32	114	3	470	14	126	4	3,437	10.0	35
Kerala	86	38	58	25	n.a.	—	n.a.	—	84	37	228	0.7	11
Karnataka	488	36	410	30	t	t	336	25	131	10	1,365	4.0	15
Orissa	655	65	233	23	n.a.	—	127	13	—	—	1,015	2.9	19
Tamilnadu	911	36	750	29	62	2	807	31	35	1	2,565	7.4	47
INDIA	13,775	40	3,986	12	6,715	19	7,577	22	2,438	7	34,491	100.0	25

*Includes Manipur, Meghalaya, Nagaland and Tripura.
† Total includes Union Territories
Source: As Table 7.3

Canal systems account for 40 per cent of the total, wells for 41 per cent and tanks for 12 per cent. Other methods include low lift pumps which raise water from rivers or ponds, and minor, often temporary, diversions of streams and river channels. In Table 7.4 the national totals are broken down into the major states and their regional groupings.

As surface water resources become harnessed, additional irrigation water has to be found mainly from groundwater reservoirs. The spread of rural electrification and the increasing popularity of diesel and petrol driven pumps have enabled many farmers to equip themselves with tube wells, which to a varying degree free them from dependence on state-managed canals.

Table 7.5 shows for the five regional groupings of States their percentage share of India's total irrigation area and the proportions within each region accounted for by canals, tanks, tube-wells and other wells and other sources of water. The maps in Figure 7.16, 7.18 and 7.19 show the distribution of the areas irrigated by canals, tanks and wells respectively.

Fig. 7.16

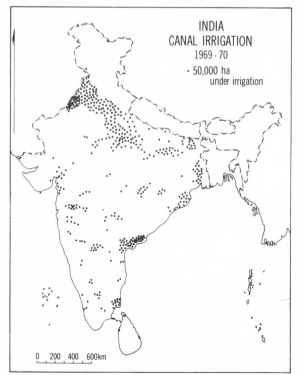

INDIA
CANAL IRRIGATION
1969 - 70
· 50,000 ha
under irrigation

0   200   400   600km

Understandably, canal irrigation is concentrated in the plains where the waters of large rivers can be diverted to command an extensive area of cropped land. In Figure 7.17 the major river development projects are located. It is clear that the wetter regions of India, like the east generally and the west coast of the Peninsula, have relatively little canal irrigation, while the areas with less than 1,000 mm rainfall *and* access to large rivers have most.

Tanks are widespread in the 'hard rock' terrain of southern India. Since they control only small catchments they are very susceptible to the seasonal variations in rainfall, and merely concentrate for an area below and around the tank (if farmers have pumps) the rainfall from a larger area. The gently rolling landscape provides only shallow valleys for tank construction, by simply raising a low earth dam, sometimes faced with granite blocks, across a river. The tanks are not designed to withstand severe flood waves, and failure of a whole series of tanks in a valley is not unknown. Seldom do tanks store water for the dry season, their principal function being to provide enough water during and immediately after the rainy season to enable irrigated crops, like rice and sugar cane, to be taken in a region where these might not otherwise be raised. As they dry out, the floors of the tanks are used for grazing, for cutting fodder grass, and in the dry season for excavating the accumulated silt for brickmaking.

The concentration of wells in the Ganga Plain is related to the extensive aquifer in its deep alluvial deposits. The depth to which wells are excavated to find a good aquifer is limited by cost and the technology available for lifting the water. The increasingly general availability of electricity and diesel engines for pumping has popularised their use not only in conjunction with the traditional well, but also from tube-lined wells which can be sunk to and operated at much greater depths than the traditional well.

In Table 7.6 an attempt has been made to draw up a water balance sheet for India's river basins grouped as in Figure 7.20.

Annual flow in the systems is a function of rainfall and the area of the catchment. The Himalayan rivers account for 58 per cent of the total, the Brahmaputra alone yielding 31 per cent. The regimes of these rivers are less extremely biased to

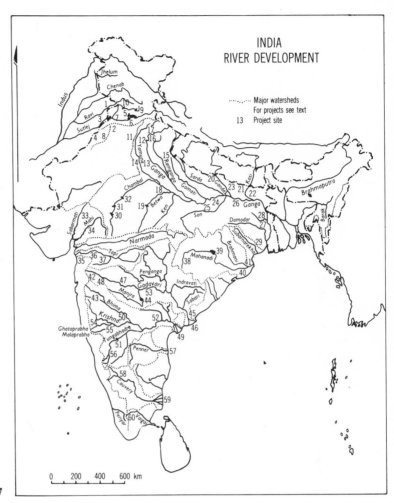

Fig. 7.17

the rainy season of the summer monsoon as they drain extensive snowfields that catch winter precipitation, particularly in the west, and yield the stored water in the spring melt. Furthermore, the huge dams of the Sutlej and Beas have a capacity to store 35 per cent of the flow, thus ensuring *rabi* season irrigation from the surplus arising from the *kharif* rains.

It can be seen that the Ganga basin is much more liberally watered by the Himalayan tributaries and main stream Ganga than by those entering from the Peninsula to the south, which contribute but a third of the total. However, because of the greater need for irrigation of the drier lands of these southern basins (Chambal and Son, principally) and of flood control and industrial water in the east (Damodar Valley), storages have been constructed to hold 23 and 9 per cent of the flow

of these tributary systems respectively. A major drawback to storage on the Himalayan tributaries is that the most suitable sites for dams on several of the important rivers lie over the border in Nepal, though some of these are being developed under treaties for the countries' mutual benefit.

The pattern of river basins in the Peninsula is highly asymmetric. Apart from the Mahanadi and the minor catchments adjoining it, the major basins have the remotest part of their watershed close to the coast on the opposite side. This is specially true of the Godavari and Krishna systems, giving them very extensive catchments which tap the heavy rainfall of the Western Ghats. The Mahanadi drains extensive uplands in Orissa and Madhya Pradesh. In all three basins, the Mahanadi, Godavari and Krishna storages have been built to hold 11, 13 and 47 per cent of flow, respectively.

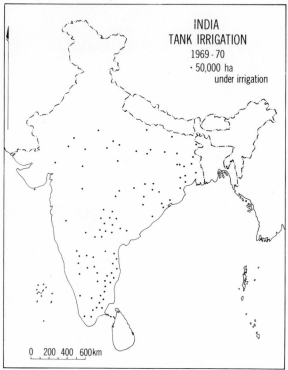

Fig. 7.18

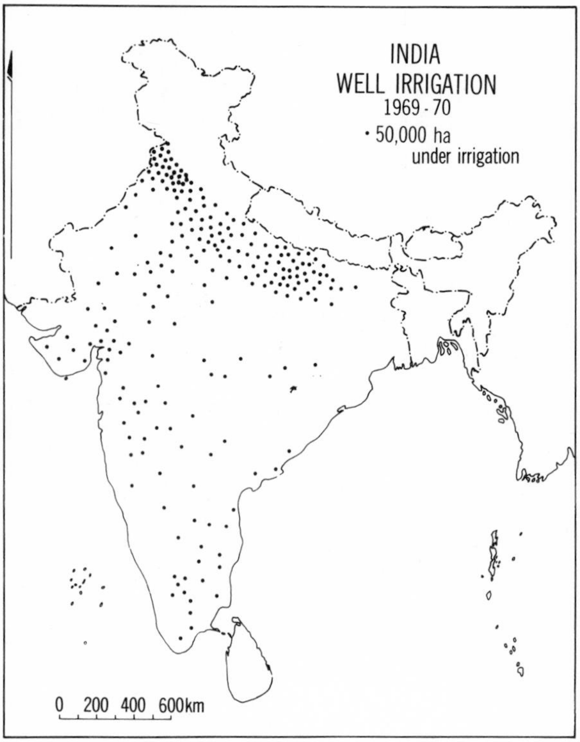

Fig. 7.19

Table 7.5   Irrigation by regions and sources, 1975–76

Region	% share of Indian net irrigated area	% of regional total by sources				
		Canals	Tanks	Tube-wells	Other wells	Other
1. *Northwest* Haryana, Himachal Pradesh, Jammu and Kashmir, Punjab, Rajasthan	23	50	3	29	20	2
2. *North Centre* Bihar, Uttar, Pradesh	31	34	4	38	14	10
3. *Northeast* Assam, Manipur, Meghalaya, Nagaland, Tripura, West Bengal	6.5	59	14	—	1	26
4. *West Centre* Gujarat, Madhya Pradesh, Maharashtra	14.5	28	8	3	55	6
5. *South & Southeast* Andhra Pradesh, Kerala, Karnataka, Orissa, Tamilnadu	25	44	30	2	20	4
INDIA	100	40	12	19	22	7

Source: As Table 7.3

Table 7.6 Water resources and utilisation by river systems (thousand million cubic metres and megawatts installed capacity)

River system	Annual surface flow	% total	Storage	% of flow	*Water utilisation* From surface water	From ground water	Total	% of flow	% From ground water	% India total	*Hydro-electric potential* Potential MW at 60% load factor	% India total	Installed capacity MW	% India total
1. Indus tributaries in India	73	3.8	14	35	47	14	60	82	23	10.9	7,750	16	3,027	20.8
1.1 Ravi, Beas, Sutlej	40	2.1	—	—	—	—	55	138	—	10.0	3,500	7	—	—
1.2 Jhelum, Chenab	31	1.6	—	—	—	—	5	16	—	.9	4,250	9	—	—
1.3 Ghaggar	2	—	—	—	—	—	—	—	—	—	—	—	—	—
2. Ganga	557	29.2	31	—	132	42	173	31	24	31.3	6,000*	13	2,512	17.2
2.1 Himalayan rivers	424	22.4	7	2	82	32	113	27	28	20.5	—	—	1,593	10.9
2.2 Right bank tributaries, Chambal-Son	88	4.6	20	23	22	8	30	34	27	5.4	—	—	815	5.6
2.3 Damodar, etc.	45	2.4	4	9	28	2	30	80	7	5.4	—	—	104	0.7
3. Brahmaputra, Barak	591	31.2	—	—	8	1	9	1.5	8	1.6	12,000	25	276	1.9
4. Between Ganga and Mahanadi	44	2.3	4	9	10	0.3	10	23	3	1.8	1,100	2	130	0.9
5. Mahanadi	71	3.7	8	11	25	0.4	26	37	1	4.7	1,000	2	270	1.9
6. Between Mahanadi and Godavari	17	0.9	—	—	10	0.2	10	59	2	1.8	—	—	—	—
7. Godavari	118	6.2	15	13	51	8	59	50	13	10.7	6,000	13	1,349	9.3
8. Krishna	63	3.3	30	47	57	9	66	105	13	12.0	1,500	3	1,893	13.0
9. Between Krishna and Cauvery	25	1.3	2	8	27	6	33	132	17	6.0	—	—	—	—
10. Cauvery and southwards	28	1.5	5	20	32	4	36	130	11	6.5	1,000	2	975	6.7
11. Rivers of Saurashtra and Kutch	12	0.6	—	—	5	13	17	141	73	3.1	—	—	—	—
12. Mahi, Sabarmati, etc.	16	0.8	5	31	9	4	13	81	30	2.4	100	—	—	—
13. Narmada, Tapi	64	3.4	11	17	14	5	19	30	27	3.4	2,000	4	300	2.1
14. West Coast rivers	218	11.5	14	6	18	1	20	9	6	3.6	4,500	9	3,846	26.4
INDIA TOTAL	1,897	100	139	7	451	108	551	29	20	100.0	47,950†	100	14,578	100.0

* Includes 2,000 on Nepal border rivers
† Includes 5,000 for minor systems

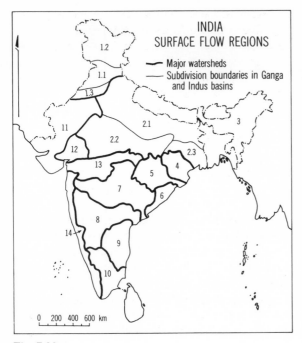

Fig. 7.20

It should be stressed that the data for storages cover only the large ones, and a very considerable additional volume is held in the thousands of tanks that are rarely out of sight on the plateaux of Andhra and Karnataka. The catchments between the Krishna and Cauvery are individually small and do not stretch far enough to the west to collect water from a rainfall regime different from or more prolific than their own. The Cauvery, however, is better favoured in this respect and 20 per cent of the flow from its Western Ghats headwaters is stored before the river spills onto the Tamilnadu plains. Together, the eastward flowing rivers of the Peninsula have 19 per cent of the country's surface water resources. The regimes of the Peninsula rivers closely follow the pattern of rainfall.

Towards the northwest the Narmada and Tapi, with long narrow catchments reaching east on either side of the Satpura Range, are the largest rivers flowing to the west coast; the catchments of the southern Aravallis in Gujarat and Rajasthan are very limited in both area and rainfall. The rivers draining the Western Ghats to the Arabian sea are all short but collectively account for 11.5 per cent of the total. Six per cent of their flow

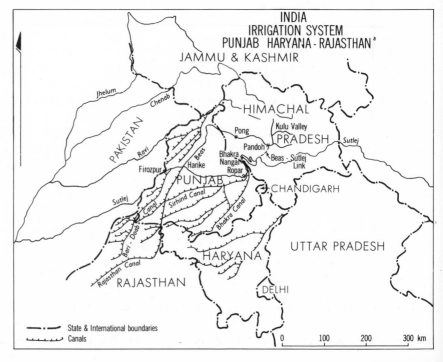

Fig. 7.21

is stored, mainly to provide constant flow to power stations that make effective use of the steep drop of the Western Ghats. Heavy rainfall, with a short dry season in the south, accounts for the high yield of these rivers.

Water Utilisation

When considering the utilisation of the water resources of a drainage basin, water should not be conceived of as a commodity which once used is necessarily lost to the ocean until it reappears as rain in a subsequent 'turn' of the hydrological cycle. Some of the rain falling on a catchment immediately enters the groundwater reserve, and more is added by seepage from canals, tanks and drainage downwards from fields. Water within the system may be used and re-used several times as it progresses towards the sea. Absolute loss occurs when it is incorporated in the tissues of living matter or passes to the air through evaporation or evapo-transpiration. Thus some of the percentages shown for utilisation of annual surface flow exceed 100 per cent. The data for utilisation cover canals and tanks as sources of surface water, with wells accounting for the groundwater figure.

In terms of utilisation, several basins are outstanding in that the level of utilisation is disproportionately high in comparison with the basic flow. Thus the Indus tributaries have 11 per cent of the utilisation as against 4 per cent of the flow of India's rivers. Intensive canal and well irrigation raised utilisation here to 138 per cent of the surface flow, and the proportion coming from groundwater is correspondingly high at 23 per cent. In the Ganga basin, its share of utilisation more nearly matches its share in flow. Groundwater is relatively important in the Ganga system, except in the eastern tributary basins where dry season *rabi* cropping is as yet not much developed, making two rain-fed *kharif* rice crops possible.

The ideal of multi-purpose development of river basins is often thwarted by a conflict of interests among the potential beneficiaries. This has been the case with the largest of all India's schemes, the Bhakra–Nangal on the Sutlej (Fig. 7.21).

Here, the first big storage dam built in the Himalaya is called upon to generate electricity and to provide irrigation water through the *rabi* season to an extensive canal system watering Punjab, Haryana and northern Rajasthan. In order to conserve water for power, the irrigation supply has sometimes to be curtailed. The farmers' misfortune may be doubled in that in those years when canal water is deficient, so too may be electricity. They are then frustrated in their efforts to make good the shortage of canal water by extracting groundwater using electrically powered pumps. The Bhakra–Nangal scheme is examined in some detail here as an example of the considerable modification that man is bringing about in the Sutlej and Beas River systems.

The Bhakra–Nangal scheme is part of a complex of works that harnesses the waters of three Indus tributaries for India's use. The main elements are complete or nearing completion. Before Independence the British had built barrages across the Ravi to supply the Upper Bari Doab Canal (1879), and the Sutlej, for the Sirhind Canal (1887), both at the points of emergence of these rivers onto the plain. Another barrage diverted the Sutlej at Firozpur, below its confluence with the Beas, to feed the Gang Canal (1928) and the Eastern Canal (1933). After Independence a minor system has been provided for the Bist Doab between the Beas and Sutlej. This is fed from the Sutlej at Ropar with some supplementation from the Beas at Tanda. The major works, however, have been the high dam on the Sutlej at Bhakra, with a 'live' (unstable) storage of almost 8,000 million m³, and the Nangal Barrage, 13 km downstream. The latter diverts water into a canal for hydro-electric development, and thence into the Bhakra Canal system below Ropar, to irrigate nearly 15 million ha in Punjab, Haryana and Rajasthan. Just below the confluence of the Sutlej and the Beas Rivers, a barrage at Harike supplies the Rajasthan Feeder Canal which carries water to the Rajasthan Canal system in the arid districts of Ganganagar and Bikaner, though its ultimate extent in this direction is in some doubt. To reinforce these schemes, particularly the storage and power capacity of the Bhakra Dam, a link has been dug to carry water from a diversion on the River Beas at Pandoh. Bhakra will receive an additional 4,590 million m³ and 990 MW of power will be generated *en route*. Lower down the Beas, the Pong Dam is being constructed to store 6,908 million m³ to provide for the canal systems taking-off below Harike.

Drought and Scarcity

A major benefit of the considerable development of water resources that has characterised India over the past 100 years is the reduction in the level of uncertainty under which farmers have always lived. In the past, when the economy was poorly developed and communications were rudimentary, drought could cause extreme hardship, and millions of people died as a result of starvation or, more directly, from epidemic disease which struck hard at populations weakened by hunger. Some of the most devastating famines that occurred during the nineteenth century were in regions where rainfall is normally adequate to support dense populations as in Bengal, Orissa and UP. Yet maybe ten million died in Bengal in a famine of 1770, 800,000 in UP in 1836, and one million in Orissa in 1865–66. Extensive areas in the sub-humid belt of the Peninsula suffered in 1876–78 when, in two successive years of scarcity, five and a half millions are estimated to have died in Gujarat, Maharashtra, Andhra Pradesh and Tamilnadu.

Famines on this scale, and the lesser shortages that have occurred more recently, have not been due simply to rainfall deficiency, though that undoubtedly triggered off the process of economic impoverishment that could ultimately lead to the starvation of the poorest in the sight of plenty. The first and hardest hit in any famine are the landless labourers for whom there is no work in times of extreme drought, and who have no property or possessions against which to borrow. For these, a famine is primarily 'a famine of work not a famine of food'.* Without work they lack the wherewithal, with which to buy food. The share cropper, the tenant farmer, the small marginal owner farmer, and all those in the village community who depend for their livelihood on the fortunes of those with land and resources are soon affected, and even the landowning farmers, starting with the smallest, may find their resources inadequate to withstand the strain of prolonged drought. Unscrupulous opportunists have been ever ready to take advantage of natural calamity by buying and hoarding food, and by striking hard bargains over loans with all in need.

*K. Suresh Singh, *The Indian Famine 1967*, New Delhi, 1975

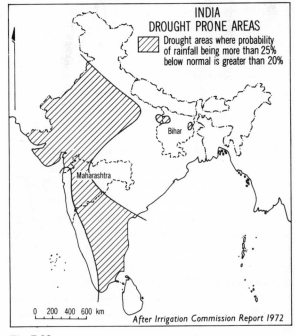

Fig. 7.22

Despite the great advances in the economy in recent decades, and the greater awareness of the administrators of the warning signs of impending scarcity, the spectre of scarcity cannot be said to have disappeared entirely from the Indian scene. Population pressure on land resources encourages farmers to grow the most profitable crops and those that will provide most food for his family. These are not necessarily the crops that could best survive in a season of drought. Rice tends to be the preferred food crop wherever conditions are normally suitable, yet this crop is probably the most sensitive of all to water shortage during growth. This fact seems to lie behind the paradoxical situation that some of the worst famines and scarcities have occurred at the margin of rice-growing regions, when these have been stricken by drought.

The Bihar famine of 1967 is a case in point. Most of the State has an average annual rainfall in excess of 1,000 mm. As a result of the failure of the July rains, essential for the survival (in an agricultural environment largely unprotected by irrigation schemes) of crops planted at the start of the monsoon, the harvest of winter (*kharif*) rice was deficient by 68 per cent of normal. The lack of late monsoon rains reduced the *rabi* wheat crop to 23 per cent. In a population in which 82 per cent of the economically active depended on agriculture such levels of crop failure were calamitous, and but for a remarkable effort by national and international organisations the disaster in human terms would have been much worst than it was. At its peak, 534,000 were employed on famine relief works in order to earn money with which to buy food, and a further 707,000 were in receipt of free hand-outs.

Maharashtra in the years 1965–66 suffered a period of serious scarcity due to poor early and late monsoon rains in 1965. Production of the major crop, rabi jowar, fell by 27 per cent over the whole State and of rain-fed rabi jowar by 67 per cent in one district. Again, famine relief works helped half a million earn their food.

It is interesting that while central Maharashtra lies within the drought prone areas as defined by the Irrigation Commission of 1972, only a small part of Bihar is so regarded (Fig. 7.22). The Commission regarded as drought-prone those areas where the probability of rainfall being more than 25 per cent below average is greater than 20 per cent (i.e. more than one year in five). It will be noted that two of the worst famines of the nineteenth century occurred well outside the drought-prone zone, underlining the significance of factors other than rainfall deficiency in creating conditions of food scarcity. While scarcity may be triggered off by the collapse of an inflexible land-use system in the face of climatic stress, it may also be the result of non-climatic stresses working on an agricultural economy which lacks adequate reserves. The Orissa famine of 1865–66 has been blamed on traders who were denuding the region's granaries of stocks in the immediate pre-famine season when only a slight crop deficiency was enough to precipitate disaster. In the case of the Bengal famine of 1943 (prior to Independence and Partition) the disruption of rice supplies owing to the military loss of Burma, combined with wartime overloading of the communications system and of the administration which proved incapable of preventing hoarding of stocks by merchants, created a famine situation in which maybe three million died as a consequence.

Modernisation

The modernisation of the socio-economic environment within which the cultivator operates has long been accepted as essential to the achievement of the goals of national self-sufficiency and social justice. The latter may currently be interpreted to mean as wide a distribution as possible throughout the community of the ownership and right to cultivate land.

The land-holding system has been the subject of much legislation. There is not enough land for those who are or who would be farmers, and the country suffers from intense rural overpopulation. Operational holdings, the units actually farmed by agricultural households as distinct from areas owned or rented by individuals, are often too small to provide subsistence for a family. Many families must supplement their income by casual employment when agricultural work is slack, or by having one or more members more or less permanently absent in some urban or non-agricultural occupation. The *average* size of operational holdings ranges from less than a hectare in Kerala, the Vale of Kashmir, the UP Himalaya and parts of West Bengal (all areas of intensive rice cultivation), to over six hectares in the dry lands in the centre of Maharashtra, western Gujarat and western Rajasthan.

Efforts have been made to control the upper limit of the size of land holdings by the 'land-ceilings policy'. States are required under a Central Government Act to introduce legislation to distribute to the landless and to smaller holders the lands held surplus to the ceiling levels determined in each State or region. Ceilings vary with the quality of land within the State, and lie generally well above the minimum required for subsistence. In the States where rice growing predominates, the lower ceiling ranges from 3.7 ha in Jammu and Kashmir to 5 ha in West Bengal, most states using 4.05 or 4.86 ha. The wheat–millets States have ceilings ranging upwards from 7 ha in Punjab to 7.25 in Haryana, UP, Maharashtra and Rajasthan. The upper limit (applicable to the least productive land) is most commonly 21.85, but wide variations occur; Assam uses 7 ha, Himachal Pradesh 28.33 ha. The Draft Fifth Five-Year Plan bemoans the meagre results of all this legislation, suggesting that ceiling levels were set too high, and that landowners have been able, aided and abetted by dilatory and unenergetic implementation on the part of the State authorities, to avoid the intentions of the laws by *mala fide* transfers of land and by dividing a property up among close relatives while continuing to operate it as a single holding.

Aggravating the small size of many holdings is their common fragmentation into separate parcels of land often at opposite ends of a village or in a neighbouring village, making the farmer's access to work wasteful in time and close supervision of all his fields difficult. In several States, holdings have been or are in an advanced state of being consolidated, but the process is terribly laborious and slow, bedevilled with legal niceties and problems of establishing ownership. The northwestern States and Maharashtra have gone furthest in consolidation, but elsewhere little has happened. One major consideration that may have deterred administrators and tenants is that the procedures can become the opportunity to evict legally insecure occupiers from the land.

Tenancy conditions are a more fundamental handicap to modernisation than the size of holdings or their fragmentation. Traditional tenancy and crop-sharing arrangements for using land are relics of the rent-capitalist system, the disappearance of which from the western world was part of the agricultural revolution in the eighteenth and nineteenth centuries. The essence of rent-capitalism was that the landowner was content to draw rents from his land while minimising his investment. In productive capitalism which replaced this system in the west, the landowner saw land as a medium through which he could increase his income by investing in its high productivity irrespective of who managed the enterprise. W. Ladejinsky has pointed to the indirect connection between land reform and modernisation as comprehended in the concept of the 'green revolution', the success of which depends on the occupier of land, whether owner or tenant, being able to acquire credit to finance his farming operations.* Dating from the Second Five-Year Plan, the call has been to give 'land to the tiller', with the abolition of tenancy as the objective. Many of those who

farm lands they do not own do so under various forms of informal verbal agreement with the landlord, which are very difficult to establish in law. Thus, much of the legislation to give land to tenants who have cultivated it for a number of years has proved abortive. Laws to limit the rental to not more than one fifth or a quarter of the gross product of the land are difficult to enforce in a semi-literate, tradition-bound population.

Attempts are being made to out-flank the handicap of non-ownership of land, by government agencies becoming more closely involved in the process of providing credit to small and marginal tenant farmers.

The Green Revolution

Too often it is popularly supposed that the essence of the 'green revolution' has been the introduction of newly developed high yielding strains of wheat, rice and other crops, as listed in Table 7.7.

While this was an important element, equally important were the provision of irrigation at the place and time required, and the availability of other material inputs such as fertilisers and chemicals for plant protection. The wider provision of credit with which to dig wells, to purchase pumps, and to apply manures and pesticides, has had an impact upon agriculture as a whole and not merely on the cultivation of the specifically HYV crops.

The HYV Programme began in 1966–67 with the introduction of new fertiliser-responsive dwarf wheats developed in Mexico. In that crop year, 4.2 per cent of the area under wheat was HYV. By 1970–71 this all-India figure had risen to 35 per cent, and to 70 per cent in 1976–77. In the more important wheat-growing states the proportion

Table 7.7 High yielding varieties, 1976–77

Percentage of crop area under HYV	
Wheat	70
Rice	35
Jowar	15
Bajra	21
Maize	18

*W. Ladejinsky, 'Ironies of India's Green Revolution', *Foreign Affairs*, **48**(**4**), 1970, pp. 756–768

was even higher: 89 per cent in Haryana, 92 per cent in Punjab, and 73 per cent in UP and Bihar. Apart from fertiliser the major constraint on the cultivation of HYV of wheat is water availability, since they require five to six shallow waterings as against the two to four needed for local varieties.

The high income to be made from growing the new varieties enabled many farmers to invest in their own independent supply of water from pumped wells or tube wells. These, however, generally depend on electricity which tends to be in short supply in the same season as the canal waters are inadequate – and for the same reason, that is, shortage of storage in the multi-purpose reservoir. The smaller farmers are hardest hit in these circumstances, as they often rely on water purchased from the larger operators who understandably look after themselves first. Undoubtedly HYV have had an impressive effect on wheat productivity, whether measured in increased tonnage or in yields per ha. Production in Punjab rose from 2,494,000 tonnes in 1966–67, at an average yield of 1,544 kg/ha to 6,639,000 tonnes, 2,537 kg/ha, in 1977–78, an increase in yield of 64 per cent.

The same degree of success has not yet been achieved with rice for a number of reasons. Several HYV of rice have been available from the late 1960s and have been found suitable to particular areas. All, however, are dwarf varieties, so bred to give them strength of stem to prevent wastage due to lodging, which reduces photosynthesis in the leaves flattened and shaded by those bent above them. Shortness of stem is a handicap in many lower parts of the deltas where rice is the main crop, and where the traditional varieties have

been selected over time to cope with flooded conditions. The natural environments in which rice has to grow in much of eastern India are far from ideal for the new varieties so far available, though better adapted HYV are being bred. In the irrigated plains of the upper Ganga and Indus tributaries, close control over the depth of water can more readily be maintained, and the HYV dwarfs have done well. In 1976–77, 35 per cent of the all-India area under rice was in HYV, compared with 2.5 per cent in 1966–67, and 19 per cent in 1971–72. Adoption of HYV has been greatest in Punjab (86 per cent of the area), Tamilnadu (92 per cent), and Andhra Pradesh (57 per cent). In the States of eastern India where more reliance is placed on direct rainfall and where control of water depth in the fields is difficult, adoption has been lower: Bihar (19 per cent), Orissa (13 per cent) and West Bengal (25 per cent).

It is in the dry *rabi* season, wherever irrigation can be assured, that HYV rice has proved most popular because then the risk of deep flooding is absent, and conditions approach the ideal, the clear skies and low humidity discouraging pests and diseases.

The potential impact of HYV rice in areas where water levels can be controlled is seen in Punjab, where an overall yield of 3,362 kg per ha was recorded for 1977–78, an increase of 183 per cent over 1966–67. Hooghly in West Bengal reached 3,450 kg/ha for *rabi*-grown *boro* rice in 1971–72 in contrast to the autumn *aus* crop at 893 kg and the winter *aman* crop at 1,342 kg/ha.

After availability of HYV seed and of irrigation water, fertiliser is the most important input re-

31 The dairyman milks his buffalo at the customer's request in the street in Kolhapur, Maharashtra, a scene indicative of the level of economic life in much of India today.
(Courtesy Margaret Scrivenor).

quired. Since fertiliser costs are linked to petroleum costs, prices have risen sharply in recent years with the result that farmers have tended to apply less to their crop and yields have fallen.

In response to the demands for fertilisers a huge new industry has sprung up all over India with a capacity exceeding four million tonnes. The consumption of fertilisers has increased five and a half times since 1965–66 and now exceeds 20 kg/ha of cropped land in 9 states. One advantage claimed for the widespread adoption of HYV, especially where it permits more multiple cropping, is that it will create more work on the land for the increasing numbers of landless labourers. The demand for labour is, however, notoriously seasonal, and while there is often a shortage of labour over short periods of intensive activity these are separated by long periods of slack demand and underemployment. In such a situation the question of mechanising farming to replace the slow labour-and-fodder-consuming bullock teams with tractors driven by fossil fuel becomes one without an answer that can be applied universally. There are situations where tractor cultivation can be justified on the grounds that they do not consume food when not in use, and because they may in some circumstances so speed the processes of cultivation as to permit a higher intensity of land-use.

Chapter 8

India: Industry

High among the priorities in the struggle to reduce the rate of population increase and to improve living standards, demographers place the related objectives of industrialisation and urbanisation. India, ever since Independence, has been progressing along the path of transition from an economy dominated by traditional semi-subsistence agriculture and industry to one in which modernised forms of enterprise in both these areas are the rule.

In the short run India's problem is to create new employment opportunities without destroying existing jobs. Consequently, labour-intensive industries are favoured at the expense of economically more attractive capital-intensive ones, and traditional craft industries are protected against the competition of efficient modern industry. A mixed system such as this is difficult for planners to control in the national interest. Efficient exporting industries seek maximum modernisation in order to compete with overseas competition, and they need a share of the home market from which to make their merchant ventures. The reservation of a part of the domestic market for village industries can run counter to the interests of the former group. It remains to be seen whether a satisfactory integration of modern and traditional can be achieved.

In the 1971 Census (see Table 6.3) 10.7 million workers were recorded as employed in manufacturing industry 'other than household manufacturing' and 6.4 million in the household 'village' or cottage sector. In addition nearly one million were employed in mines and quarries and over a million on plantations – both primary economic activities with important manufacturing implications.

The range and scale of industrial production is impressive, as Table 8.1 shows. India has the capacity to manufacture almost all the kinds of goods and machines needed for a modern nation; it is,

however, at the stage when not all the quantity required can be produced.

Energy Resources

One of the hallmarks of the industrial revolution as it occurs in any country, is the substitution of inanimate power for muscle. India's industrial revolution starts with electricity as the main form of industrial energy, obtained from coal and water power for the most part, with nuclear energy an important alternative in areas far from the coalfields. Able to obtain power through an extensive grid system, Indian manufacturing industry is much less locationally tied than was industry in the developed countries in the past. Petroleum is still the major basis for energising transport, and its use is being discouraged for static power raising in view of domestic scarcity and recently escalated import costs.

Coal
The coal mining industry (see Fig. 8.1) has been called upon to raise production from about 105 million tonnes in 1978 to 150 million tonnes by the end of the current Plan in 1982–83. By then electricity generation will be the major consumer of coal (36 per cent) followed by the steel industry (23 per cent) and transport (12 per cent). Most production comes from the Lower Gondwana formations in the Damodar Valley extending westwards from the Raniganj field in West Bengal to the Jharia, Bokaro, Karanpura and Ramgarh fields in Bihar (see Fig. 8.8). These account for about two-thirds of India's Gondwana coal production, but future expansion is likely to come from the hitherto minor fields of central India and their extensions into the Mahanadi and Godavari

Table 8.1   Industrial production, 1977–78

Item	Unit	1977–78
Coal	million tonnes	105
Petroleum crude	million tonnes	10.1
Petroleum products	million tonnes	23.2
Electricity, installed capacity	million kW	26.1
Electricity, generated	thousand million kWh	99
Iron ore	million tonnes	41
Steel ingots	million tonnes	8.6
Aluminium	thousand tonnes	179
Copper	thousand tonnes	21
Lead concentrates	thousand tonnes	35
Zinc concentrates	thousand tonnes	86
Manganese ore	million tonnes	1.8
Motor vehicles	thousand	84
Tractors	thousand	41
Motor cycles, etc.	thousand	225
Bicycles	thousand	3,184
Diesel engines (stationary)	thousand	133
Electric motors	thousand h.p.	4,040
Power pumps	thousand	352
Radio receivers	thousand	1,857
Sewing machines	thousand	364
Nitrogenous fertiliser	thousand tonnes N	2,013
Phosphatic fertiliser	thousand tonnes P_2O_5	670
Sulphuric acid	thousand tonnes	2,076
Caustic soda	thousand tonnes	520
Paper, paper board	thousand tonnes	965
Newsprint	thousand tonnes	56
Cement	thousand tonnes	19,300
Cotton yarn	thousand tonnes	1,128
Cotton textiles, cloth	million m	8,141
mill made	million m	4,181
hand-loom, etc.	million m	3,960
Jute textiles	thousand tonnes	1,178
Rayon yarn	thousand tonnes	129
Sugar	million tonnes	6.5
Tea	million kg	560
Coffee	million kg	119
Vanspati cooking oil	million kg	572

Sources: India – A Reference Annual, 1979; Times of India Directory and Year Book 1979.

valleys. The structural extension of the Damodar Valley trough embraces the Sangrauli field in Madhya Pradesh, south of which a number of extensive fields include the important Korba coal, exploited for power for aluminium reduction and for coal to blend with Damodar coking coal at the Bhilai steel works. Several outcrops of Gondwana coal lie to the southeast, parallel to the Mahanadi and Brahmani Rivers, the principal being at Talcher in Orissa, developed for power. Further west four groups of small fields may be noted roughly aligned with the Pench-Wainganga and lower Godavari valleys.

Qualitatively, the Gondwana coals are by far the best and include valuable coking coals which are still being wastefully consumed for steam raising. Their importance as a diminishing resource of metallurgical significance is recognised, and the railways are progressively adapting locomotives to use less efficient but more abundant non-coking grades or are electrifying their lines. Indian production is about 23 per cent in coking coals, 74 per cent in non-coking and 3 per cent in lignite.

Poorer quality coal and lignite are mined from Tertiary formations in Assam, Meghalaya and Arunachal Pradesh, Darjiling, Jammu and Kashmir, and the lignite deposits of Rajasthan and Tamilnadu. Tamilnadu's lignite at Neyveli is used to generate power, for making briquettes, and as a basis for the manufacture of urea fertiliser; that at Bikaner in Rajasthan is used for briquettes for railway locomotives.

Fig. 8.1

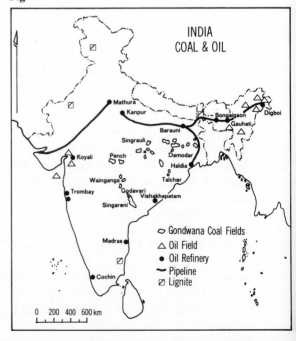

Petroleum

India is now able to supply about 43 per cent of her petroleum needs for domestic production, a proportion that is likely to rise when the Bombay High structure reaches full development. Output is at present 10.8 million tonnes of which Bombay High provides about a quarter. Imports run at 14.1 million tonnes of crude and 2.6 million tonnes of petroleum products. Demand is rising however, and the search for oil-bearing structures is being vigorously pursued, especially in off-shore areas. The oldest oilfield in the country, in Assam, is still in production (see Fig. 8.1). Since Independence the Gujarat fields around the head of the Gulf of Cambay have been developed. Refineries for domestic crude have been established in the Assam Valley at Digboi (0.53 million tonnes capacity), Gauhati (0.75 million tonnes) and Bongaigaon (1 million tonnes), connected by a pipeline which also carried crude further west to Barauni (3 million tonnes) in Bihar. The latter is connected to the deep-water port and refinery at Haldia (2.5 million tonnes) which uses imported crude, and to Kanpur for distributing products in

32   The shipbuilding yards at Vishakhapatham on the Andhra Pradesh coast, have an annual capacity of up to three ships of 12,500 d.w. each and are expanding to produce six totalling 80,000 d.w. Other shipyards are in Calcutta, Bombay and Cochin. (Courtesy Govt. of India).

33   Quarrying high grade iron ore in Goa for export, mainly to Japan.

34   Off-shore oil drilling rig. Bombay High structure off the Maharashtra coast, now contributing a valuable resource. Development is under the Oil and Natural Gas Commission, a government agency. (Courtesy Govt. of India).

UP. The Gujarat crude is refined at Koyali (3 million tonnes) which is linked by pipes to its several tributary fields. The line from Salaya, a new deep-water off-shore terminal in the Gulf of Kutch, to Mathura (6 million tonnes) will feed imported crude to the largest Indian refinery. Other refinery capacity is located at major ports, two at Trombay (5.5 and 3.5 million tonnes), in Bombay harbour, and the rest at Cochin (3.5 million tonnes), Madras (2.5 million tonnes) and Vishakhapatnam (1.6 million tonnes).

Electric Power

Since Independence, India's capacity to generate electricity has increased tenfold, yet demand continues to outstrip supply. Power cuts in areas of heavy load, particularly during periods of drought, have been a serious embarrassment to industrial and agricultural production alike. In total, India's power output was 99,000 million kWh in 1978, giving over 150 kWh per head of population.

The greatest demand is from industry which uses 67.3 per cent of the total; domestic and public lighting takes 14.7 per cent, agricultural pumps 12.5 per cent, railways 3 per cent and public water and sewage undertakings 2.3 per cent.

The rapid expansion in electricity generating capacity is seen in Table 8.2. As potential hydro-electric sites are harnessed the emphasis inevitably changes towards coal and nuclear energy.

The hydro-electric potential of India's rivers is estimated at 48 million kW of which some 30 per cent has been harnessed (see Table 7.5 and Fig. 8.2; cf. also Fig. 7.20).

Table 8.2 Electricity generation (millions of kW Installed Capacity)

	1965–66	*1974–75*	*1977–78*
Steam	4.5	11.0 ⎫	15.3
Diesel	0.4	0.3 ⎭	
Hydro	4.1	7.0	10.0
Nuclear		0.6	0.6

The Himalayan rivers together have 32 per cent of India's installed capacity (Fig. 8.2). The east-flowing rivers account for 34 per cent of installed capacity, the Krishna, Godavari and Cauvery being outstanding. Power sites on these rivers are located in their upper or middle reaches where gradient can be concentrated. Outstanding in the number of sites with abrupt falls on strong perennial rivers, are the west coast rivers, notably those descending the Western Ghats. Including the small development on the Narmada, they account for almost 29 per cent of installed capacity. If the power development on the westward-diverted eastward-flowing rivers like the Koyna is transferred to the west coast's budget, their share rises to 36 per cent of the nation's total.

35 The 'doubling' process in a modern cotton mill at Coimbatore, Tamilnadu. (Courtesy Govt. of India).

36 The Chittaranjan Locomotive Works in the Damodar Valley makes diesel and steam engines for the Indian Railways. (Courtesy Govt. of India).

The seasonal irregularity of flow in a monsoon climate makes it difficult and expensive to exploit potential fully. Where water storage for irrigation and to check flood surges is an urgent need, multipurpose river developments are politically and economically attractive. Fortunately hydel potential and coalfields where thermal power can most cheaply be generated do not generally overlap, and the only substantial areas where local energy resources must be augmented with materials brought in from elsewhere are northwestwards from Bombay to Delhi. The location of nuclear power stations at Bombay and in Rajasthan is entirely justifiable at such a distance from coal. Others are being constructed at Kalpakkam near Madras, and Narora, UP.

Fig. 8.2

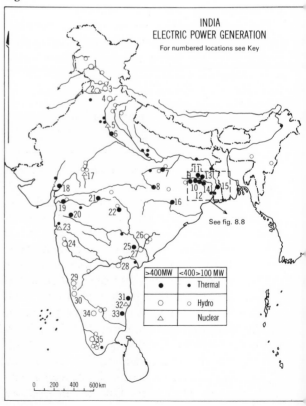

1 Salal (R. Chenab)	
2 Bhakra-Nangal	19 Ukai
3 Beas Link (Pandoh)	20 Nasik
4 Yamuna	21 Satpura
5 Narora (nuclear)	22 Nagpur
6 Harduaganj	23 Tarapur (nuclear)
7 Obra-Rihand	24 Koyna
8 Korba	25 Kothagudam
9 Pathratu	26 Balimela
10 Bokaro	27 Lower Sileru
11 Chandrapura	28 Srisailam
12 Santaldih	29 Kalinadi
13 Durgapur (DVC)	30 Sharavati
14 Durgapur (W. Bengal)	31 Ennore
15 Bandel	32 Kalapakkam (nuclear)
16 Talcher	33 Neyveli
17 Ranapratap Sagar (nuclear)	34 Kundah
18 Dhuvaran	35 Idikki

Other Localised Resources

India is fortunate in possessing, or being able to produce, a wide range of industrial resources – mineral, vegetable and animal. The principal industrial minerals in which India is deficient are lead and zinc, nickel, tin, silver, mercury and cobalt. In several minerals there is a surplus available for export (see Fig. 8.3).

Fig. 8.3

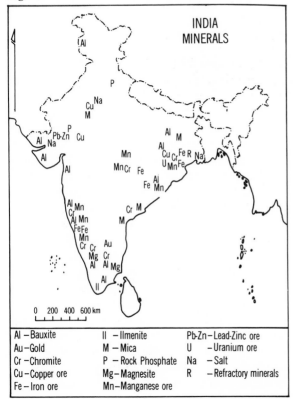

Al – Bauxite	Il – Ilmenite	Pb-Zn – Lead-Zinc ore
Au – Gold	M – Mica	U – Uranium ore
Cr – Chromite	P – Rock Phosphate	Na – Salt
Cu – Copper ore	Mg – Magnesite	R – Refractory minerals
Fe – Iron ore	Mn – Manganese ore	

Iron ores of high quality are worked in several parts of the Peninsula and have been a major factor in the establishment of the iron and steel industries in West Bengal, Bihar, Orissa, Madhya Pradesh and Karnataka. The most productive region extends from Singhbhum in southern Bihar through Orissa into Madhya Pradesh. Its surplus ore is exported through Paradip in Orissa and Vishakhapatnam and Kakinada in Andhra Pradesh (see Fig. 8.7), Karnataka's ores are at present used locally, but with the completion of the railway down the Western Ghats from Hassan to Mangalore, export will be facilitated. Goa already exports huge quantities from its immediate hinterland, through Marmagao. Goa led in iron ore

production with 12.1 million tonnes in 1973; the other major producers were Madhya Pradesh 8.1 million, Orissa 5.9 million and Bihar 4.7 million tonnes in a total of 35.4 million tonnes, of which 21.3 million were exported.

Manganese ore production runs at 1.7 million tonnes annually, almost half of which is exported. The Nagpur – Bhandara region in northeast Maharashtra is the principal source. Production of chromite, another ferro-alloy, is on a less important scale. Deposits are found in Bihar, Orissa, Maharashtra, Andhra, Tamilnadu and Karnataka. Figure 8.3 shows the importance of the peninsular shield as the principal mineralised region of India.

India's endowment of non-ferrous metals is less lavish. Reserves of bauxite are more than adequate and allow for increasing exports beyond domestic needs for the aluminium industry. Bauxite is found in laterite formations in many parts of the country, but particularly around the coastal margins of the Peninsula, and in its more humid eastern interior (Madhya Pradesh and Bihar). 1.5 million tonnes were mined in 1977–78.

Copper is mined in the multi-mineral belt of Singhbhum in Bihar (see Fig. 8.7) and in the newly developed Khetri belt in Rajasthan. Output at *c.* 21,000 tonnes in 1977–78 should increase to

37 Hauling hardwood logs aboard a sailing coaster at Mangalore, Karnataka. The timber will be shipped to Bombay or Cochin for despatch abroad.

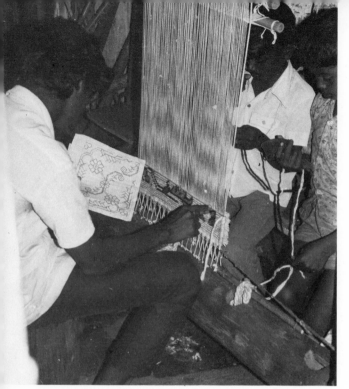

38 These boys are being taught how to make woollen rugs on a hand-loom typical of the craft level of household industry. At Eluru in Andhra Pradesh.

meet over 40 per cent of needs as the Khetri operation comes into full production. In 1977–78, 2.6 million tonnes of ore were extracted. The metal is also found in southern Rajasthan but it is the lead – zinc complex of that area, in Udaipur district, that has attracted exploitation. This is India's only present source of these metals; in 1977–78 86,000 tonnes of zinc concentrates and 35,000 of lead concentrates were obtained.

Gold has been produced steadily in small amounts from very deep veins in the Kolar field near Bangalore.

With the coming of nuclear power, India is fortunate in having a source of uranium ore in Bihar and in the Himalaya, but as yet it has relied on imported nuclear fuels. Other minerals for atomic use include monazite, a source of the element thorium which, with ilmenite – for titanium oxide is extracted from the beach sands of Kerala.

Non-metallic minerals of importance include mica, for which India has long been famous as the major world producer, from primitive shaft mines in central Bihar, Andhra Pradesh and Rajasthan. Common salt occurs in rock form in the sub-Himalayan belt, but most production is from evaporating sea water notably in the Little Runn of Kutch in Gujarat, and around the Bay of Bengal

in Calcutta, Tamilnadu and Andhra Pradesh. Naturally concentrated evaporites are worked in the Sambhar Lake in Rajasthan. With the increasing demand for fertilisers, the search for rock phosphate has been intensified, since the output from Udaipur and Dehra Dun (UP) falls well short of need. Another essential in the fertiliser industry is sulphuric acid, obtained using pyrites in Bihar, 31,000 tonnes being mined in 1977–78, but the country still relies heavily on imports.

Manufacturing Industry

There are three fairly distinct levels of manufacturing enterprise in India. At the simplest level of organisation and the lowest level of capitalisation, is village or household industry employing essentially family labour. This merges with small-scale industry, in which wage labour and a modest degree of capitalisation exist. Another distinction is in their measure of modernisation. Household manufacturing tends to be confined to traditional crafts little affected by modernisation, whereas the small-scale industries are essentially modern technologically speaking, and as advanced in this respect as the third category of industry, the 'organised' sector, registered and regulated under various acts. To a considerable extent the three levels correspond to three types of location: household industry is found obviously in the villages and small towns; small-scale industry is most common in towns and non-metropolitan cities; organised industry in the larger cities and in settlements created specifically for them.

Household Industry
The total number of men, women and children occupied in household industries is undoubtedly much more than the 6.4 million recorded in the Census, as many craftsmen are part-time farm labourers. The handloom industry, muscle powered, dominates village manufacturing. Some home-spun cotton yarn may be used, but most weavers use mill-made yarn.

Village industries are kept alive by indirect subsidies through the provision of cheap machine-made yarn, and by the reservation of a sizeable part of the textile market – the making of saris which almost every woman wears – for the village and small-scale sectors, but the economic wisdom of such protection is strongly questioned, even though it is inevitable for social and political reasons.

In a few areas of enterprise like silk-spinning from home-bred cocoons, coir production from domestic coconuts, making jaggery (crude sugar) from the farmer's own cane, and the manufacture of simple pottery, metal utensils and carpentry articles for the immediate local market, village industry continues to hold a viable position, but inevitably it must give way to the processes of modernisation, and is doing so through the expansion of the small-scale industrial sector. Attempts to link them to larger markets expose them to exploitation by middlemen from outside. A few trades of high craftsmanship following traditional designs capable of commanding markets in the tourist industry and overseas will no doubt survive.

Small-scale Industry

Small industries are defined as those having a capital investment of not more than Rs 1 million, or Rs 1.5 million in the case of industries ancillary to an industry in the 'organised' sector. They are usually proprietary or small partnerships, a fact that limits their ability to raise credit and to expand the scale of their operations. Their entrepreneurs' lack of technological qualifications places limits on the range of processes they can undertake, though government agencies are trying to bridge the 'information gap' for them. The Small Industries Development Organisation helps entrepreneurs get started in appropriate fields.

One important incentive is the establishment of industrial estates provided with the services essential to small industry, but which in the Indian urban area may be difficult for a manufacturer to arrange at a site of his own choosing. In many respects small industries are complementary to those in the large-scale sector.

Many process the raw materials that large-scale industry requires (cotton ginning is an example), others utilise the products of heavy industry, fabricating goods for local markets, like spun cast concrete pipes for irrigation, metal furniture, etc. They exist because of enterprise, and are located because of the personal preference of the entrepreneur.

The ability of small industry to create jobs (unskilled, semi-skilled and experience-giving), and to raise the level of economic activity in the small towns (in activities beyond the competitive reach of large-scale centralised industry), thereby interacting with the village agricultural economy, makes it a most essential element in the process of Indian modernisation.

Manufacturing in the Organised Sector

From the outset at Independence India has pursued a policy of industrialisation in which public ownership and private enterprise have well defined fields of interest. From 1956 government reserved to itself exclusive responsibility in certain basic industries listed as Schedule A industries, while sharing others with private enterprise, – the Schedule B industries – and leaving the remainder for the private sector to develop within the general system of licensing under government control.

Schedule A industries include the mining of coal, iron, petroleum, and the major non-ferrous metalliferous ores; the basic iron and steel, and non-ferrous metal industries; heavy engineering and machine tool manufacture; air and rail transport; nuclear energy and electric power. Schedule B covers aluminium, chemicals, fertilisers, road and sea transport and pharmaceuticals. It will be noted that textiles and food processing industries are not scheduled.

Direct government involvement in industry has grown to be very considerable. Among the 20 largest companies 15 are in the public sector – in steel, food, heavy electrical machinery and engi-

39 Typical of rural commodity transport throughout South Asia: bullock carts bringing sacks of grain into market at Kolhapur Maharashtra.

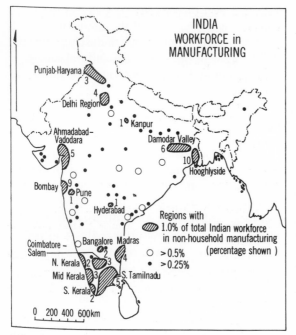

Fig. 8.4

significant advantages of nodality in most cases. Figure 8.4 and Table 8.3 show the distribution of the population engaged in the manufacturing industry (other than household industry) and mining. At the present stage of India's development which, as has been pointed out, is far from being fully integrated, one should not seek to find (in the clustering of the industrial population in particular areas) the kinds of closely knit industrial regions one associates with a highly developed country. Hooghlyside, the Damodar Valley and Greater Bombay – Thana most nearly correspond to the conventional idea of industrial regions, but the other areas of concentrations are more loosely structured.

The Annual Survey of Industries lists for each State the man-hours worked, the number of factories and the value added by manufacturing. These data have been mapped as percentages of the Indian total in Figure 8.5 from which the dominant position of Maharashtra (mainly Bombay) and West Bengal is clear on all counts. Tamilnadu ranks third on each criterion, followed by Gujarat and Uttar Pradesh. The value added by the latter, the largest of the States, is only a quarter of that by Maharashtra.

The major employer of labour, the textile industry, has wide distribution, but is responsible in large measure for the concentration of industrial employment in the regions listed in Table 8.3 with the exception of the Damodar Valley. There were 689 cotton mills in 1974. Many are mapped in Figure 8.6. The jute mills are highly localised, 62 of the 74 recorded being in Hooghlyside conurbation

neering, petroleum, fertilisers, aircraft, shipping, coal and lignite, air transport and copper.

Government investment in large enterprises like Bharat Heavy Electricals, Hindusthan Machine Tools, etc., enables it to locate plants in order to spread the benefits of central government expenditure over the states hungry for employment opportunities. Bangalore, Hyderabad, Bhopal, Madras, Ranchi and Lucknow are examples of locations where various State-owned engineering industries have been established without specific material or market advantages in their location, but with

Fig. 8.5

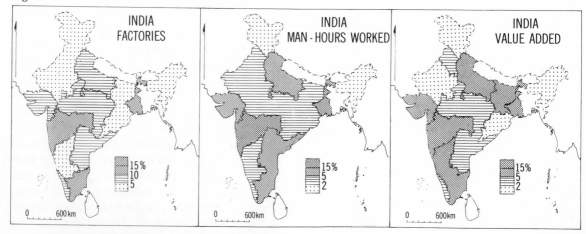

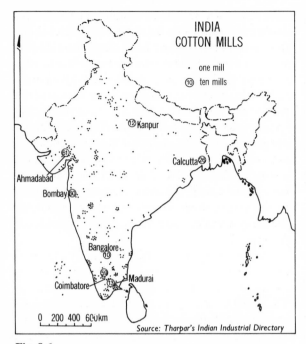

Fig. 8.6

Table 8.4 Steel ingot production 1977–78 (thousand tonnes)

Bhilai	2,371
TISCO, Jamshedpur	1,968
Rourkhela	1,409
Durgapur	1,092
IISCO, Burnpur	651
Bokaro (under development)	933
Bhadravati	103
Others	97
TOTAL	8,624

where they employ 250,000 workers. The reason in this case is clearly the proximity of East Bengal raw jute in the early days of the industry, which now has to find fibre grown domestically in West Bengal Assam and Bihar, and imports some from Bangladesh, now its major rival as a jute manufacturer.

The iron and steel industry is the most important component of the minerals and metal working group. It is now to all intents a nationalised industry,

Table 8.3 Labour force in industry and mining (in regions as per cent of India total)

Bombay – Thana	9.2	
(with Pune)		10.5
Hooghlyside	9.7	
Damodar Valley		
(incl. Singhbhum)	6.2	
Ahmadabad group	5.1	
N. Tamilnadu group	4.0	
Coimbatore – Salem	3.1	7.6
S. Tamilnadu	4.5	
N. Kerala	1.7	
Mid-Kerala	2.9	6.4
S. Kerala	1.8	
Delhi group	3.8	
Punjab – Haryana	2.6	
Bangalore	1.7	
Hyderabad	1.1	
Kanpur	1.1	

since government has a large share in the two privately established firms. The whole industry is coordinated by the Steel Authority of India (SAIL) set up in 1973 to restructure the management in its several plants, and to direct future development. The major steel works in production (1977–78 data) are shown in Table 8.4.

In a general sense, all these plants are oriented towards materials, but 'proximity to materials' may mean distances of 100 km for the nearest ingredient. Jamshedpur is the oldest of the steel plants, established in 1907–11. High grade iron ore is mined in the hills to the south and west (see Fig. 8.7 and 8.8), but although manganese and chromite for alloy steels are available in the same Singhbhum district, better quality materials are brought in from Madhya Pradesh and Orissa. Coking coal is railed in from the Damodar Valley about 120 km distant.

Next in order of age is the Indian Iron and Steel Company's plant at Burnpur with a capacity of one million tonnes. Originally based on ironstone shales in the Damodar coal measure series at Kulti (est. 1919) from which good cast iron could be made, the firm set up a plant at Burnpur 16 km to the east, near Asansol, to make steel using non-phosphoric Singhbhum ores (up to 70 per cent iron content) brought from over 300 km to the south. The smaller but more specialised Bhadravati plant in Karnataka dates from the same era, and was set up to use charcoal fuel.

Rich silica-iron ore from the Bababudan Hills (55–64 per cent iron) is brought to the site on the Bhadra River by ropeway. Coke has now to be railed in from the Damodar Valley, but fuel transport costs are minimised by pig iron in electric smelters. Bhadravati is an important plant for alloy and special steels made in electric furnaces, such as stainless, spring and tool steel, ferro-silicon and ferro-manganese.

The steel plants established since Independence have been set up with foreign participation – Bhilai and Bokaro with Russian assistance, Durgapur with British help, and Rourkhela with West German aid. To date, Bhilai is India's biggest steel plant, laid out on many hectares of level terrain alongside the electrified railway line linking it to the Damodar Valley (whence its coking coal must come 745 km) and to Calcutta, and other lines to ports at Vishakhapatnam and Kakinada on the Andhra coast, and to western central and northern India. Iron ore (67 per cent iron) is brought from Dalli Rajhara 97 km to the south. Originally it was intended to use coal from Korba, only 225 km distant to the northeast, but this proved unsuitable for coking unless blended with stronger Jharia coal from the Damodar in a 30:70 ratio. Manganese can be obtained from Balaghat about 200 km to the west.

Durgapur, on the banks of the Damodar River, brings its ore from Naumundi in Singhbhum 329 km away, but is close to coking coal and to lower quality fuel for power generation. Alloy steels are made in an adjoining works. Rourkhela is near to the Brahmani River just over the border in Orissa on the electrified line from Calcutta and the

Fig. 8.7

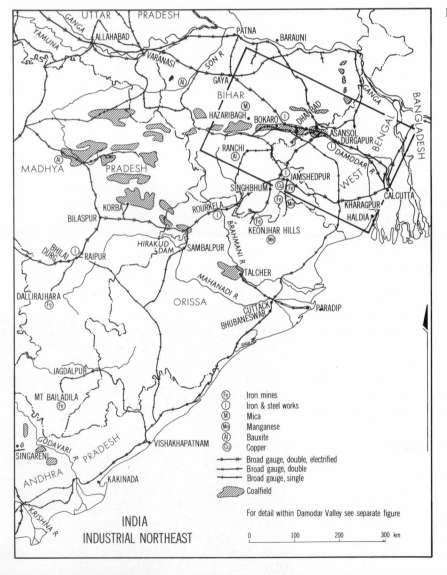

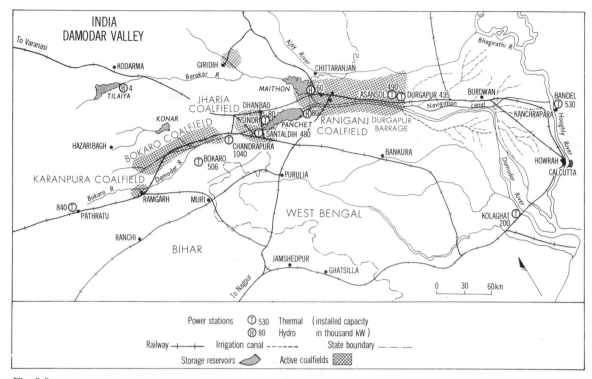

Fig. 8.8

Damodar Valley. The iron ores of the Orissa–Bihar border hills are close at hand, and the plant brings in coking coal from the Damodar, back-loading in the wagons that carry ore to the Damodar works. Bokaro promises to dwarf these earlier plants of the post-Independence period. Its locational advantages are similar to those of Durgapur. It is expected to develop to 4.75 million tonnes capacity and the feasibility of further increasing this to 10 million is under study. A major feature of the plant is a hot strip mill of more than 3 million tonnes capacity.

Meanwhile plans are going ahead to establish new steel plants still further from coal than any of those discussed above. The Salem steel plant is under construction in Tamilnadu, to utilise low grade magnetite ores. Vijayanagar close to Tungabhadra Dam in Karnataka will produce billets and strip products within a capacity of 3 million ingot tonnes, while at Vishakhapatnam a plant of similar size will make sectional steel.

After 20 years of development the Indian steel industry has reached the point where it has become a net earner of foreign exchange from its products which are among the cheapest in the world.

40   In this small dry dock at Goa a steel barge used for carrying iron ore out to bulk carriers anchored offshore, is being repaired.

Industrial Regions

Table 8.5 breaks down into major categories of industry the employment data for the 11 regions having over one per cent of the total. Some of the characteristics of these regions are elaborated below. Bombay – Pune constitutes a functional economic region despite the distance separating their centres. A fast electrified line connects them, and Pune is inevitably drawn within Bombay's dominance. The region is much involved in the textile industry, which in 1971 occupied 30 per cent of the factory workers. More forward-looking electrical and mechanical trades have been developing, however.

Tata make buses and heavy trucks; International make tractors; Premier Automobiles make cars, trucks and buses; and Mahindra monopolise the manufacture of jeeps, all of them in Bombay. Pune has two factories, making motor scooters and mopeds.

Chemicals, pharmaceuticals and film-making are further evidence of Bombay's technologically advanced status. A combination of factors account for Bombay's industrial pre-eminence, shared by

41   A hydroelectric power scheme in the Western Ghats. Such dams serve also to control flooding and to even out the flow downstream, thus contributing to the value of the river for irrigation. (Courtesy Govt. of India).

Pune as a satellite. As the major port nearest to Europe (especially when the Suez canal is open) Bombay was the principal point of entry for the ruling British. Fuel and power have always been a problem so far from the coalfields but the foresight of the Parsee family of Tata promoted development of hydro-electricity, exploiting the steep Western Ghats slope. It was a shrewd locational decision that put India's first nuclear power station at Tarapur, near Bombay, to serve this concentrated demand for power. As the port most accessible from the Middle East, Bombay has two petroleum refineries, providing the materials for the petrochemical and plastics industries as a byproduct. Many branches of the rubber industry are represented in both Bombay and Pune, as are paper making, precision instrument and radio manufacture.

Ahmadabad-Vadodara (Baroda) is a more nearly mono-industrial textile region around the head of the Gulf of Cambay. The smoke stacks on Ahmadabad's skyline are reminiscent of prints of nineteenth century industrial Lancashire. The region as a whole had 32 per cent of its full-time workers in textiles in 1971, and Ahmadabad 45 per cent (see Table 8.5).

The initiation of petroleum refining at Koyali (using local oil) has stimulated the petrochemical industry, while at Vadodara textile- related chemicals, including chlorine and caustic soda are made as well as more traditional fine pottery.

Hooghlyside conurbation, with Calcutta as its focus, is separated by barely 110 km of paddy fields from the coalmines of the Damodar Valley (see Fig. 8.8). Together they may be considered an economic entity, Calcutta depending a good deal on the power resources and semi-manufactured raw materials of the Damodar which, however, has links to industrial foci throughout the country on account of its dominance in coalmining. The map shows the salient features of the Damodar basin which debouches below Durgapur onto the low floodplains west of the Hooghly. The Damodar River and its principal tributaries the Bokaro, Konar and Barakar have been brought under control since Independence to reduce flooding, produce power, and provide irrigation for the floodplains, and water for industry. The hydro-electric stations are now overshadowed by production in the thermal stations along the coalfield,

Table 8.5 Workers in major industrial regions (by percentage categories of manufacturing)

Region	Total (thousand)	Food, drink, tobacco	Cotton, wool, synthetic textiles	Jute textiles	Clothing	Wood, paper printing etc.	Leather etc.	Chemical, oil etc.	Non metal	Base metals, etc.	Machinery, transport and equipment repairs	Others
Bombay – Pune	857	5	30	–	5	7	1	12	3	10	18	9
Bombay	*662*	*5*	*30*	*–*	*5*	*7*	*1*	*12*	*2*	*11*	*17*	*9*
Ahmadabad – Vadodara*	450	14	32	–	7	5	2	5	6	5	6	14
Ahmadabad	*126*	*7*	*45*	*–*	*7*	*4*	*1*	*3*	*4*	*6*	*9*	*9*
Hooghlyside	921	10	8	13	6	7	3	8	7	10	20	8
Calcutta	*319*	*34*	*1*	*2*	*7*	*14*	*4*	*11*	*4*	*8*	*24*	*13*
Damodar etc†	267	24	3	0.1	4	12	0.2	7	18	20	8	10
N. Tamilnadu‡	238	16	14	–	6	9	4	7	6	8	12	17
Madras	*93*	*4*	*10*	*–*	*8*	*14*	*1*	*6*	*3*	*10*	*21*	*18*
Coimbatore – Salem	243	15	45	–	9	4	0.4	2	3	4	5	13
S. Tamilnadu§	290	20	23	–	9	8	0.4	15	3	6	1	18
Kerala	480	39	10	–	16	8	0.3	7	6	4	3	7
Cochin – Ernakulam	*65*	*26*	*7*	*–*	*12*	*9*	*0.5*	*12*	*5*	*7*	*9*	*11*
Bangalore	173	6	21	–	5	5	0.5	5	4	4	45	6
Hyderabad	70	13	2	–	7	11	1	17	5	7	21	16
Kanpur	112	10	41	3	6	4	7	4	1	6	12	6

* Includes the seven districts Mehesna, Ahmadabad, Kheda, Vadodara, Baruch, Surat and Valsad
† Includes ten districts: Hazaribagh, Ranchi, Dhanbad, and Singhbhum (Bihar), Purulia, Bundwan, Bankura, Midnapore and Birbhum (West Bengal), and Sundargarh (Orissa)
‡ Includes four districts: Madras, Chingleput, North and South Arcot
‡ Includes six districts: Madurai, Tiruchirapalli, Thanjavur, Ramanathapuram Tirunelveli, and Kanyakumari

Source: Census of India, 1971: Establishment Tables Part III B (for each state. These figures differ from those in the General Population Tables. The latter are derived from the replies of individuals to the enumerators' questions. The Establishment Tables analyse the more or less full-time workforce. A very large number of casual workers are excluded from the tables

42   Brickmaking in Kerala: after sun-drying (in the background) the bricks are fired using timber fuel. The clay used is dug from the paddy fields.

and now can most effectively be used to provide additional power to meet peak loads four hours daily, the base load being maintained by the thermal stations. The hydro-electric stations are at Tilaiya (4 MW) in the headwaters of the Barakar, Maithon (60 MW) near this river's confluence with the Damodar, and Panchet (40 MW) downstream. The Konar Dam is a flood regulator and reservoir for industry. The rapid industrial development of this and the Hooghlyside regions has kept the demand for power ahead of capacity to supply, and has led to the siting of several large thermal stations along the valley, utilising local coal as fuel and the river waters for cooling purposes; similarly the iron and steel plants. The Durgapur stations were designed to utilise waste gases from the coke ovens at the steel works; that at Chandrapura supplies power for the electrified line from Calcutta to Bhilai. A pipeline carried surplus gas from the steel works to Calcutta.

The major features of the iron and steel industry in the Damodar and adjacent areas have already been described. An important ancillary industry is making refractory bricks for furnaces, found at Dhanbad and Burdwan, using local clays from the Gondwana series. The fertiliser industry has developed at Sindhri using naphtha, a byproduct of the coke ovens, as feed-stock, with coal-based electricity. Super-phosphate manufacture is also located here. Purulia and Muri, south of Bokaro, process bauxite from Lohardaga west of Ranchi, sending the alumina to Sambalpur at the Hirakud Dam in Orissa and the Alwaye in Kerala for electrolytic reduction using hydel power. Dhanbad refines lead and zinc and is a centre for toolmaking and radio industries. Heavy engineering is strongly represented in the railway locomotive works at Chittaranjan, at Jamshedpur where rolling stock are made, the Durgapur plants for constructional steel and mining machinery, and the heavy cable works at Rupnaraianpur, a list far from exclusive. The overall industrial mix may be gauged from Table 8.5.

To the visitor to India from an industrialised country, the visual impression of the Damodar Valley is at once familiar yet bizarre. Pit-head gear rises from the paddy fields; aerial ropeways sweep across the countryside to bring sand from the Damodar's bed for stowing in the mines to minimise subsidence and fire due to spontaneous combustion; sari-clad women are seen at work around the pit-head, pushing trolleys of pit-props, or at sidings head-loading baskets of coal into railway trucks; in open-cast coal workings grass-thatched bamboo huts serve as offices and workmen's shelters, only explosives meriting brick stores in such a transient landscape. Modernisation progresses, and efficient mechanical loading is seen at some mines, and neat rows of miners' cottages and houses for the executives, some flat-roofed and maybe topped with a stack of rice straw to feed the family cow. Casual labourers, especially common in the open-cast section of the coalmining industry, fare less well as squatter settlers in simple shacks of matting, mud, wood, bamboo and straw erected on some patch of as yet unclaimed land, the familiar home of the newcomer in search of work in each and every urbanising centre in India.

As far as industry is concerned, Calcutta and Hooghlyside form a huge sprawling mass of well over one million workers, and untold numbers of seekers after jobs. Industrially, Calcutta owes its origins to being the port accessible to sea-going vessels on the Hooghly, which gave access to the Ganga. Early Calcutta could tap the wealth of the whole Ganga valley as far as Delhi, the Moghul capital, when European traders were seeking to exploit the possibilities of India. The French established their 'factories' at Chandernagore, the English at Calcutta, thus laying the foundations for India's mercantile metropolis.

When the British became the rulers of India Calcutta was their capital, until this was moved to Delhi in 1912. Commerce bred industry, for long dominated by the manufacture of jute goods, using raw material brought in by country boats and dumb barges from areas in East Bengal now in Bangladesh. The industry survived partition from

its material base by turning to domestic sources and remains strung out along both banks of the Hooghly and in sites a little back from the river. Its viability is at present seriously in doubt through the strong competition from Bangladesh and from synthetic substitutes. The engineering trades are important also, more important in fact nowadays, though their pre-eminence in India is being challenged by Calcutta's rival, Bombay. Machinery for factories, air-conditioners, typewriters and radios are specialities.

Now that the Hooghlyside region includes its new out-port of Haldia, with its petroleum refinery, the industrial mix contains as many ingredients as Bombay's, with the addition of jute, and a lesser concentration on cotton textiles. Calcutta itself accounts for about a third of the conurbation's workforce. It is more strongly oriented to engineer-

43 Blast furnaces at the Soviet-built Bhilai Iron and Steel Works in Madhya Pradesh. India's largest. (Courtesy Govt. of India).

ing and less towards textiles than is Hooghlyside as a whole.

The industrial clusters of India southwards from Bangalore contain almost one-fifth of the industrial population. There are some important nodes of sophisticated modern industry as at Bangalore, Madras and Cochin where various branches of engineering prosper, but in general the familiar dominance of the cotton textile mills persists. This is particularly true of the Coimbatore–Salem and Southern Tamilnadu regions, industrial amalgams of several distinct and well-separated towns. The characteristic industrial mix is that of Coimbatore which has steel re-rolling, boiler-making, paper, batteries, electrical heat exchangers, compressors, printing, tool forging, paints, instrument making and so on, strung out along its approach roads. Madras with its immediate hinterland has lagged somewhat in comparison with its port rivals, Bombay and Calcutta, largely on account of its lesser importance in British India. The development of the Neyveli lignite as a source of power, the establishment of an oil refinery and of a nuclear power station, and its selection as the location of several vehicle industries, and the making of film and of films for the Tamil speakers augurs well for Madras's future. The printing trades account for the high percentage in the wood, paper and printing category (Table 8.5).

Apart from Cochin and its twin town Ernakulam, Kerala is employed industrially in processing its plantation and agricultural products: tea, coconuts for oil and coir fibre, cashew nuts from home and abroad, coffee, rubber, tapioca and rice. Fishing provides another resource for freezing prawns and canning sardines and tuna for export. Timber working for veneers and plywood, and timber-based rayon and paper-pulp industries draw heavily on forests, which are in danger of being over-cut. Cochin, one of India's finest harbours and a major port, has a new ship-building yard, petroleum refinery, chemical and soap manufacturing, and is likely to provide industrial leadership in a State that badly needs to develop factory employment to absorb its excess population. With the completion of the Idikki hydel scheme, Kerala will have power in abundance and to spare.

Inland in Karnataka, in part because of its equable climate at 900 m, Bangalore has become a centre of specialised engineering. The aircraft industry has its main plant here, and other public sector enterprises include telephones, watches, radios and television sets, transformer equipment, machine tools and soap. There are several textile mills, but their former predominance is giving way to more highly skilled occupations.

Industrial development at Hyderabad, the most isolated of India's millionaire cities, has been encouraged by locating key public sector plants there to make cables and heavy electrical equipment, precision bearings, machine tools and electronic equipment, a mixture not unlike Bangalore's.

As the nation's capital, Delhi has attracted considerable industrialisation. Its region, as here defined, includes the neighbouring districts of Meerut and Gurdaspur, the former an industrial city in its own right. Engineering has overtaken the textile trades as the main employer but the total picture is one of considerable diversification. By contrast, Kanpur, set in the middle of UP, is still very much a mill town making cotton and woollen goods. It has the highest proportion of workers in leather of any large centre, a relic from its past as a provider of military equipment for the British. Although it has plants dealing in chemicals, rubber, paint, metal castings etc., it appears relatively weak in the kinds of industry that go with modernity, a fact of concern to its economic planners.

Chapter 9

India: Population Distribution and Urbanisation

India is still a land of villages; the expectation that the arrival of the industrial revolution might herald a period of rapid urbanisation has yet to be realised. The level of urbanisation reached 19.9 per cent in 1971, a far cry from the 86 per cent of Australia for example, another country with an economy strongly rooted in the land.

The patterns of overall population density (Fig. 9.1) and of urbanisation (Fig. 9.2) are inter-related in an interesting way. Granted that agriculture is the mainstay of the rural population and the predominance of that population in the total, high densities of the latter reflect productive alluvial soils and humid climate (over 1,000 mm rainfall), with or without supplementary irrigation. Thus one can explain the high densities in a belt extending from eastern Uttar Pradesh, through Bihar, rural West Bengal, the Assam Valley and the Kerala coast. Urbanisation is rarely at above average throughout this area. The upper Ganga plain in western UP and the Indus plains in Punjab–Haryana have similarly high to very high densities, in part based on rich irrigated agriculture and in part by above average urbanism. The remainder of the Peninsula coastlands, extending inland in the south to cover all Tamilnadu,

Fig. 9.1

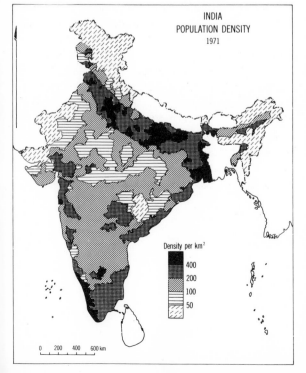

Fig. 9.2

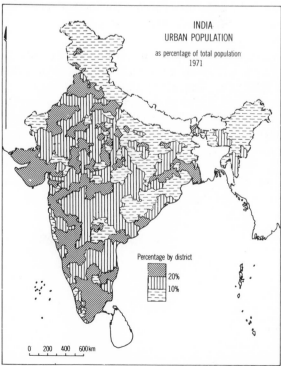

are less well watered by rainfall than the north-eastern portion, but intensive irrigation in places, and in some a high degree of industrial urbanism or a combination of both, results in high population densities overall, from Vishakhapatnam port through the Andhra deltas, Tamilnadu and the coastal belt from Bombay north into Gujarat. In the interior, large urban centres at Indore, Hyderabad and Bangalore account for the high densities of their districts which could otherwise support only modest populations.

At the other extreme, low overall densities correlate with low levels of urbanisation in the hilly and inaccessible areas of the Himalaya, the Northeastern Hills, the Bastar Plateau and the hills of Orissa, where conditions favour neither agricultural nor urban concentration. Through central India into Rajasthan and Kutch, low population

density usually coincides with poor plateaux, rocky ranges or desert, all inimical to productive agriculture. The pattern of urbanisation is less consistent with these physically based criteria. In the case of many districts there is a correspondence of low overall density with low percentages of urban population, but several instances of high urbanisation also occur. The latter is an outstanding characteristic of Gujarat at all levels of population density, and the explanation of this phenomenon probably holds for most of central India also. Before Independence these areas were broken up among a large number of princely States of varying size, each with its own capital where the raja held court and centralised his administration and much of whatever development took place in industry, commerce, and education. Once established, centres like this tend to be self-

Fig. 9.3

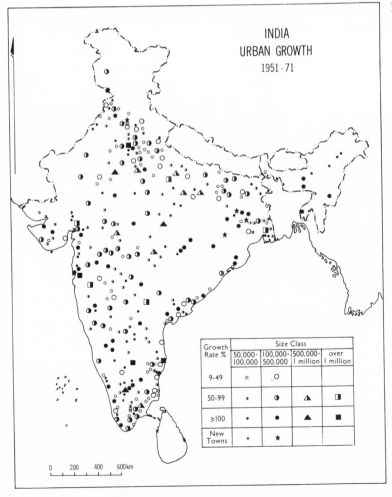

perpetuating despite the changing administrative structure and the loss of princely patronage. Urbanisation in the desert areas of Rajasthan and Kutch may be explained similarly, but an additional factor here is the mode of life, part nomadic and pastoral, part extensive and very seasonal dry farming. A lower premium was placed on permanent rural settlement than on urban clustering for mutual protection from marauders in the past and from the unfriendly elements, and for commerce and the generation of supplementary or alternative means of livelihood to those available in the harsh environment.

Between the extremes may be noted the large tracts of the Peninsula whether on the Deccan Lavas or on the ancient rocks of the Shield, which support around average densities, high as they may well be in relation to the resource base. Urbanisation here tends also to lie within the middle range of values (10–19 per cent) which is below the national average. Notable exceptions occur in the highly urbanised zone along the Bombay–Calcutta corridor.

Urban Growth

Figure 9.3 shows the present size of each urban centre of over 50,000 population in 1971 and its growth since 1951. It covers two-thirds of the total urban population. With this increasing at 73 per cent in the double decade, the three categories of growth rate used correspond to low, average and high levels of growth.

Table 9.1 shows the distribution of urban popu-

lation by classes and their growth in the decade 1961–71.

The overall growth rate for the urban population was 38 per cent, but this was exceeded only in the town classes of over 50,000 population. Growth in the millionaire section of Class 1 was at the national urban average of 38 per cent, but this obscures the fact that only two of the nine cities, Calcutta and Kanpur, were below this level, Bangalore equalled it, and the remaining six bettered it – Delhi and Madras quite substantially as Table 9.2 shows.

Table 9.2 Millionaire cities; population and growth rate (%), 1971.

Delhi	3,647,023 (55)
Calcutta	7,031,000 (20)
Bombay	5,971,000 (44)
Madras	3,170,000 (63)
Hyderabad	1,796,000 (44)
Ahmadabad	1,742,000 (44)
Bangalore	1,654,000 (38)
Kanpur	1,275,000 (31)
Pune	1,135,000 (44)

In the middle group of Class I, the ten semi-millionare cities have as a body a slower growth rate (31 per cent) than the national average: Nagpur (35 per cent), Indore (45 per cent), Jabalpur (46 per cent) and Jaipur (52 per cent) exceed the mean for the group, while Varanasi and Allahabad (with 19 per cent) are at the bottom of the table; Coimbatore (23 per cent), Agra (25 per cent), Lucknow (26 per cent), and Madurai (29 per cent) are strung-out in between. The vitality of the smaller cities in this class, with 100,000–499,999 inhabitants, is

Table 9.1 Growth of urban population, 1961–71

Class	No. of towns	Urban popn. 1971 (million)	Per cent of total urban	Growth 1961– 1971 (million)	Growth 1961– 1971 (%)
Total	**2641**	**109.10**	**100**	**30.16**	**38**
Class I	147	61.09	56	20.10	49
Over 1 M	9	27.42	25	7.54	38
500,000–999,999	10	6.43	6	1.52	31
100,000–499,999	128	27.24	25	11.14	69
Class II, 50,000–99,999	185	12.00	11	3.95	41
Class III, 20,000–49,999	583	17.46	16	3.93	29
Class IV, 10,000–19,999	874	12.00	11	2.55	27
Classes V and VI, less than 10,000	852	6.56	6	0.15	2.3

Sources: Census of India, Census Centenary 1972: Population Statistics: and Paper I of 1971 Supplement

44 Workers' tenements in the cotton-manufacturing section of Bombay.

remarkable by contrast. As a group they have increased their population by 69 per cent, but growth has been strongest among those in the upper half of the size range. Thus, among towns between 250,000 and 499,999, 65 per cent had a growth rate of over the national average of 38 per cent, while in the lower half only 36 per cent exceeded that figure.

The Class II towns more than held their own, but those in Classes III to VI could not maintain the national level. This supports a subjective impression that urbanisation involving the attraction of population towards modern style development is a negligible process in towns below 50,000, and becomes really effective in the Class I towns. The latter account for two-thirds of the urban growth, more than half of it in the section below 500,000, and most of the rest among the millionaires. The relative stagnation of most of the cities in the middle range of Class I is significant. The most vigorous expansion here is in a new State capital, Jaipur, and the other two cities exceeding the average, Indore and Jabalpur, are centres of engineering. The laggard five are mostly ancient cities dominated by the textile industry and traditional trades; three of them are in Uttar Pradesh.

The distribution of urban centres can be resolved into a basic pattern of corridors following trunk broad gauge railway routes, with a number of clusters reflecting regional resource development or past political factors. The system of corridors is presented diagrammatically in Figure 9.4 and provides a frame of reference. The concept of growth corridors as applied to India is derived from a Russian geographer's interpretation of the structure of the Indian economy.*

India now has at least nine 'millionaire cities'. Four of the nine millionaire metropolitan centres form the basic pivots to the urban network: Delhi, Bombay, Calcutta and Madras. Two others, Kanpur and Pune, lie within corridors linking the main pivots. Ahmadabad lies at the hub of a cluster of towns that itself overlaps the Bombay–Delhi corridor. Only Hyderabad and Bangalore are outside the primary network.

In terms of developmental growth the Bombay–Calcutta corridor appears to show the most vigour. East of Nagpur (930,459), which by now has almost certainly joined the millionaires and which – with a medium growth rate – lies close to mid-point in the corridor, very strong growth is associated with the outer bastions of India's metallurgical industrial complex in Durg–Bhilai–Raipur and Bilaspur. Further east, Sambalpur, which is based on Hirakud hydel power, lies a little off the main corridor on a branch line carrying iron ore and surplus pig iron and steel to the port city of Vishakhapatnam. The main line continues through the steel towns of Rourkhela and Jamshedpur–Tatanagar into the Hooghlyside conurbation via Khargpur. Alternative routes form a web that ties the Damodar Valley towns, mostly showing fast growth, both to their ironfields south of Jamshedpur, and to the Calcutta region, thus broadening

*Galina V. Sdasyuk, Urbanisation and the Spatial Structure of Indian Economy, in A. Chandra Sekhar, Gen. Ed. *Economic and Socio-Cultural Dimensions of Regionalisation: an Indo-USSR Collaborative Study*, New Delhi, 1972

the corridor at this eastern end, so dominated by heavy industry of importance to the whole of India.

Nagpur, at the centre of the corridor joining the rivals for industrial and commercial primacy, provides a minor pivot at which lesser corridors tie in to Delhi, Hyderabad and Madras. As an important node in the road network also, Nagpur is likely to develop very strongly in future. To its west, five towns of third rank (100,000–500,000, Class I in the Census definition) are strung along the line to Bombay as it crosses the Kandesh Deccan, and three others with more purely local functions lie a little off the corridor. Most have average growth rates, while at the approaches to Bombay, as around Calcutta, fast-growing commuter satellites are typical.

By far the oldest urban corridor in the whole sub-continent follows the Grand Trunk Road the length of the Indo-Gangetic Plain, a line now parallelled closely by railways. The route is studded with historic cities: Varanasi (606,721) the most holy city of the Hindus; Allahabad (513,036) a centre of pilgrimage for Muslim and Hindu; Agra (634,622) and Delhi, both great Moghul alternative capitals; Amritsar (458,029) sacred to the Sikhs. Lucknow or Lakhnau (813,982) on a branch of the Grand Trunk Road and an alternative railway route between Varanasi and Delhi, continues its traditional role as capital of the middle Ganga Plain, now covered by the state of Uttar Pradesh. On the more direct line from Allahabad to Agra, Kanpur, brash and horribly industrial, has insinuated itself into this string of nobler beads. Between Calcutta and Delhi there is no city of first or second rank that has grown at better than

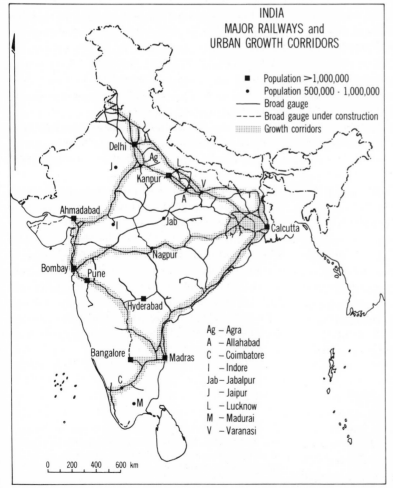

Fig. 9.4

middling rate, and outside Delhi's ring of satellites, only Aligarh in the third rank shows strong growth.

This is true generally of the whole broad belt of the Ganga Plain through UP and Bihar, in which there are almost as many centres stagnating in the lowest bracket as there are in the middle growth bracket, yet another indicator of this region's economic backwardness.

North of Delhi the picture is more promising. Chandigarh as a new capital city for the Punjabis, Sikh and Hindu, has been the focus of a remarkable growth from nothing to 232,940 by 1971, no doubt diverting potential that might otherwise have gone into Ambala (102,493 and stagnating). Amritsar with sluggish growth suffers from its exposed position on the Pakistan border, though it is well placed on the Grand Trunk Road to exploit the flow of trade with India's neighbour. By contrast Jammu (164,253) displays strong population increase, compensating for its flank position on the border by commanding one of the gateways into the Vale of Kashmir where Srinagar (423,253) shows moderate growth. Towns a little back from the frontier like Ludhiana (401,176) have good records of growth, largely due to settlement by refugees and their subsequent vitality as entrepreneurs and parents. Jullundur (296,106) and Patiala (151,041) are in the middle range.

The Delhi–Bombay corridor is less clearly defined by urban development in the section traversing the Chambal Basin, much of it semi-arid and rocky. However, both Kota (212,991), which has experienced phenomenal growth at 227 per cent in the double decade, and Ratlam (119,247), in the middle growth range, demonstrate as railway junction towns, the value of nodality. Ratlam links westwards to Ahmadabad and the ports on the Rann of Kutch. At Vadodara (Baroda, 467,487) the corridor is reinforced by carrying the Ahmadabad–Bombay link through Surat (493,001) and the Bombay satellites.

A fourth corridor linking Bombay to Madras is clearly marked at its northern end by the satellite Thana (207,352) and by Pune, almost within the commuting range of wealthy businessmen. Pune, like Gulbarga (145,588) in northeastern Karnataka and several smaller towns along the line through the dry zone of southern Andhra, evidences average growth at best. The large city of Sholapur (398,361) is an example of the stultifying effect of overdependence on the cotton mill textile industry which has held it to low level growth.

The last inter-metropolitan corridor runs along the east coast from Calcutta to Madras, fortuitously stringing together groups of cities and towns of quite independent development (in contrast to the historic interdependence of the cities along the Grand Trunk Road). Several of these were seaward-looking, exporting towns in colonial times. The modern railway links the fast-growing twin towns of the Mahanadi delta, Cuttack (205,759) and Bhubaneshwar (105,491) through Berhampur (117,662 medium growth) to the fast-growing port of Vishakhapatnam (363,467), and to Vijayawada (344,607) and Guntur (269,991). Rajamundry (118,805) and Kakinada Port (164,200) on a short spur line with other centres of moderate growth in the Godavari–Krishna delta, are clearly within the influence of the corridor whose ties to the main network are further strengthened in this area by the line northwards through Warangal to Nagpur (and ultimately to Delhi) and westwards to Hyderabad–Secunderabad (and ultimately to Bombay). Southwards, the route to Madras passes through the economically rather limited districts of Ongole and Nellore. That the line is now double-tracked or provided with alternative loop routes throughout its length from Calcutta to Madras is an indication of the growing importance of this eastern side of the Bombay–Calcutta–Madras triangle.

From Madras to the southwest, a major corridor, again a cul-de-sac like that   northwards from

45 Shanties for squatters on a vacant plot in Bangalore, Karnataka. Roofing materials range from plastic sheets to traditional woven thatch. Although crude there is an air of pride of possession in the settlement.

Delhi, ties into the main network the vigorously growing chain of Tamilnad towns extending from Salem (416,440), through Erode (169,613) to Coimbatore (736,203) and beyond to Cochin–Ernakulam (439,066) on the Kerala coast. Northwards along the coast, a branch of the broad gauge runs through Calicut (333,979) to Karnataka's port Mangalore (215,122), linked to plateau Karnataka through the spectacular metre gauge line up the escarpment of the Western Ghats to Hassan, and designed to carry iron ore exports. South of Cochin the broad gauge is being extended to replace the metre gauge up to Trivandrum and serve hitherto railless areas in the far south of Kerala and the Arabian Sea coast districts of Tamilnadu. The clusters of cities in southern Tamilnadu centring on the temple city of Madurai (711,501) are served by a metre gauge system, their sole link to the broad gauge network being a spur line from Erode to Tiruchirapalli (464,624). Only one of the cluster of some 25 towns south of Pondicherry shows better than middle range growth, and several of the smaller rank appear to be more or less stagnating.

One corridor of towns characterised by medium to high growth rate runs south from Pune to Bangalore through Sangli (201,597), Kolhapur (267,513), Belgaum (213,872), Hubli–Dharwar (379,166), Davangere (121,110), with a branch to the steel town of Bhadravati (101,358). The broad gauge line terminates at Kolhapur, from which a metre gauge track continues the corridor south to Bangalore, but a fine highway provides an alternative and door-to-door service by heavy trucks.

Madhya Pradesh is a region traversed by railway routes as much constructed to link the major corridors and metropolitan centres as to carry the relatively small traffic generated locally. The inheritance of former princely State capitals and of some embryonic industrial centres of British military inception like Jabalpur (534,845) provides nodal cities such as Bhopal (384,859), Jhansi (198,135) and Ujjain (208,561) on broad gauge junctions, and Indore (560,936) and Gwalior (406,140) at a confluence of such lines with metre or narrower gauge tracks laid down by economically minded princes to serve their domains. Jabalpur and Bhopal, the latter selected to be the capital of Madhya Pradesh, have grown rapidly; Gwalior, Indore and Ujjain at medium pace.

A high level of urbanisation has long been typical of desert Rajasthan and semi-arid western Gujarat. Jaipur (636,768), like most State capitals, has enjoyed the brisk growth that comes with local primacy, and its attraction for tourists guarantees it a better place in the roadway and airline networks than it has on its metre gauge railway system. Further west, Bikaner (208,984) and Jodhpur (317,612), cities of medium growth, have nodal positions in the same system, which no doubt follows more ancient camel tracks searching out these urban oases. Growth at Udaipur in the south of Rajasthan has been boosted by the development of mineral wealth. Southwest of this, in Kathiawar and Kutch, all towns but one show moderate growth or better, indicating economic vitality. The Rann of Kutch provides a deep-water port closer to Delhi and the north than increasingly congested Bombay. The new free port at Kandla and the oil terminal at Salaya are served by broad gauge extension from Ahmadabad, and by a pipeline under construction from the latter to Mathura, thus linking the region via Ratlam to the mainstream of the Bombay–Delhi corridor, which can be expected to develop even more strongly as a result.

46 A village near the coast in Andhra Pradesh. The high conical roof thatched with palm leaves keeps the interior of the houses cool but dark; the walls are of mud brick. The charpoy (bedstead) serves as a couch by day. The woman on the right has been to the well to fetch water in the brass pot on her head, carried on a cloth pad; in her hand is a scoop made from a palm leaf. Chickens are running in the background. Characteristically Hindu villages are kept scrupulously clean around the houses.

Chapter 10

Pakistan: Political Geography

With the dissolution of the already spatially divided state of Pakistan in 1971 by the secession of its eastern wing to become Bangladesh, a new Pakistan came into being which achieved for its people a measure of physical identity hitherto unknown.

Pakistan occupies the basin of the easternmost of the three great rivers that traverse the steppe deserts of the Old World: the Nile, the Tigris-Euphrates and the Indus. That these basins were the cradles of early civilisation gives to the Indus a distinctiveness lacking in other basins in South Asia. Pakistan lies at the eastern limits of the sub-tropical steppe desert zone that stretches west through Iran and Arabia to the Atlantic coast of the Sahara. In the heart of this zone Islam developed as a faith uniting its adherents in a vigorous culture and a powerful political organisation. The modern Pakistanis tend to see their cultural affinities in this Islamic world.

In more recent times Pakistan is the successor to a western frontier established in the nineteenth century by the British for their Indian Empire. Its eastern frontier with India is one of the products of the partition of India in 1947 when Lord Radcliffe had to arbitrate the separation of a Muslim Pakistan, West and East, from the rest of the Indian Empire. That process established in the erstwhile West Pakistan the long sought after sense of political unity. The in-migrations of Muslim refugees from the new India and the out-migrations of non-Muslims subsequent to partition accentuated the sense of cultural unity based on religion within the western wing of the new nation, even though it was some way short of cultural homogeneity. Parallel processes were at work in East Pakistan, but at a much lower level of intensity. Ultimately, Islam and a common antagonism towards 'Hindu' India proved insufficient to hold the young nation together against the fissiparous strains of linguistic and other cultural differences and physical separateness.

To a degree unmatched elsewhere in South Asia, the peoples of Pakistan are unified by the common heritage of their Islamic religion. More than 97 per cent of the population are Muslim. Islam was first introduced to the Indus basin in 711 AD by the Governor of Basra who established control as far north as Multan. Later, vigorous proselytisation was carried out by invaders from the north-west, and in the eleventh century Punjab with Lahore as its capital became the eastern province of an empire ruled from Ghazni in Afghanistan. Much of Baluchistan and sometimes Sind, was ruled from Ghazni. The centre of Muslim power moved to Delhi in the thirteenth century under the Delhi Sultans and the link with Ghazni was lost for three centuries, until Babur coming from Afghanistan in 1525–26 founded the Moghul Empire in Delhi. Under the Moghuls, Muslim power spread almost throughout the subcontinent. With its decline, Sind was lost to Persia for a while from 1739, and power in the Punjab was seized by the Sikhs early in the nineteenth century. From Lahore, Ranjit Singh came to control Kashmir and formerly Moghul lands west of the Indus, right into the hill country occupied by the Pathan tribes through whom Afghan influence had usually reached as far as the Indus.

The Sikhs' conflict with the British resulted in the surrender of Kashmir, subsequently to be sold to a Hindu Raja thus placing its mainly Muslim population under non-Muslim rule and establishing the grounds of the major bone of contention persisting between Pakistan and India to this day. After the second war with the Sikhs the British succeeded to their frontier with Afghanistan athwart the northwestern hills, a frontier which divided the Pushto speakers, a third lying west of the border and two-thirds to the east. The issue of Pakhtunistan, nationhood for the Pushto speakers in association with Afghanistan, has sometimes produced tension between Pakistan and Afghanistan, but commands little serious support on the Pakistan side.

In Sind, British annexation led to its attachment to Bombay Presidency whence it was administered until it became a separate province in 1936 with Karachi as its capital.

On Partition, Pakistan inherited several princely states which have become provincially administered districts. The peculiar problems of the tribal groups in NWFP and Baluchistan are recognised in special local arrangements, sometimes administered directly from Islamabad, sometimes by the appropriate provincial government through the adjacent district. Economic and social development is relied upon gradually to bring these formerly extremely independent and sometimes fanatically fractious peoples into harmony with the more advanced and advantaged plainsmen.

Figure 10.1 shows the provinces, districts and the tribal areas. The map has remained remarkably stable since Partition, in contrast to India's which has undergone much reorganisation on linguistic grounds. Pakistan has been fortunate in having adopted Urdu as its national language which, as the mother-tongue of only 8 per cent of the population, is probably understood at a rudimentary level by the majority. It has the virtue of not being the language of any regional majority group. As the language of the Moghul court it is still most strongly represented in the urban areas, a tendency strengthened after Partition when many Urdu speakers came as refugees from India to settle in towns.

Punjabi, mother-tongue of two-thirds of the

Fig. 10.1

population, has its speakers in strength in every province and might be said to be the language of socio-economic dominance. No district of the Punjab has less than 89 per cent claiming Punjabi as mother-tongue. Sindhi is next in importance, with 13 per cent. Negligible in most of the Punjab and NWFP, it is relatively quite significant in Baluchistan, the adjacent backward province, economically most closely linked to Sind. Pushto, spoken by 8 per cent is most concentrated in trans-Indus NWFP and the northern districts of Baluchistan. The predilection to travel in search of work explains the scatter of Pushto speakers throughout the country, with 105,000 in Karachi alone. Balochi (2 per cent) and Brahui (1 per cent) are nationally unimportant, but as the languages of the more backward groups in Baluchistan they may yet have political significance. Balochi is also spoken in eastern Iran. Some linguistically interesting but politically minor languages are found in the remote valleys of the far north – Kafiri, Kohistani, Khowar, Shina and Kashmiri are Dardic languages, Balti a Sino-Tibetan tongue, while the ancestry of Burushaski is unknown (Fig. 10.2).

Partition of the Punjab Plains between Pakistan and India disrupted the irrigation system based on the Ravi, Beas and Sutlej Rivers. The resultant problems have now been resolved through the

47   An Afridi boy on the way to buy kerosene, outside his village in the Khyber Pass, N.W.F.P. The towers are traditional points of vantage from which to watch for feuding enemies. Complete seclusion of the household is ensured by the high stone and mud brick walls. The Afridis are Pushto-speaking tribesmen much given to smuggling and the transport trade with Afghanistan.

Fig. 10.2

Indus Waters Agreement of 1960. Of less economic consequence, but a deep-seated unhealed wound to its pride, the issue of Kashmir remains unresolved–at least in Pakistan's eyes. In its simplest terms, India sees the problem as effectively closed and administers the portion of Jammu and Kashmir it occupies as a State of the Indian Union, resting its legitimacy on the fact that the Maharaja of Kashmir elected to join India–which he was legally free to do–even if in so doing he went against the advice of the instruments of partition to accede 'to the contiguous dominion, bearing in mind geographical and ethnic considerations'. Pakistan rests its case on the fact that the issue is before the United Nations Security Council for resolution, and shows the area as 'disputed territory' on its maps. Not so the two small enclaves in the Kathiawar Peninsula of Gujarat, Junagadh and Manavadar, whose Muslim rulers wished to join Pakistan but were absorbed by India. Pakistan refuses to accept their loss and shows both on its maps as part of its territory.

The '*de facto*' situation in Kashmir is a partition along a 'line of control' supervised by the UN, dividing 'Azad' (Free) Kashmir from the Indian controlled state of Jammu and Kashmir.

Democratic government has not flourished in Pakistan as well as it has in India or even Sri Lanka. Several periods of military dictatorship, the latest starting in 1977, have interrupted periods of parliamentary government, though the latter tended to more autocratic leadership than is customary in the Westminster model.

Internationally Pakistan has pursued policies aimed to protect it against the perceived threat from India. Thus, while India has been antipathetic towards China (having suffered warfare on the border) and friendly towards the USSR, Pakistan has actively cooperated with China, even to the extent of opening their frontier with the Karakoram Highway, while also accepting Soviet sponsorship of the Karachi Steel Mill. The USA also aids both countries which can reasonably claim to be 'non-aligned'! A marked trend, especially since the secession of Bangladesh, has been to develop relations with the Middle East, particularly with Iran and the oil-rich states of the Persian Gulf.

48 The Badshahi Mosque, Lahore, viewed from the Fort. The quadrangle of the mosque is crowded with worshipping men on festivals. Pink sandstone and white marble are the building materials used in this magnificent Moghul structure.

Chapter 11

Pakistan: The People and the Economy

The population of Pakistan is estimated at over 81 million at the end of 1979, with another million living overseas, mainly in the Middle East and Britain. Official sources use 3 per cent per year as the current rate of population increase, but forward projections are more than usually difficult in Pakistan where the census taker must add to the common enough handicaps of conservatism, suspicion of all forms of governmental enumeration, and mass illiteracy, the practice among orthodox Muslims of keeping women (and so babies also) in seclusion, thus making a direct head count impracticable. Such attitudes are also reflected in the rather poor progress made in family planning. Governments, sensitive to popular feelings and the power of the Muslim mullahs to stir up reaction, have been lukewarm in their support compared with India.

The future pattern of population growth is likely to follow closely that of India (Fig. 5.1). Table 11.1 shows how the total may well achieve a fivefold increase in the 80 years since 1901. Forward projection suggests that by the year 2000 there may be 170 million and that zero growth is unlikely to be achieved before about 2075.

Migration has played a larger part in Pakistan's demographic history than in that of the other South Asian countries. The colonisation of the Punjab in the late nineteenth century brought 443,500 immigrants to the Chenab Canal Colony alone, mainly from areas now in India's Punjab. Following Partition in 1947 the flow was reversed as far as non-Muslims were concerned, of whom Pakistan lost 5.5 million to gain 7.5 million Muslim refugees from India. In the population of 1961, 15 per cent were born outside Pakistan. Over time their significance will diminish, but the importance of refugee families' votes in Karachi, for example, where they make up more than 43 per cent of the population, should not be overlooked.

Characteristically, the dependency ratio* is high, 94.9 in a population with almost 44 per cent under 15 years of age. Figure 11.1 shows the popu-

Fig. 11.1

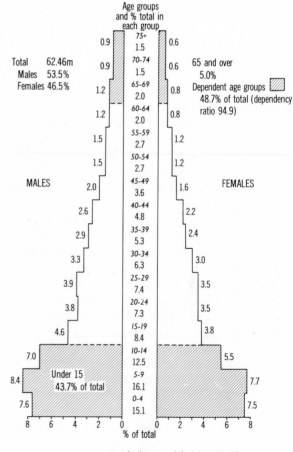

PAKISTAN
1972
Total population by age group and sex

Total 62.46m
Males 53.5%
Females 46.5%

65 and over
5.0%
Dependent age groups
48.7% of total (dependency
ratio 94.9)

MALES   FEMALES

Under 15
43.7% of total

% of total

* Dependency ratio: $\dfrac{\text{population aged } 0\text{–}14 + \geqslant 65}{\text{population aged } 15\text{–}64} \times 100$

lation pyramid for 1972. For the urban population the dependency ratio (86.2) is lower than that for the rural population (98) on account of the tendency for people in the economically active age groups to migrate perhaps only temporarily to towns, returning to retire to their villages.

The occupational structure of the population contributing to the economy is certainly understated in the participation rate, which takes no account of children who help their parents. The dominance of agriculture is clear. Women account for about 10 per cent of the agricultural workforce, many more of them working unpaid on their husband's farm.

It is normal for the young to contribute directly or indirectly to the family income. Only 17 per cent of the rural 10–14 age group is in school, 25 per cent of the boys and 6 per cent of the girls. The urban figures are better, 42 per cent of the total, 49 per cent of the boys and 32 per cent of the girls being at school, and a much higher proportion of youth in towns stay on at school after 14, 20 per cent of the 15–19 years' group compared with 5 per cent in rural areas.

Literacy is another measure of general education with great significance for modernisation. Farmers who cannot read are at a disadvantage when new ideas are abroad. Overall, 14 per cent of the population is literate. As in schooling, women trail the men; in only four cities are more than 29 per cent of women literate, while in the same four more than 40 per cent of the men can read.

The differences between urban and rural dwellers can be extended to differences between regions. In Figure 11.2 levels of development have been mapped for all 45 districts to provide a consistent picture of regional inequalities in Pakistan. Nine factors have been used to arrive at a score for a district which enables it to be ranked alongside other districts. The nine indices are:

1.   A measure of production.
2.   Level of urbanisation.
3.&4. Measures of modernisation in agriculture–tractors and fertilisers.
5.&6. Measures of education–percentage literate and percentage attending school.
7.   A measure of social welfare–the population served by each medical practitioner.

8.   A measure of social modernisation and emancipation – the ratio of females in the school population aged 10–14.
9.   Industrialisation – the percentage of the non-agricultural labour engaged in manufacturing industry.

Some of the data dates from the 1961 Census, and were it possible to update them, Islamabad and its neighbour Rawalpindi would be in the highest ranking group. As mapped, the top nine districts are each dominated by a strong urban centre. Eight of the second group of nine form a continuous

Table 11.1   Population of Pakistan, 1901–78

Million		Average intercensal increase per cent
1901	16.6	—
1911	19.4	0.7†
1921	21.1	0.9
1931	23.5	1.1
1941	28.3	1.8
1951	33.8	1.7
1961	42.9*	2.4
1972	64.98‡	2.9†
1978	78.5§	
1979	81.0§	

*46.1 if adjusted for under-enumeration
†from the adjusted total for 1961
‡Census taken at end of year
§ Estimates for end of year at 3.2 per cent increase

Fig. 11.2

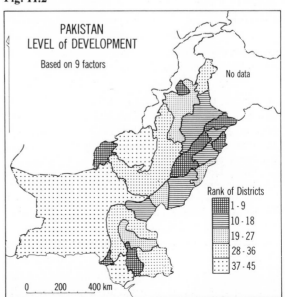

PAKISTAN
LEVEL of DEVELOPMENT

Based on 9 factors

No data

Rank of Districts
1 - 9
10 - 18
19 - 27
28 - 36
37 - 45

0   200   400 km

49 Punjabi women making cow-dung balls for fuel, mixing in straw as binding material. They find a ready market in Lahore nearby.

block with the main core of Punjab districts in the top group. The ninth, Sukkur in Sind, has appreciable industry. In the fourth and fifth groups are the more backward districts. The lowest ranking form most of Baluchistan plus the Indus delta region, while the next lowest includes much of the western upland margins and the Thar desert fringe in Sind. Were data available for the Tribal Territories and the northwestern districts of NWFP

these areas would be similarly ranked. Some regional contrasts will be further elaborated in later sections.

The National Accounts

The structure of a country's Gross National Product (GNP) provides a good perspective view

Table 11.2   Structure of Gross National Product at constant factor cost 1959/60, and per cent of total

Sector	1971–72		1973–74		1976–77		1978–79	
1. Agriculture	38.5		35.6		34.5		29.7	
2. Mining and quarrying	0.5		0.5		0.5		0.4	
3. Manufacturing	15.3		15.6		14.4		14.2	
large-scale		11.6		12.2		10.9		9.9
small-scale		3.7		3.4		3.5		4.3
4. Construction	3.6		4.0		5.1		4.9	
5. Electricity and gas	2.4		2.8		2.4		2.7	
6. Transport, storage, communications	6.2		6.6		6.2		6.5	
7. Wholesale and retail trade	13.5		14.3		13.6		13.0	
8. Banking and insurance	2.0		2.3		2.8		2.8	
9. Ownership of dwellings	3.6		3.4		3.5		3.0	
10. Public administration and defence	7.0		7.3		8.1		9.8	
11. Services	7.3		7.1		7.1		6.8	
12. Gross Domestic Product	99.8		99.5		98.2		94.0	
13. Net Factor Income from/to rest of the world	0.2		0.5		1.8		6.0	
14. Gross National Product	100.0		100.0		100.0		100.0	
15. Per Capita Income (Rs)	517		559		551		646	
16. Per Capita Income (current values) (Rs)	774		1116		1730		2,459	

*Provisional figures for 1978–79 from *Pakistan Economic Survey* 1978–79 GNP totalled Rs 191,584 million at current values
Source: National Accounts 1973–74 to 1976–77 and *Pakistan Statistical Yearbook 1974* (for 1971–72)

of the relative importance of the various economic activities of its population, the value of which is not necessarily tied directly to the numbers involved in the different sectors. Changes over time in the contribution to GNP from the various sectors can indicate whether the economic structure is in a static or dynamic state. Divided by the estimated population, GNP allows calculation to be made of per capita income, a grossly simplified concept, but one commonly used especially in a time series, to chart the movements in the economy, for better or for worse.

The composition of GNP is set out in Table 11.2 which shows the 11 sectors constituting Gross Domestic Product and the Net Factor Income from the rest of the world, the balance of invisible receipts over expenditures which convert GDP to GNP. Since the secession of Bangladesh economic growth has been sluggish. Agriculture is still very dominant although its share of the total has been declining. Unfortunately manufacturing has not been expanding proportionately and the increases have been in 'non-productive' areas like defence, public administration and construction. The effect on per capita income of the periods of political unrest accompanied by industrial troubles, curfews and consequent loss of production is seen in its decline between 1973–74 and 1976–77 from which date there has been some improvement under the stability of Martial Law Administration.

The structure of Pakistan's trade reflects its

50 The patient overloaded donkey is a common sight on Pakistan's roads. Singly or in caravans these little beasts do a vast amount of the country's carrying.

predominantly agricultural character. Agricultural products, raw or manufactured, are exported to pay for mainly manufactured imports. Table 11.3 shows the composition of exports. For a country no longer self-sufficient in foodgrain production, the large share of the export trade accounted for by rice calls for comment. The item is mainly *basmati* rice of very high quality (and price) for which there is a keen demand abroad.

In a 'normal' year, if such ever existed, unprocessed raw materials would make up 40–50 per cent of the total, but the share represented by semi-manufactured goods (such as processed raw materials) and by fully manufactured articles, is increasing. Cotton fabrics lead the list of manufactures, but the smaller items, sports goods and surgical instruments, indicate the range of Pakistani enterprise and craftsmanship. The Free Trade Zones planned for Karachi and later, Lahore, to encourage foreign investment in manufacturing industry for the export market are aimed at further increasing industry's share, while expanding employment opportunities for local labour.

Imports shown in Table 11.4 are dominated by machinery, vehicles and manufactures generally, and increasingly by the fuel to energise them. The abrupt rise in oil prices since 1974 is responsible for much but not all of the increase in the fuel bill. Fertilisers have been an expanding item to provide the essential inputs for an agriculture trying to reduce the need to import foodstuffs of any kind. The list of Pakistan's major trading partners (Table 11.5) is indicative of its lack of pronounced political bias, though the fact that

Table 11.3 Exports

Main group	Per cent of total value 1971–72	1977–78
Raw cotton and waste	29.1	8.5
Cotton fabrics and yarn	29.4	22.1
Raw wool	0.6	0.6
Woollen carpets	3.2	9.0
Raw hides and leather	5.7	4.9
Leather products and footwear	1.2	0.6
Rice	8.1	18.6
Fish and products	3.3	2.6
Tobacco and products	0.8	1.7
Guar and products	1.2	1.6
Petroleum products	1.2	4.8
Sports goods	1.5	1.5
Surgical instruments	0.7	1.2
TOTAL (Rs millions)	3,371.4	12980.4

Table 11.4   Imports

Main group	Per cent of total value	
	1971–72	*1977–78*
Machinery and transport equipment	30.0	26.5
Manufactured goods	16.4	12.6
Food and live animals	13.9	5.6
Chemicals, fertiliser, etc.	8.0	9.2
Mineral fuels, etc.	7.3	17.7
Animal and vegetable oils and fats	2.4	5.6
TOTAL (Rs millions)	3,495.4	27,814.7

the percentage of trade with the Middle Eastern countries has more than doubled since 1971–72 underlines a significant change in which cultural affinities march with economic advantage.

Figures for the balance of trade present a dismal picture, all too familiar among the countries of the less developed world. Exports currently pay for little more than half the imports. In 1977–78 imports cost Rs 27,815 millions against exports valued at Rs 12,980 millions, leaving a negative balance on the visible account of Rs 14,835 millions. To keep balance with the rest of the world Pakistan has to borrow extensively, and currently carries a debt of $9,230 million of which almost 25 per cent is with the USA, 22 per

cent with international bodies, and 13.8 per cent with Middle Eastern countries including 8.4 with Iran. The cost of servicing these debts was calculated as equivalent to 13 per cent of foreign exchange earnings at the end of 1978. Burdens of this magnitude are not uncommon among the less developed countries and clearly stand in the way of improving living standards significantly. Unless some change can be brought about in the way these countries finance development they will

Table 11.5   Major trading partners, 1977–78

	Share of exports (per cent)	Share of imports (per cent)
USA	5.0	12.6
EEC countries	20.6	25.9
E. Europe, USSR	4.5	3.8
Middle East	26.5	19.4
Japan	8.5	11.9

find themselves working harder and harder to stay in the same place.

Economic planning in Pakistan was disrupted by the loss of Bangladesh and political uncertainties that followed. From 1971–72 there was a series of Annual Plans until 1978, when a Fifth Five-Year Plan was published for 1978–83. The sectoral

51   Rubber-tyred camel carts in convoy near Dulle Wala in the Thal region. The old fashioned iron clad cart wheels are generally forbidden on bitumen surfaced roads because of the damage they cause. The tyres are lorry cast-offs.

allocation of public capital resources under this plan are shown in Table 11.6.

To the Rs 148,170 million in the public sector must be added Rs 62,000 million approved for investment in the private sector, distributed among various heads as follows: agriculture 18 per cent, industry and mining 31 per cent, transport 18 per cent, housing 21 per cent, and miscellaneous 12 per cent. Of the combined total, public and private, agriculture's share is 12.4 per cent and that of industry and mining 20 per cent. Much of the allocation to water benefits agriculture through irrigation, as does some of the expenditure on power. Industry's share is disproportionately large in comparison to its contribution to national income but is aimed to lead to a more balanced structure of GNP. Half of the allocation is for the Karachi Steel Mill which is unlikely to make any contribution within the Fifth Plan period.

Table 11.6 Sectoral allocation of Fifth Five-Year Plan, 1978–83 (per cent of total)

Total (Rs million)	*148,170*
Agriculture	10.1
Water	11.6
Power	18.8
Industry	14.2
Fuel	3.8
Minerals	1.3
Transport and communications	18.5
Housing, etc.	6.6
Education	6.9
Health	4.5
Population planning	1.2
Social welfare	0.1
Manpower	0.5
Rural development	1.0
Mass media	0.5
Tourism	0.4

Source: Fifth Five-Year Plan 1978–83

52 Interior of a textile weaving mill in a Punjab town. All the operatives are men. (Courtesy Govt. of Pakistan).

53 Hauling rock salt from the Khewra Mines in the Salt Range, Punjab. (Courtesy Govt. of Pakistan).

Chapter 12

Pakistan: Water, the Key to Subsistence

To a very large extent the human geography of Pakistan is an expression of man's ingenuity in harnessing exotic rivers and groundwater resources in order to survive in an arid region. More than three-quarters of the country has less than 250 mm of rainfall annually, and the small portion with over 500 mm amounts to only 7 per cent of the total. Much of that is in the mountains, but it includes the valuable piedmont plain from Sialkot northwest to Peshawar (Fig. 3.5). The dispersion diagrams (Fig. 3.8) suggest how precarious agriculture must be where direct rainfall is the sole source of moisture.

There is no escaping the fact that Pakistan is at best a semi-arid region, with a rainfall so low and so unreliable that it may best be looked upon as a gratuitous accident of nature reviving native forage plants and supplementing whatever supplies have been engineered by irrigators. From Dera Ismail Khan on the Indus or Sahiwal in the Bari Doab, through both of which passes the 250 mm isohyet, it is a full 800 km to beyond Hyderabad before that isohyet is crossed again and for half this distance the rainfall fails to average even 125 mm.

Northwards from the 250 mm isohyet in the Indus Plains, an increasingly large proportion of the rainfall comes in the cool season from passing depressions (see the dispersion diagrams for Lahore and Peshawar) and is consequently of much greater benefit to agriculture than the same amount received in summer. The importance of the winter rains, whether as the sole or as a supplementary supply of moisture for agriculture is seen in the ratio of *rabi* (cool season) to *kharif* (summer) crops (Fig. 12.1).

Apart from Peshawar, where winter and summer rains are more or less in balance, and Baluchistan (e.g. Quetta) where in a very low total the winter

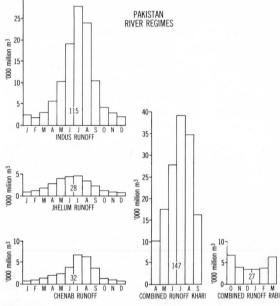

Fig. 12.1

fall is dominant giving a 'Mediterranean' regime, most of Pakistan has more than half its rainfall in the three summer months, July–September, a characteristic, if short, monsoon season. Since temperatures over the plains are extremely high in summer with daily maxima often in the 40s (°C) evaporation is also high, greatly reducing the effectiveness of the monsoon rainfall. Rivers and canals flowing through the Indus Plains are subjected to intense evaporation, far in excess of what they may gain from local rainfall. Such conditions promote the capillary movement upwards of moisture in the soil, a process responsible for concentrating in the surface layers salts from the subsoil, potentially to the serious detriment of plant life.

Rain-fed agriculture without supplementation with irrigation water is fairly rare in Pakistan.

On the Himalayan slopes, where irrigation is in any case difficult, *kharif* or *rabi* crops, sometimes both, may be grown, and the loess soils of the Potwar Plateau carry rain-fed *rabi* wheat and mustard. Generally, however, irrigation is practised wherever conditions allow. In essence, irrigation is the use of precipitation which fell elsewhere, such water being obtained from the surface flow of rivers or from groundwater reservoirs below the surface.

In the Indus plains the major sources of water have been the large exotic rivers of the Indus system: the Indus, with its right bank tributary the Kabul River, and the five rivers of the Punjab – Jhelum, Chenab, Ravi, Beas and Sutlej. Under the Indus Waters Treaty of 1960 the waters of the Ravi, Beas and Sutlej were given to India. All these rivers obtain most of their flow from catchments within the mountains and their regimes are marked by extreme seasonal fluctuation. Table 12.1 shows the relative importance of the several catchments as measured close to the entry of the rivers onto the plains. Figure 12.1 illustrates the seasonality of their regimes.

Maximum flow is from April, when snow melts in the Himalaya through the summer monsoon to September. Discharge in this period may be five times that of the winter six months, a fact which underlines the importance to Pakistan and India of constructing storage dams to enable the summer surplus to be carried over into the rabi cropping season.

Irrigation Methods

Although canal irrigation now accounts for five-sixths or more of the total area irrigated, it is of relatively recent introduction. Small-scale irriga-tion methods have been in use for several mil-lennia. Probably as old as agriculture in the Indus Plains are the shallow wells sunk to the water table, from which water is raised by a variety of means, the most common being the Persian Wheel driven by bullocks or other farm animals. Such wells are particularly numerous in the Himalayan Piedmont Plain where groundwater is close to the surface and where the need is merely to supplement the moderate rainfall. They are also important along the margins of the active floodplains of the rivers in locations where groundwater is accessible (Fig. 12.2). Water from wells costs the farmer more in personal initiative, capital investment, and labour than does canal water, and for this reason it tends to be more carefully used. The few acres which it is economical to water from a well are usually intensively farmed, the fields nearest the well often having the aspect of a well-tended garden.

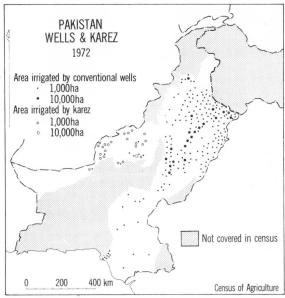

Fig. 12.2

Table 12.1 Run-off and discharge in the Indus rivers

Catchment	Average annual runoff (thousand million m³)	Discharge (thousand m³ per second) maximum	minimum
Indus (including Kabul)	115	26	0.48
Jhelum	28	22	0.11
Chenab	32	20	0.11
Ravi	9	7	0.03
Beas	16	10	0.06
Sutlej	17	14	0.08

Where the water table is beyond the reach of hand-excavated wells (or where adequate capital is available) mechanically drilled, metal-lined tube wells are common. Driven by diesel engines or electric motors, tube wells can command a larger irrigated area. Another important use of tube wells is to drain areas which have become water-logged through years of canal irrigation (Fig. 12.3).

Fig. 12.3

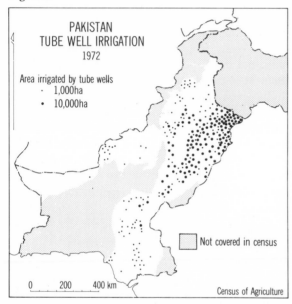

There are other methods of bringing water to cultivated lands, though none is responsible for any appreciable proportion of Pakistan's sown area. In the Himalayan valleys, streams and small rivers are diverted to water terraced slopes or the valley-floor alluvium. The broad active flood-plains of the Indus and the Punjab rivers are

54 Pakistan's largest storage dam and H.E.P. scheme is at Tarbela on the Indus. The service and auxiliary spillways are seen here. (Courtesy W.A.P.D.A.).

similarly watered to some extent by diversion of braided channels during the low water period With wells, these were probably the basis of agriculture in the Indus Civilisation of 2500 BC. Along the Piedmont Plain that skirts the Sulaiman and Kirthar ranges, an unreliable and variable proportion of the infrequent but normally violent discharge of hill-fed torrents or *rod kohi* is held up behind crude barrages in the steep-sided river beds, and is led to bunded fields to soak into the soil so that a crop can be taken (Fig. 12.4). Lastly, the *karez* system of Baluchistan epitomises the basic problem of agriculture in an arid region, that of concentrating upon a restricted but cultivable patch of land the sparse precipitation that occurs over a wider area (Fig. 12.5). In essence, a karez system consists of a near-horizontal tunnel driven from the level of the cultivable land near the centre of an intermontane basin to intersect the water table in the gravelly detritus, which constitutes the fans along the mountain foot where intermittent streams from high catchments soak away into the coarse material. At the lower end of the tunnel emerges a small stream of water which is led to the fields. An important advantage of the karez is that the water travels most of its way underground, and so with the minimum risk of loss by evaporation. Canal irrigation is altogether a more elaborate matter and conducted on a larger scale than the minor systems just des-

Fig. 12.4

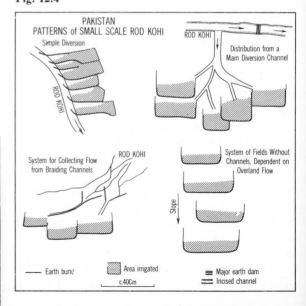

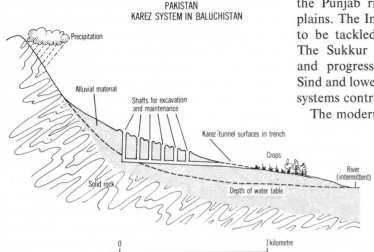

PAKISTAN
KAREZ SYSTEM IN BALUCHISTAN

Precipitation

Alluvial material

Shafts for excavation
and maintenance

Karez tunnel surfaces in trench

Crops

River
(intermittent)

Solid rock

Depth of water table

0   1 kilometre

Fig. 12.5

the Punjab rivers close to their entry onto the plains. The Indus itself was too formidable a river to be tackled until engineering skills advanced. The Sukkur Barrage was constructed in 1932, and progressively inundation canal systems in Sind and lower Punjab have given way to perennial systems controlled by barrages.

The modern canal system (Fig. 12.7) is the end

cribed. In the nineteenth century, following the earlier example of the Moghul governors of Multan and the Emirs of Sind, the Sikhs and the British cut inundation canals to divert the summer floods. Such canals were fed from cuts made in the banks of the rivers and would fill only when the river level rose sufficiently. The cultivated area commanded was usually in the meander floodplain parallel to the river and close to it. The principal aim was to water *kharif* crops during the high flood season when maximum flow was available, but early watering for *rabi* crops might be possible where the canal intake was at a low level, allowing water to flow late in the season. Some inundation canals used anabranches of the rivers from which water could be raised by Persian wheels or shadufs. Inundation canals were most common south of the latitude of Multan, on the Indus and the lower Chenab and Sutlej, where the banks were not too high. In the upper Punjab the rivers are slightly incised into the meander floodplain and such canals were of limited value.

Canal irrigation of the Punjab awaited the construction of gated barrages across the rivers to raise and control the level of the off-take channel. The Upper Bari Doab Canal (1859–61) enabled water to be diverted onto the higher interfluves – the scalloped interfluves – of the Punjab rivers at all seasons (Fig. 12.6). Thus canals came effectively to command the whole of the Indus plains, though seasonal scarcity of water – in winter particularly – was the main constraint on the area to be commanded. Barrages were first built across

product of progressive elaboration in the manipulation of Pakistan's water resources over the past 75 years. The basic problem has been that the water resources of the eastern rivers, the Ravi, Beas and Sutlej, were inadequate to meet the demands in southern Punjab and Bahawalpur State (as it was), while the western rivers, Jhelum

Fig. 12.6

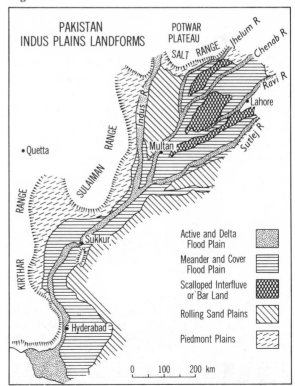

PAKISTAN
INDUS PLAINS LANDFORMS

POTWAR PLATEAU

SALT RANGE

Jhelum R

Chenab R

Ravi R

Lahore

Multan

Sutlej R

Quetta

RANGE

SULAIMAN

KIRTHAR

RANGE

Sukkur

Hyderabad

Active and Delta Flood Plain

Meander and Cover Flood Plain

Scalloped Interfluve or Bar Land

Rolling Sand Plains

Piedmont Plains

0   100   200 km

and Chenab, had water surplus to requirements in their less extensive doabs. Engineers hit upon the ingenious expedient of transferring water from the western rivers to supplement those further east. In the Triple Canals Project, carried out between 1905 and 1915, Jhelum water from Mangla was transferred by the Upper Jhelum Canal to the Chenab above its Khanki Barrage; Chenab water was extracted further upstream at Marala to feed the Upper Chenab Canal leading ultimately to the Ravi, which it crosses at Balloki to feed the Lower Bari Doab Canal flowing past Harappa. The Triple Canals Project was to provide a blueprint for solving the post-partition problems of water distribution between India and Pakistan. Figure 12.8 shows the link canals now operating to bring water eastwards to command areas deprived of their pre-partition supply. The Indus has been brought in to supply the Jhelum and Chenab across the Thal.

It had long been realised that efficient irrigation in the Punjab would depend ultimately on the creation of storage dams to carry over the summer surplus for use in winter, when a given quantity of water goes twice as far as in summer. Partition in 1947 brought matters to a head for Pakistan which lost the three eastern rivers whose headworks now lay in India. This forced Pakistan to transfer more water from the western rivers to make good the loss, but even so a seasonal deficit in winter remained which could only be overcome by storage dams. Under the Indus Waters Treaty and with huge sums of aid from the World Bank and friendly governments, notably the USA, the Mangla and Tarbela Dams have been built on the Jhelum and Indus respectively. Storage at Mangla, 6,500 million m^3, represents 23 per cent of the mean annual flow. Tarbela stores 11,500 million m^3, 14.5 per cent of annual flow. The sediment load of the Indus is a serious problem and is likely to render the dam almost useless as a storage reservoir within 55 years. A storage of equivalent volume can be built on the Indus using its gorge between Attock and Kalabagh.

Fig. 12.7

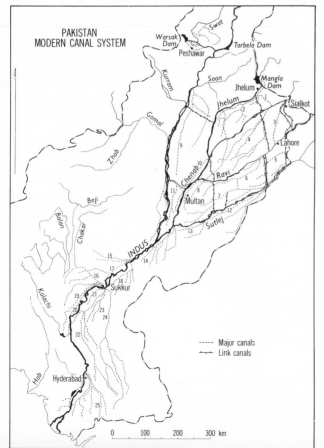

Fig. 12.8

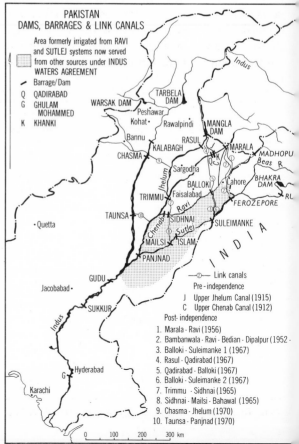

The Water Budget of the Indus System

The flow characteristic of the Indus and of the combined rivers available to Pakistan are shown in Table 12.2 with the actual water used in 1957 and in prospect for 1985. It is expected that by 1985 both Mangla and Tarbela Dams will be fully operational. Tarbela is capable of storing an amount equivalent to its total *rabi* season flow. With Mangla added, the total storage represents 61 per cent of the *rabi* flow of all three rivers, and the expectation is that water utilisation in the *rabi* season will expand. Before Mangla Dam was built, on average (1961–66) 105×10^9 m³ was used in a year, 33×10^9 m³ in rabi, 72×10^9 m³ in *kharif*. By adding 6.3×10^9 m³ to the combined *rabi* flow of 27.3×10^9 m³, Mangla restored Pakistan to its position prior to the Indus Water Treaty. Water from Tarbela Dam has enabled real expansion to take place though technical difficulties have delayed full realisation of the potential. By 1985 *rabi* use will have increased 22 per cent, and *kharif* use by 17 per cent.

The water budget of the canal commanded areas of Pakistan is shown diagrammatically in Figure 12.9 based on a World Bank projection. It will be noted how little rainfall contributes to crop growth, a mere 8.6 thousand million m³ in

55 Persian Wheel, in its modernised version with steel wheels and metal buckets replacing more cumbersome timber wheels and earthen pots on rope chains, near Rawalpindi. The horse and buffalo are blindfolded to prevent them becoming dizzy. Water for irrigation can be seen pouring into the metal trough on the left.

a total of 80.2 actually used by crops. Evaporation takes its toll of water on the surface but a substantial amount infiltrates to groundwater from canals and fields, some of it to be recycled through the irrigation system by pumping.

Where groundwater is not saline it can be regarded as a valuable resource which can be tapped for irrigation. Usable groundwater underlies much of the Indus Plain particularly in the vicinity of the major river floodplains and in the Himalayan piedmont. Where it is close to the surface, traditional wells have long been used to exploit it. At

Table 12.2 River flow characteristics and use (all figures thousand million m³)

	Indus at Tarbela	Indus (Attock) + Jhelum + Chenab	Actual use	Projected use
		1968	1957	1985
Oct	3.3	6.8	9.3	9.9
Nov	2.0	3.9	4.6	4.9
Dec	1.6	3.5	4.3	4.9
Jan	1.4	3.5	4.9	6.2
Feb	1.4	3.7	7.3	7.4
Mar	1.9	6.3	6.9	7.4
Rabi season	*11.5*	*27.6*	*37.3*	*40.7*
Apr	2.6	10.1	6.3	8.6
May	5.4	17.5	8.8	9.9
June	12.7	28.0	13.0	16.0
July	20.7	39.5	13.6	17.3
Aug	19.7	35.0	13.8	17.3
Sept	8.4	16.3	12.2	14.8
Kharif season	*69.6*	*146.5*	*67.6*	*83.9*
Year	*81.0*	*174.2*	*104.8*	*124.6*

Note: Totals may not match exactly owing to roundings in conversion

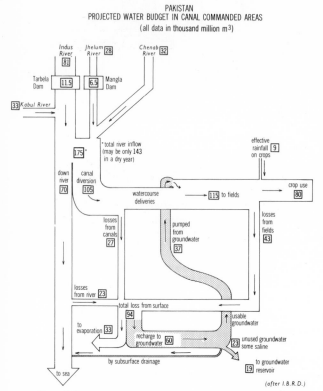

PAKISTAN
PROJECTED WATER BUDGET IN CANAL COMMANDED AREAS
(all data in thousand million m³)

Indus River 81
Jhelum River 28
Chenab River 32
Tarbela Dam 11.5
Mangla Dam 6.5
Kabul River 33
* total river inflow (may be only 143 in a dry year) 175
effective rainfall on crops 9
down river 70
canal diversion 105
watercourse deliveries
to fields 115
crop use 80
losses from canals 27
pumped from groundwater 37
losses from fields 43
losses from river 23
total loss from surface 94
usable groundwater
to evaporation 33
recharge to groundwater 60
unused groundwater some saline 23
by subsurface drainage
to groundwater reservoir 19
to sea

(after I.B.R.D.)

Fig. 12.9

greater depths and for maximum efficiency, tube wells equipped with power pumps are now often used. The role of groundwater resources in the total water budget is increasing. The more that groundwater is exploited in the Punjab, the less water will ultimately flow to Sind, since every cycle of use in irrigating crops involves some loss through evaporation, transpiration and fixation in the crop itself.

The budget illustrated supported an average cropping intensity of 110 per cent, i.e. 10 per cent of the fields irrigated carried a second crop in the year. Projections forward to 1985 and 2000 increase the intensity to 126 and 142 per cent respectively, levels achieved by a higher factor of utilisation of water on its way through the system, particularly by the re-use of groundwater.

Water-logging and Salinity

The completion of the works proposed under the Indus Waters Treaty will not remove from Pakistan every problem connected with irrigation. The design of early irrigation schemes did not usually provide for the long-term changes in hydrology

that massive irrigation can produce, namely water-logging and salinity. In simple terms, water-logging arises from the introduction of irrigation water into a region without adequate provision being made for drainage (Fig. 12.10). Water neither used by crops, nor evaporated nor transpired nor drained away on or below the surface, accumulates as groundwater, until such time as its level rises to the surface to produce a swamp. In many areas groundwater has not accumulated, as subsurface drainage removes it elsewhere, but where the subsurface structure inhibits free drainage, as in the case of the sub-alluvial rock ridge running southeast across the Punjab from Shahpur, or where reduced permeability occurs, extensive water-logging may result at the surface. Impediments to surface drainage, such as road, railway, or canal embankments running across the slope of the land, are a major cause of ponding back surface run-off, which then has time to percolate to groundwater. Seepage from unlined canals and distributary channels further adds to the groundwater reservoir and often induces a rise in the water table.

An even greater menace than water-logging is salt in the soil. All river water contains salts in solution, and so the irrigator applies to his fields a normally very dilute saline solution. When crops transpire, and when water evaporates, it is pure water vapour that goes into the air, leaving behind the saline content to accumulate. Often, therefore, the surplus water from irrigation that joins the groundwater body is of increasing salinity. Salts in the soil itself may also be taken into solution. Where saline groundwater lies close to the surface, many crop plants will be unable to tolerate the condition and land may have to be abandoned unless remedial action is taken. This has been happening on a large scale in Pakistan as a result of several generations of irrigation. A major defect in the design of early schemes, only now fully appreciated, was to provide only enough water for a crop to be taken. Under-watering prevented the leaching out of accumulated salts, under-draining encouraged their retention in the soil. Up until now it has been no exaggeration for an engineer to say 'Heroic measures are essential if the Punjab is not to be destroyed'. The form that the rescue operation is taking is first to separate the saline water table from the surface zone where

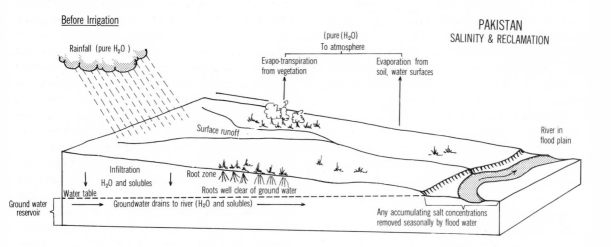

Before Irrigation

Rainfall (pure H₂O)

(pure (H₂O)
To atmosphere

Evapo-transpiration
from vegetation

Evaporation from
soil, water surfaces

PAKISTAN
SALINITY & RECLAMATION

Surface runoff

River in
flood plain

Infiltration
H₂O and solubles

Root zone

Roots well clear of ground water

Water table

Ground water
reservoir

Groundwater drains to river (H₂O and solubles)

Any accumulating salt concentrations
removed seasonally by flood water

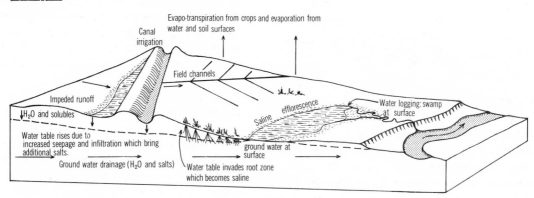

Under Irrigation

Evapo-transpiration from crops and evaporation from
water and soil surfaces

Canal
irrigation

Field channels

Impeded runoff

Water logging: swamp
at surface

H₂O and solubles

Saline efflorescence

Water table rises due to
increased seepage and infiltration which bring
additional salts.

ground water at
surface

Ground water drainage (H₂O and salts)

Water table invades root zone
which becomes saline

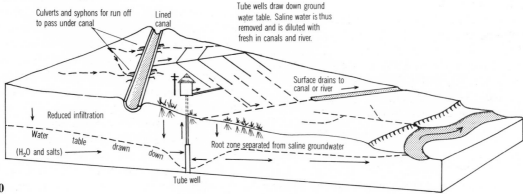

Reclamation and Proper Maintenance

Culverts and syphons for run off
to pass under canal

Lined
canal

Tube wells draw down ground
water table. Saline water is thus
removed and is diluted with
fresh in canals and river.

Surface drains to
canal or river

Reduced infiltration

Water
(H₂O and salts)

table

drawn

down

Root zone separated from saline groundwater

Tube well

Fig. 12.10

irrigation is supporting crops. This is achieved by closely spaced tube wells which pump the saline water into canals where it can be diluted to safe levels, or into river courses. Surface drains may have to be dug to prevent surplus irrigation water sinking to add to the groundwater and so bringing the water table closer to the surface.

Figure 12.11 shows the extent of severe salinity and water-logging of the farm area: it does not reveal the whole picture as much land has been rendered unusable and consequently has been

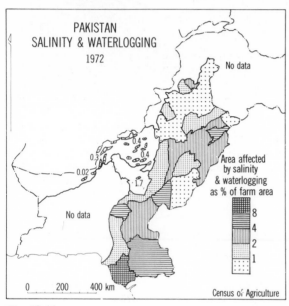

Fig. 12.11

abandoned. The major areas in which groundwater is saline are shown on Figures 12.12 and 12.13. It will be noted that these areas are generally in the middle zone of interfluves and not close to the active floodplains as a rule. In Lower Sind the problem is more extensive. The water table is not close enough to the surface in all of these areas to create a toxic environment for crops, but nonetheless the groundwater cannot be regarded as a usable resource and needs to be prevented from invading the root zone. The first major reclamation programme or Salinity Control and Reclamation Project, SCARP I, was undertaken in the Rechna Doab, between the Rivers Chenab and Ravi, in 1959. Others SCARPs followed, SCARP II in the Chaj Doab (Chenab–Jhelum interfluve) in 1962, III in the Lower Thal Doab in 1965, IV in the Upper Rechna Doab. By 1974, 6,844 tube wells and 460

km of surface drains had been installed to reclaim 1.6 million ha of canal command in the Punjab alone.

Fig. 12.12

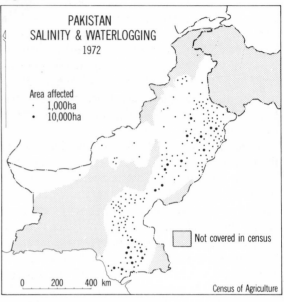

Fig. 12.13

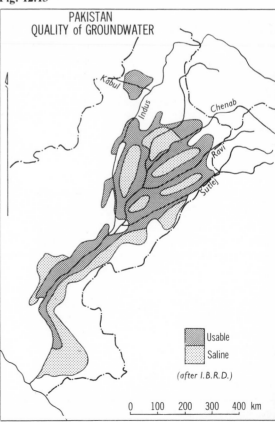

Tables 12.3 and 12.4 below summarise the extent of the problems of water-logging and salinity respectively.

Where it is fresh, groundwater is of course a valuable and accessible reservoir of irrigation water and the pumping of tube wells to reclaim water-logged areas can have its compensations. Under the SCARPs, public tube wells are delivering almost 10,000 million m³ of water annually while private wells yield a further 24,670 million m³, together making a very substantial contribution to the water circulating in the Indus Basin irrigation system (cf. Fig. 12.9).

In the Sind the problems of salinity loom larger than in Punjab, and groundwater is seldom a welcome resource. When extracted to reduce the level of toxic groundwater, the effluent has usually to be removed to the river or to canals with sufficient capacity to dilute its saline content. Where the terrain becomes increasingly flat as the Indus passes through Sind to the sea, the removal of saline drainage water becomes difficult. Futhermore, as the alluvium becomes finer downstream, it is often impracticable to drain affected areas

56   A government tube well, electrically powered on a SCARP area in the Rechna Doab west of Lahore. Such wells are used to control the level of groundwater and so to counter waterlogging and salinity. The water may be useable directly or after dilution with fresher canal water.

Table 12.3   Extent of waterlogging (million ha)

	Gross canal commanded area (CCA)	Area affected Severely (water table 0–1.5 m)	% of CCA	Moderately (1.5 – 3 m)	% of CCA	Total	% of CCA
Punjab	8.2	0.6	7	2.7	33	3.3	41
Sind	5.1	1.2	23	1.8	33	3.0	56
NWFP	0.4	0.04	10	0.01	1	0.11	11
Baluchistan	0.24	—	—	—	—	0.002	0.3
TOTAL	13.94	1.84	13.2	4.5	32	6.41	46

Note: Waterlogging is measured as in April when at a minimum. By September–October it rises to 1.5–2 times the April level

Table 12.4   Extent of soil salinity (million ha), 1973–74

Province	Area surveyed	Area affected Moderately (0.2–0.5%) %		Severely (>0.5%) %		Alkali affected %		Total (%)	
Punjab	8.2	0.4	5	1.2	15	2.1	26	3.7	45
Sind	5.1	3.2	63	1.9	37	—	—	5.1	100
NWFP	0.4							0.04	9
Baluchistan	0.24							0.04	18
TOTAL	13.94	3.6	26	3.1	22	2.1	15	8.9	64

Source: Annual Plan 1976–77

by pumping from wells, so surface drains and subsurface tile drainage beneath the fields are being used increasingly. Fortunately, in the short run, the level of salinity while excessive for wheat, can still be tolerated by appropriate rice varieties in many areas.

Agricultural Patterns

The dominant modes of irrigation in the Indus plains are summarised in Figure 12.14. Perennial canal supply has been the ultimate target for as much of the basin as can be so commanded. Seasonal inundation irrigation canals still serve broad tracts in the Sutlej Valley, now the 'tail-end' of systems deriving water from the western rivers. Wells dominate in only a few areas. They are being increasingly converted from muscle to electric or diesel power. While overall water availability increased 35 per cent between 1965–66 and 1975–76, public tube well supplies increased 150 per cent and private tube wells 193 per cent, compared with a 9 per cent increase for canals.

Fig. 12.14

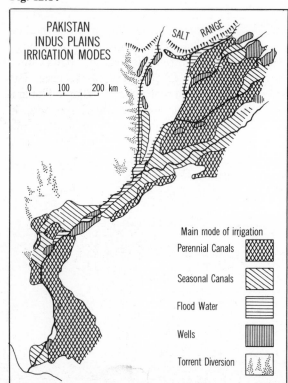

The proportion of the cropped area irrigated is mapped in Figure 12.15 which shows the paramount importance of irrigation in agriculture. Over a very large part of Punjab and Sind, the percentage of the cropped area irrigated in one way or another exceeds 80, and is often over 90.

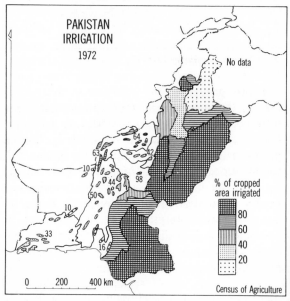

Fig. 12.15

The rain-fed or *barani* lands of the Punjab Piedmont, and the southern areas of Thal, less fully provided with canal supplies, have over 60 per cent of their crop land irrigated none the less. The low figure of 30 per cent for Mianwali is because the district covers a large area of the rolling sand plain in central Thal together with some rocky hill country. Some districts in Sind fall below the 80 per cent level, but only barely so in the cases of Sukkur and Dadu. Jacobabad (52 per cent irrigated) is on the fringe of canal commands and has a substantial area reliant on torrent watering or 'sailaba'. There is a problem of definition that can distort the picture somewhat. In Sind for example, it used to be common under the earlier inundation canal system and may still be the practice when supplies are short, to grow a *rabi* crop without irrigation in season, on the basis of moisture remaining from late *kharif* 'pre-watering' of land. Some of the apparent deficiency in irrigation in Sind, in districts that can hardly rely on the very low and unpredictable rainfall, may be explained in this way.

Crops

The principal crops grown are shown in Table 12.5.

Table 12.5 Principal crops (thousand ha), 1977–78

Wheat	6,724	Gram	1,099
Rice	1,976	Sugar Cane	755
Bajra	688	Rape, etc.	412*
Jowar	428	Cotton	2,038
Maize	604	Tobacco	53*
Barley	167		

Source: Economic Survey 1978–79
* 1976–77

Those grown in the *rabi* season are wheat, barley, the pulse gram, rape and mustard, and tobacco, to which should be added the following (whose area in thousand ha are for 1971–75): the pulses masoor, 75 and mattar, 186; chillies, 34; fodder crops, 1,215. The *kharif* crops are headed by rice, the millets bajra and jowar, maize and cotton. In addition the pulses mung, 67, and mash, 43, guar seed, 230, groundnut, 41, sesamum, 23 and *kharif* fodder, 1,917, merit mention. Sugar cane straddles the two seasons, remaining in the ground 11 months or more.

As the staple food, wheat is grown in every district, and generally dominates the *rabi* season. Conditions are least favourable in the extreme south because of saline soils and high temperatures in the Indus Delta. Almost two-thirds of the crop is HYV Mexi-Pak variety. The need to apply fertilisers for optimum yields militates against HYV in the *barani* (rain-fed) areas like the Potwar Plateau and Thal. On the sandy soils of the latter, wheat is sometimes less important than pulses which can better tolerate droughty conditions.

In the main irrigated tracts of the Punjab and Sind almost 100 per cent of the wheat crop is HYV. Wheat yields under irrigation average 1.56 tonnes per ha. HYV yielded 1.63 t/ha in 1974–75 compared with 0.78 t/ha for traditional varieties.

Although conditions are ideal for closely-controlled, irrigated rice cultivation, HYV rice occupies only 39 per cent of the total under this crop, largely on account of the much greater profits to be made growing high quality basmati rice for export, which occupies 31 per cent of the rice area, and contributed 36 per cent of production. Basmati rice commands Rs 7,667 per tonne against Rs 4,335 for HYV IRRI-Pak rice, and Rs 2,589 for traditional Joshi rice. Basmati is particularly important in the districts immediately north of Lahore, but it is in the lower Indus plains below the Sukkur Barrage that rice becomes the major significant crop in several districts, particularly on the right bank where water retentive clay soils are a factor. In terms of yield, HYV achieves 1.75 t/ha against 1.23 for other varieties.

Cotton vies with rice for second place by area. It is by far the most important cash crop, and is vital for Pakistan's export trade either in the raw state or converted into manufactured yarn or cloth. The main cotton belt in the irrigated districts of the Punjab extending from Sargodha, Jhang, Faisalabad and Sahiwal south through Multan to the three districts of Bahawalpur Division contains 65 per cent of the area. The left bank districts in Sind, from Sukkur to Hyderabad and Tharparkar account for 23 per cent. In recent years yields have been disappointing partly due to pests, diseases and floods, but also because

57 Marala barrage on the Chenab is the headworks of link canals that cross the Rechna Doab to the River Ravi. The machines for raising the gates of the barrage can be seen to the right of the road. (Courtesy Govt. of Pakistan).

of competition from alternative, more profitable crops like maize and sugar cane. Yields in 1977–78 at 0.33 t/ha showed some improvement over the previous three years and production rose to 569,000 tonnes despite a continuing fall in area.

Seasonal Cropping Patterns

A simple view of the seasonal ratio of *rabi* to *kharif* cropping is given in Figure 12.16. Overall, *rabi* cropping exceeds *kharif* in 33 of the 46 districts mapped, but in many the difference is slight, and the seasonal areas are more or less in balance over southern Punjab and the mainly left bank districts of Sind. *Rabi* crops are most clearly dominant in a trans-Indus belt extending from Chitral in the far north, through Kohat and Bannu, to Dera Ismail Khan, with extension east of the river into Mianwali, Attock, Sargodha and Muzaffargarh, and along the Punjab Piedmont in Gujrat and Sialkot. Winter rainfall is a major factor favouring *rabi* cropping in the western parts of this belt, but in the sandy Thal districts of Mianwali and Muzaffargarh it is rather the unsuitability of such soils for cropping in the high evaporation season that makes winter cropping preferable. As a rule, the tiny patches of cultivable land in Baluchistan show strong *rabi* dominance due to reliance on small-scale irrigation in an extremely arid climate where valuable water would be wasted on *kharif* crops.

Kharif dominance is limited to parts of the western Himalaya exposed to monsoon rainfall and so able to raise rain-fed maize crops on terraced fields, and to Tatta, Hyderabad and Bandin towards the Indus delta, where ample irrigation water is needed to flush salinity out of the soil and can only be obtained in summer.

A more detailed picture of Pakistan can be had in Figure 12.17 which shows for every district the proportion of the cropped area, *rabi* and *kharif*, under the major crops. The circles are proportionate to area but are so small in the case of some NWFP and Baluchistan districts as to necessitate magnified key circles. This map should be referred to (with Fig. 10.1 which shows district names) while reading the ensuing section.

Agricultural Regions

The regions shown in Figure 12.17 are basically physiographic regions within each of which there is a measure of homogeneity of agricultural activity.

The *Baluchistan Plateau* with its basins and ranges is extremely dry, almost half of the region having less than 125 mm rainfall on average, and

Fig. 12.16

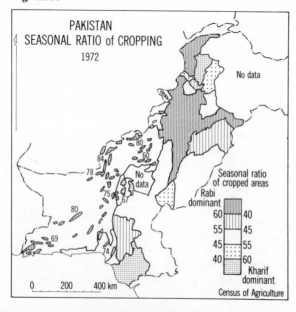

Fig. 12.17

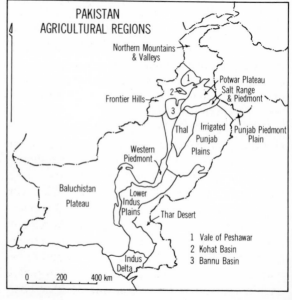

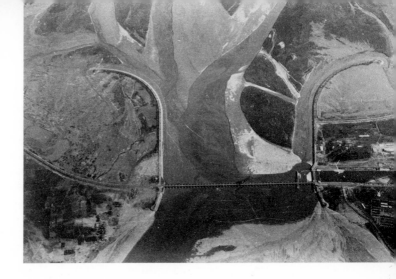

58 Aerial view of a typical barrage in the Punjab. Water is diverted into the canal on the right. Protective embankments upstream prevent flood waters from outflanking the barrage, which also serves as a road bridge.

the rest no more than 250 mm. Since there is no certainty of rain occurring in any particular year – let alone month – agriculture relies on irrigation to concentrate on a small part of the land the rain that falls over a wider area or accumulates as groundwater over time. The higher ranges trap some winter snow which, as it melts, percolates into the alluvial fill on the lower slopes, from which it may be recovered by digging *karez*. Alternatively, in some areas, *rod kohi* irrigation is practised, with even less certainty of success. Over much of the Plateau the main field crops are wheat and barley raised in *rabi*. Kharif jowar is liable to high variation in area and yield depending on the chance of rain. 'Average' climatic conditions can be said never to occur, and the agricultural statistics show a reasonable crop perhaps one year in four or five. Other crops grown include *rabi* pulses and *kharif* maize, cotton, bajra and coriander. Las Bela district in the southeast is unusual in having kharif jowar dominant: this corner of Baluchistan is open to the penetration of monsoon rains (in a good year) and has a regime similar to that of Karachi.

Fruits are relatively more important here than elsewhere in Pakistan. Melons are popular on sandy soils, as they grow quickly after a shower of rain or a flash-flood and provide human food and animal fodder. Tree fruits and vines with their deep root systems can withstand drought better than field crops. They represent the region's chief cash source, especially around Quetta where the railway provides an outlet to lowland urban markets for grapes, apricots, almonds, and apples, and in the valleys back from the Makran coast

where dates are a speciality, in addition to papaya and mangoes where water is available.

Such relatively intensive fruit farming and crop raising in oasis-like basins occupies only a fraction of the rocky and generally treeless countryside. Livestock – sheep, goats and camels – provide for man a more reliable means of exploiting the region's meagre resources of moisture since they can forage over wide areas of desert, harvesting the accumulated vegetal growth. Pastoralism (semi-nomadic and seasonally transhumant) is a common way of life in Baluchistan, but one liable to disturb the delicate desert ecosystem if flock numbers are not controlled. Wool, hair, dried meat and live camels as beasts of burden are the saleable products, while the herdsmen subsist in part on the milk and meat of their animals. The *Western piedmont* extends along the foot of the Kirthar and Sulaiman Ranges west of the Indus floodplain, and has its counterpart east of the river in a narrow belt at the foot of the Salt Range. Since the piedmont skirts the plains it is nowhere wide enough to dominate a district and so does not show up on the map of seasonal cropping patterns. By and large the belt is one of rod kohi irrigation by which fields are pre-watered for a *rabi* crop of wheat for preference. When local rainfall is adequate a *kharif* crop of jowar and even cotton may be sown. The northern part of this belt, with better prospects of winter precipitation and groundwater accessible by wells, in parts has a more secure agriculture than the southern. Where pre-watering by rod kohi has not been possible, gram may be sown as a rain-fed crop.

The *Frontier Hills* are rather better watered than Baluchistan, but share a regime bringing 70 per cent of the rain in winter. *Rabi* cropping is usually more important than *kharif*, but not by a wide margin, and not exclusively. Kurram, for example, has *kharif* cropping dominant because its good rainfall allows maize to be grown up the slopes and rice in the irrigated valley floors during summer. It should be noted how tiny are the areas cultivated in these hills. Livestock rearing and transhumance between hills and the neighbouring plains, and the carrying trade, using camels and donkeys, provide some additional income in this difficult rocky terrain.

The *Northern Mountains and Valleys*, the continuation of the Himalaya of western Kashmir, are the best watered region of Pakistan with over 1,000 mm of rain. The higher slopes are forested and provide some summer grazing. With maximum rainfall in summer in the Murree Hills in the east *kharif* crops are in the lead. Westwards, winter rains and *rabi* crops dominate, but neither season is really dry. Valley sides are terraced for maize, wheat and mustard, while narrow strips of irrigated rice are found in the valley bottoms.

North of this humid mountain belt, precipitation falls off rapidly and an arid mountain desert occurs with less than 125 mm along the Indus valley. Depending on aspect some rain-fed agriculture is possible, but fortunately minor irrigation is relatively easy from snow-melt streams which can be led to the terraced fields. There is a distinct vertical zonation of cropping. Up to 2,000 m double cropping of wheat and maize is possible. Barley, quicker growing and more tolerant of drought than wheat, is also popular and, in suitable valley locations, rice. Above 2,500 m only single cropping is possible because the cool temperature delays maturation of *rabi* and *kharif* crops. Wheat or maize, with barley at higher levels, are the usual crops, but many grow grapes to make wine – this among the Ismalia sect who are not orthodox teetotal Muslims. At higher levels, maize gives way to buckwheat, a millet (ragi in India), as a *kharif* crop. Wheat extends to 3,350 m, barley to 3,700 m. Peaches and apricots survive above 3,000 m, providing dried fruits for the diet. In Chitral notorious but valuable sources of cash are charas (*Cannabis* sp.) and opium poppy. Silk, reared on mulberry, is the basis of cottage industry and for the factories in Swat. These remote valleys may soon be made much more accessible with the completion of the Karakoram Highway which links China with the Kaghan and Swat valleys through the 'Shangri La' of Hunza.

The *Basins of Peshawar, Kohat and Bannu* are areas of intensive cultivation supported by irrigation from rivers draining from the hills to the west. With moderate rainfall (500 mm or so) which is fairly evenly distributed between seasons, a really prosperous agricultural economy has developed, based on the staples wheat and maize, and the valuable cash crops sugar cane and tobacco. In places cropping intensity exceeds 150 per cent and even 190 per cent in the tobacco area around Swabi.

To the east of the Indus the neighbouring region of the *Potwar Plateau* is similarly fortunate in its rainfall, but suffers from a lack of irrigation owing to its difficult terrain. Fair crops of rain-fed wheat are taken on the loess soils, and in a few places wells allow more intensive horticulture. *Rabi* wheat is very dominant; in *kharif* jowar and bajra rely on less certain monsoon falls, with maize on the hill slopes. Over-grazing by goats and sheep may be in part responsible for the accelerated erosion which has led to extensive gullying of parts of the plateau. Efforts are being made to control erosion and rehabilitate the areas affected by contouring the fields, damming gullies and erecting masonry barriers to check floods, and by dynamiting and bulldozing the badlands into level fields once more. The costs are very high

59 'A horizontal oasis in a vertical desert' is how Elizabeth Staley (who took this picture) describes this scene in the arid region to the west of the Karakoram. The gravelly flood plain is irrigated by channels feeding maize and rice crops. The rocky mountain slopes carry a sparce discontinuous cover of grasses and shrubs.

in relation to the only moderate potential for rain-fed agriculture.

The *Punjab Piedmont Plain* is a belt about 40 km wide along the foot of the Outer Himalaya on the borders of Pakistan and Kashmir. Its agriculture is distinguished from that of the Punjab Plains proper by the general absence of canals and its dependence on well irrigation to supplement the moderate rainfall of about 800 mm. In the west in Gujrat, where it abuts onto Potwar, the surface is a true piedmont, while eastwards around Sialkot it is part of the cover floodplain of the Chenab, underlain by good groundwater. In Gujrat, cultivation depends on rainfall and wells for the most part, *rabi* wheat being followed by irrigated fodder crops and jowar in *kharif*. Both canals and wells are available in Sialkot, and rice becomes the more important *kharif* crop in an intensive system.

Within the *Punjab Plains* south of the piedmont belt agriculture increasingly depends on canal irrigation, supplemented perhaps by wells. Rain is an occasional benefit but not to be relied upon overmuch. There are some broad regional differences in the agricultural pattern but more local variations which are not reflected in the district-wise data.

In *Thal*, the broad interfluve between the Indus and Jhelum rivers, and along the fringe of the Thar Desert, east of the lower Sutlej (in Bahawalpur) and of its continuation in the Indus, rolling sand plains with hummocky dunes and clayey depressions limit the penetration by canal-based agriculture. Parts of the Thal have been levelled for canal irrigation from the Jinnah Barrage at Kalabagh, and individual enterprise has introduced tube well irrigation into some depressions. Much of the area remains the realm of pastoralists who graze their sheep, goats and camels on the desert flora and raise spasmodic rain-fed crops of *rabi* gram and *kharif* bajra or jowar. Such a way of life as this was widespread throughout the Indus Plains before the construction of canals. In the late nineteenth century 81 per cent of Tharparkar's cultivated area (in the far southeast corner of the country) was rain-fed. Now, 98 per cent is irrigated from canals bringing water almost 400 km from the Sukkur Barrage.

Another regional pattern is that of the rice growing districts in the *Lower Indus Plains* in Sind, already mentioned. The plains on the right bank of the Indus below Sukkur, extending into the Sibi embayment as the Kachhi Plain, are Pakistan's principal concentration of rice growing on account of the water-retentive soils and a tradition built up over a century of irrigation from inundation canals – now mostly transformed into perennial systems, with the completion of barrages at Sukkur, and more recently Gudu and Kotri (Ghulam Mohammed). Rice dominates the economy of this region to a much greater extent than in the Basmati rice growing areas of the northeast Punjab.

Throughout the Indus Plains in Punjab and Sind

60 A flat roofed tightly nucleated village in inner Gilgit, with its terraced fields used to grow maize in summer, wheat and mustard in winter. On the far slope unstable screes make hazardous the maintenance of a water channel taking off from the stream in the distance. Note the poor vegetation cover including stunted pines, in the foreground.
(Courtesy Elizabeth Staley).

there is a sameness in *rabi* cropping – wheat, gram, the oilseeds, mustard and rape and fodder being the common denominators. There is more variety in *kharif* cropping. Cotton, rice and sugar cane, depending on local soils, are the cash crops, all needing irrigation, with jowar and bajra as coarse grains not so demanding of water. Fodder crops (often berseem, one of the lucerne group of leguminous plants) are irrigated for multiple cutting to feed draft animals, bullocks and buffaloes, horses and donkeys, on the farm and in the towns.

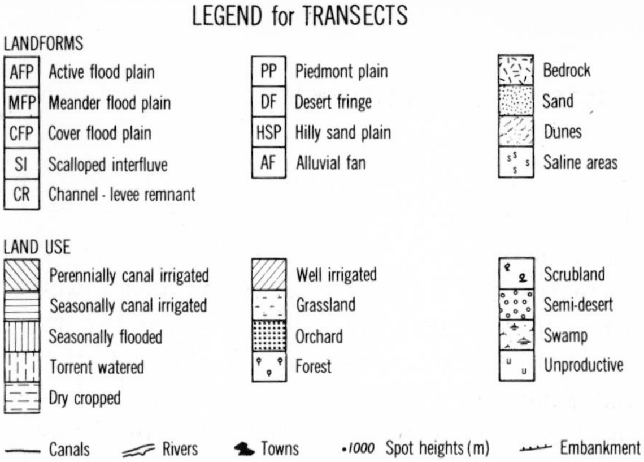
LEGEND for TRANSECTS
LANDFORMS
AFP Active flood plain
MFP Meander flood plain
CFP Cover flood plain
SI Scalloped interfluve
CR Channel - levee remnant
PP Piedmont plain
DF Desert fringe
HSP Hilly sand plain
AF Alluvial fan
Bedrock
Sand
Dunes
Saline areas
LAND USE
Perennially canal irrigated
Seasonally canal irrigated
Seasonally flooded
Torrent watered
Dry cropped
Well irrigated
Grassland
Orchard
Forest
Scrubland
Semi-desert
Swamp
Unproductive
Canals
Rivers
Towns
•1000 Spot heights (m)
Embankment

Fig. 12.18

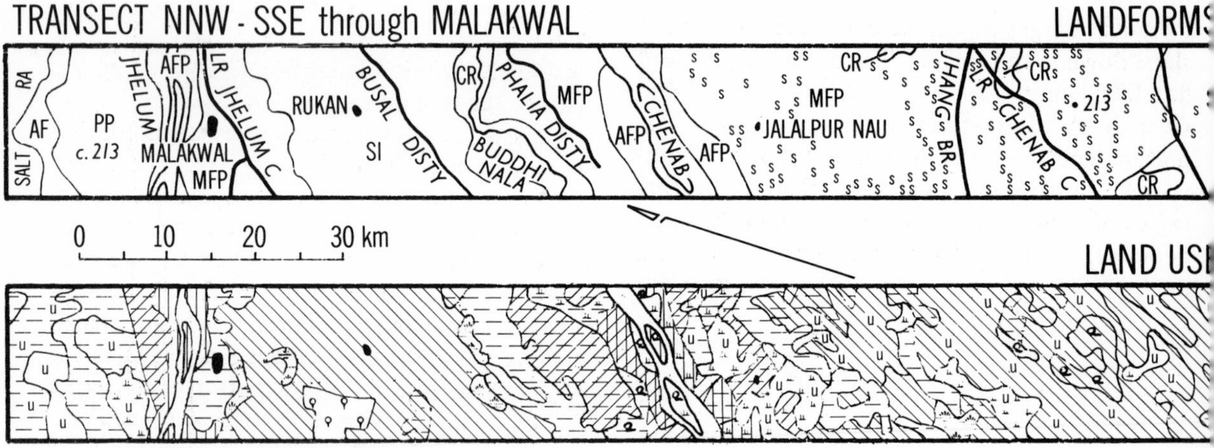
TRANSECT NNW - SSE through MALAKWAL
LANDFORMS
SALT RA
AF
PP
c. 213
JHELUM
AFP
MALAKWAL
MFP
LR JHELUM C
RUKAN
SI
BUSAL DISTY
CR
PHALIA DISTY
BUDDHI NALA
MFP
AFP
CHENAB
AFP
MFP
JALALPUR NAU
CR
JHANG BR
LR CHENAB C
CR
213
CR
0 10 20 30 km
LAND USE

Fig. 12.19

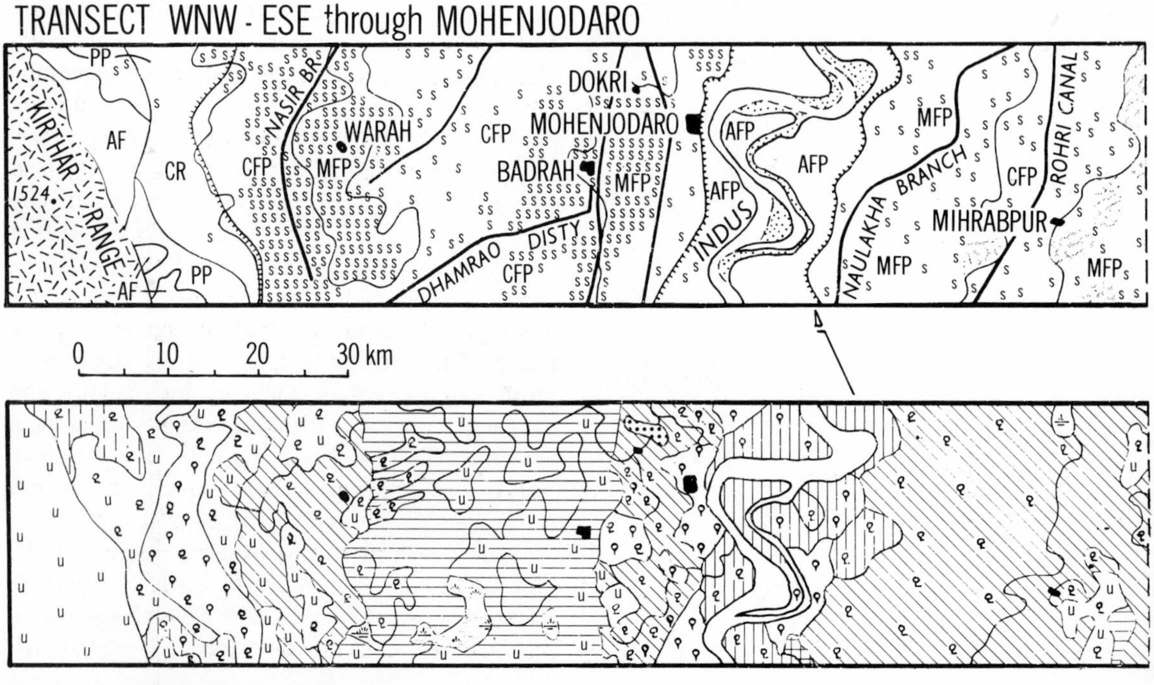
TRANSECT WNW - ESE through MOHENJODARO
PP
KIRTHAR RANGE
1524
AF
CR
PP
AF
CFP
NASIR BR
WARAH
MFP
CFP
DOKRI
MOHENJODARO
BADRAH
MFP
DHAMRAO DISTY
CFP
AFP
AFP
INDUS
AFP
MFP
NAULAKHA BRANCH
CFP
ROHRI CANAL
MIHRABPUR
MFP
MFP
0 10 20 30 km

Characteristic Transects

Within the plains the morphological elements are the basis of some variety in land use, best illustrated by reference to two characteristic transects, one across the central Punjab from the Salt Range across the Jhelum and Chenab Rivers and another across the Indus downstream of Sukkur in Larkana and Khairpur. Figure 12.18 shows the landforms and land uses associated with them in the Central Punjab. At the foot of the Salt Range scarp a belt of coarse gravel fans, much cut into gullies by torrents, merges into a piedmont plain of gentler slope down to the Jhelum. The classic sequence of floodplain units is seen between the Jhelum and Chenab. A narrow, active floodplain along the present course of the Jhelum is followed southwards by a strip of meander floodplain still bearing traces of former meander scrolls and backswamp depressions. The oldest river terrace element, dubbed the scalloped interfluve by geomorphologists because of the characteristic line of its margins, presents a degraded bluff to the meander floodplain below it. To the south, this bluff is

enhanced by the channel levee remnant at its foot, a pronounced depression with sandy rises along old levees with marshy stretches. A strip of meander floodplain and the active floodplain along the Chenab complete the symmetry of the interfluve, the Chaj or Jech Doab. Beyond the Chenab the pattern repeats itself in the Rech Doab between the Chenab and Ravi Rivers.

The gravel fans at the foot of the Salt Range are of little use because of their rugged surface into which water soon disappears. The piedmont plain is better favoured as wells here can easily reach groundwater to irrigate *rabi* wheat and tobacco, *kharif* millets, cotton, sugar cane and vegetables. Within the active floodplain of the Jhelum, sandy banks can be irrigated during the *rabi* season to grow wheat, but are awash during *kharif*. Immediately south of the river the Lower Jhelum Canal commands the meander floodplain. It is nominally perennial, but as demand exceeds supply in *rabi*, supplementary well irrigation is common. Wheat, oilseeds, gram and fodder berseem are grown in *rabi*; cotton, jowar and maize in *kharif*. On the low sandy ridges near Malakwal above the reach of irrigation, rain-fed *rabi* wheat and gram are the only crops. On the scalloped interfluve, the Kirara *bar* lands, a similar canal commanded cropping system is found, with extensive irrigated reserved forest in addition. Further over, below the bar lands, the meander floodplain and channel levee remnant provide a more complex environment. The highest levels, generally sandy in texture, grow rain-fed wheat and gram or are left in scrub. Depressions are severely waterlogged, supporting at best rice – as the crop most tolerant of the saline condition – some wheat and much scrub. Between these extremes inundation canal irrigated intermediate levels grow millets, cotton and rice while water is plentiful, and *rabi* wheat on land pre-watered at the end of the *kharif*. The active floodplain of the Chenab is more extensive than that of the Jhelum, and its floods are too strong to allow permanent structures like wells close to its changing bed. *Rabi* wheat and pulses grow on the shoals, but much is left in scrub and clumps of tough grass.

Almost a third of this transect consists of the Hafizabad Plain, a meander floodplain commanded by the Lower Chenab Canal System. The region has suffered extreme deterioration in product-

LANDFORMS

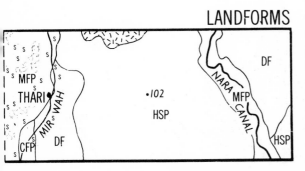

LAND USE

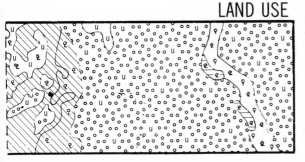

ivity owing to salinity and water-logging and reclamation now proceeds. Cropping patterns are as in the Lower Jhelum Canal Command.

The transect in *Larkana and Khairpur* Districts (Fig. 12.19) extends from a narrow belt of alluvial fans and piedmont plain at the foot of the Kirthar Range across a former channel remnant of the Indus onto a broader plain, which descends gently to the Indus through elements of decreasing age: cover floodplain, meander and active floodplain. In this lower section of the Indus system the scalloped interfluve is absent. On the cover floodplain, soil wash has obliterated the relief features of former river activity still apparent on the meander floodplain, though it can still be traced in the soil patterns. On the eastern side of the Indus the sequence of features is repeated, with aeolian influence an additional factor, this becoming more pronounced towards the margins of the Thar Desert. The Nara tract, now occupied by a canal, is another former channel of the Indus, its sandy alluvium reworked by wind into dunes separated by *patti* depressions.

Two major areas of unproductive land mark both ends of this transect, the rocky Kirthar Hills in the west, the hilly sand plains and desert fringe to the east, into which penetrates the southern tip of the rocky Rohri ridge. These tracts provide sparse forage for goats, sheep and camels. Grazing is better in the channel remnant depression where torrent water accumulates and is restrained by an embankment from flowing over the well-ordered fields of the cover floodplain. *Kharif* millets are grown on the better parts of the alluvial fans. The cover floodplain west of Warah is severely afflicted by salinity and water-logging, and much land has been lost to agriculture. Where irrigation is perennial, there are more *rabi* crops – wheat, pulses and oilseeds – than *kharif* rice, but the position is reversed under seasonal inundation irrigation. Nearer the Indus, salinity is less of a problem though some depressions are water-logged. The active floodplain of the Indus is too deeply awash to be used in summer, but in *rabi* channel diversion and the raising of water from channels by Persian wheels or low lift mechanical pumps supports the usual crops. Considerable areas of reserved forest grow shisham, tamarisk and acacia to provide firewood for the towns. East of the Indus the pattern is repeated, but salinity and water-logging are insignificant.

61 A bullock team, Dhanni breed, levelling with a board on which the driver stands. A crop of maize has been drilled in the furrows. A walled village may be seen in the background. A scene in late winter on the Maize and Millets Research Farm, Pirsabak, in the Vale of Peshawar.

Chapter 13

Pakistan: Industry and Urbanisation

Industrial Resources

Agricultural land, water and a warm climate are Pakistan's main natural resources, directly supporting a large proportion of the population as farmers. Before being used for irrigation, some of the water is harnessed to produce hydro-electricity. The rocks of the country contain large reserves of natural gas and some liquid petroleum, and there is some coal. Limestone and rock salt are reasonably abundant, and valuable deposits of chromite have long been mined for export. Copper ores are now being developed, and there are known deposits of rock phosphate. The iron ores of good quality so far discovered are inaccessible and small in volume.

The products of agriculture then are the main basis for industrial development. Most agricultural raw materials have to be processed into a form suitable either for consumption, export or further manufacture into useful articles, so there is a wide range of processing industries: flour and rice mills, cotton ginneries, oil mills, sugar mills, leather tanneries. Secondary manufacturing is dominated by the cotton textile industry, through which much foreign exchange is earned by exporting the value added by making yarn and cloth, rather than the raw cotton. Similarly leather goods are exported, rather than raw hides and skins, and represent a better income for Pakistan's workforce.

Another group of industries supports the economy by producing substitutes for manufactures previously imported, and there is plenty of scope for further development in this area using, if necessary, imported raw or semi-processed materials to be worked up or assembled by Pakistani labour.

Natural Gas

Natural gas has been an enormous boon to Pakis-tan, and now tops the list of energy sources with 38 per cent of the total. The Sui field in Sibi District leads in production, the gas being piped the length of the country, to Lahore and Peshawar in the north, Karachi in the south. Other fields are near Karachi — the Sari – Hundi and the Mari fields to the east of the Indus opposite Sui and in the Potwar Plateau (Fig. 13.1). Current production is 15.9 million m^3 per day, 5,819 million m^3 annually, (82 per cent from Sui) equivalent to about 6.8 million tonnes of furnace oil. The gas is used to produce electricity (34 per cent of production), as a feedstock for the fertiliser industry (18 per cent), in the cement industry (13 per cent), as well as in general industry (27 per cent) and for domestic (5 per cent) and commercial uses (3 per cent).

Fig. 13.1

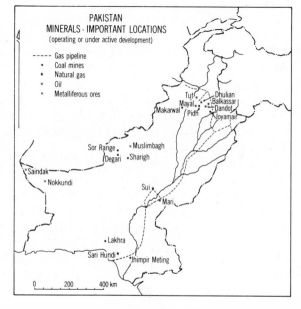

PAKISTAN
MINERALS · IMPORTANT LOCATIONS
(operating or under active development)

----- Gas pipeline
· Coal mines
* Natural gas
· Oil
× Metalliferous ores

Petroleum

Petroleum has long been obtained from wells in the Potwar Plateau, which provide 15 per cent of the country's needs. Significant expansion is expected by 1981 with the development of new structures at Dhodak. As Baluchistan is structurally continuous with Iran there are hopes that a major oil-field may some day be found there. Production is running at about 505,000 tonnes annually, and 4.6 million tonnes of crude have to be imported. The prospect of self-sufficiency during the 1980s is not unreasonable.

Hydro-electricity

Pakistan's well-watered northern mountains have considerable hydro-electric potential, some of which has been harnessed since Independence as a byproduct of creating storage dams for irrigation. By 1982, 2,500 MW will have been harnessed, and on completion of the Tarbela Project a total of 3,550 MW will be available out of a reasonably accessible potential of 10,000 MW. The major stations are shown in Table 13.1. Several small stations use the fall in canals in NWFP and the Punjab, but none exceed 20 MW. A very large proposed scheme under discussion would be located on the Jhelum in Pakistan-occupied Kashmir, where a minimum of 306 MW could be harnessed, and 3,760 at peak flow for a short period.

Coal

Coal output is about 1.1 million tonnes of mediocre quality. Coals of coking quality are lacking, though some are suitable for blending with imported coal for metallurgical use. The principal mines are near Quetta with smaller production from the Salt Range on both sides of the Indus. A lignite field just north of Hyderabad is being surveyed with the possibility in mind of supporting a thermal power station at Jamshoro.

Pakistan is moving towards a unified electricity grid to connect its scattered power resources with its population centres, themselves dispersed over great distances. Figure 13.2 shows the pattern of power generation and distribution. The major thermal generating stations are in Karachi (530 MW), Gudu (439 MW by 1980, gas based), Multan (265 MW, gas) and Faisalabad (332 MW, gas and gas turbine). A nuclear power station yields 100

MW at Karachi, and another is planned for Chasma to produce 600 MW There are several smaller thermal power stations in Lahore, Sukkur and Hyderabad.

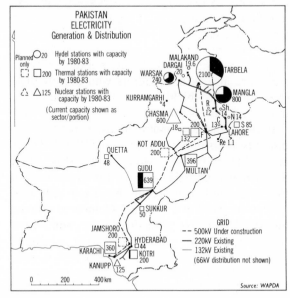

Fig. 13.2

Mineral resources

Mineral resources apart from energy sources are located in Baluchistan and the Salt Range. Chromite is mined near Quetta, 11,000 tonnes in 1977–78, but 23,000 tonnes when demand warrants. Copper is being developed at Saindak in the remote Chagai District in the west of Baluchistan, in deposits thought capable of producing 15,000 tonnes annually, of blister copper. Rock salt is mined in the Salt Range near Khewra west of the Indus, and at Kalabagh and Warcha along the scarp face east of the river. 439,000 tonnes were mined in 1977–78. Salt is also obtained by evaporating sea water near Karachi, 224,000 tonnes in the same year.

Table 13.1　Hydroelectric power stations

Installed capacity in MW	1979	Total after full development
Warsak, on the Kabul River	160	240
Mangla, on the Jhelum	600	800
Tarbela, on the Indus	700	2,000

Manufacturing Industry

Like most underdeveloped countries, Pakistan shows in its industrial structure the workings of a dual economy. There is a strong substructure of rural and urban craft industries carrying on traditional manufacture of homespun and woven fabrics in cotton, wool and silk, of carpets, footwear, pottery, ropes and cord, and products in wood, cane and metal. Many workers in these crafts are also farm labourers who occupy their spare time, of which there is often all too much, in making articles for sale, barter or home use.

Formal modern manufacturing industry as officially measured employs over 550,000, 39 per cent of them in the textile industry (Fig. 13.3). Seven industrial cities account for 69 per cent of this total, and their details by major industrial groups are given in Table 13.2. Compared with the industrial structure of a developed country, the trades associated with engineering, electrical goods and vehicles are very poorly represented.

62 Tractor delivering sacks of grain for weighing at a collecting centre in a Thal village. Men on the charpoy, goats on the ground take their ease. Flat roofed mud houses without windows are the rule.

Under the 1972 legislation nationalising the basic industries, ten impressive-sounding corporations were put in charge of chemicals, ceramics, fertilisers, light engineering, automobiles, cement, machine tools and heavy engineering, petroleum refining and petrochemicals, and the Pakistan Steel Mill. There was not a great deal to nationalise

Fig. 13.3

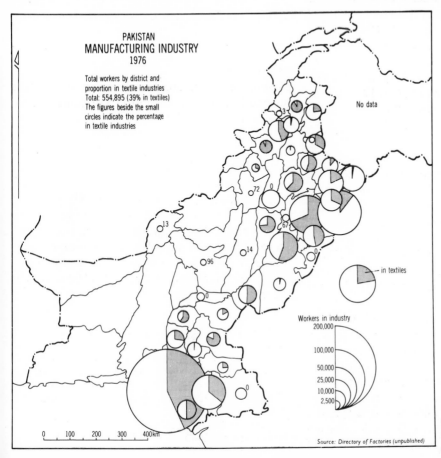

PAKISTAN
MANUFACTURING INDUSTRY
1976

Total workers by district and
proportion in textile industries
Total: 554,895 (39% in textiles)
The figures beside the small
circles indicate the percentage
in textile industries

No data

in textiles

Workers in industry
200,000
100,000
50,000
25,000
10,000
2,500

0   100   200   300   400 km

Source: Directory of Factories (unpublished)

Table 13.2 Major industrial groups in seven major industrial cities, 1976 (thousands employed and percentage)

Industrial group	Karachi	%	Lahore	%	Faisalabad	%	Hyderabad	%	Multan	%	Sialkot	%	Gujranwala	%	% of total for these cities
Food and drink	18.0	9.3	2.9	5.3	6.1	15.7	3.4	10.2	2.9	11.8	0.1	0.5	2.1	12.6	9.3
Tobacco	3.6	1.9	0.2	0.4	—	—	13.0	39.0	—	—	—	—	—	—	4.4
Textiles and carpets	83.6	43.0	6.2	11.2	26.9	69.5	12.2	36.4	13.6	55.7	0.3	2.0	3.3	19.2	38.4
Leather	2.7	1.4	0.5	0.9	—	—	0.4	1.0	0.5	1.9	t	0.3	0.1	0.7	1.1
Footwear	1.4	0.7	1.7	3.0	0.3	0.6	0.3	0.9	—	—	0.3	1.6	—	—	1.0
Woodworking	1.3	0.7	0.7	1.3	0.2	0.6	t	t	t	t	—	—	0.1	0.5	0.7
Printing, etc.	6.0	3.1	2.8	5.1	0.9	2.3	0.2	0.4	t	0.1	—	—	—	—	2.4
Medical, chemical	8.0	4.1	3.1	5.7	0.1	0.3	0.1	0.2	1.5	6.3	—	—	0.1	0.5	3.6
Rubber	3.4	1.8	1.8	3.3	0.3	0.7	—	—	—	—	0.3	1.7	0.3	1.7	1.6
Iron and Steel, foundries rolling mills	10.3	5.3	8.8	16.0	0.3	0.7	t	0.1	t	0.2	t	0.2	0.5	2.9	5.4
Metal working	10.0	5.2	1.8	3.2	t	t	0.1	0.2	0.4	1.6	1.8	10.1	6.4	37.4	5.4
Engineering	3.5	1.8	5.7	10.3	2.9	7.4	0.2	0.5	0.4	1.6	0.6	3.5	1.5	8.7	3.9
Electrical goods	4.5	2.3	6.0	11.0	t	0.1	0.1	0.3	—	—	t	t	1.8	10.4	3.4
Transport equipment	10.1	5.2	4.8	8.8	t	t	t	0.1	0.1	0.3	0.1	0.5	0.2	1.2	4.1
Precision equipment	1.1	0.6	0.7	1.3	t	0.1	—	—	—	—	3.1	18.0	—	—	1.3
Other specialities	—	—	—	—	—	—	—	—	4.5	18.4*	1.0	5.5†	—	—	1.4
TOTAL (incl. others)	194.5	100.0	55.0	100.0	38.8	100.0	33.4	100	24.4	100.0	17.4	100.0	17.0	100.0	100.0

*Cotton ginning; † sports equipment
Note: t < 0.1% or < 0.1 total

Table 13.3   Manufacturing industries, output 1971–72, 1975–76, and 1977–78

Item	Unit	*1971–72*	*1975–76*	*1977–78*
Cotton yarn	Thousand tonnes	336	350	298
Cotton cloth	Million m²	628	520	391
Jute textiles	Thousand tonnes	30	42	33
Mild steel products	Thousand tonnes	166	231	315
Cement	Thousand Tonnes	2,876	3,093	3,324
Particle board (straw, paper, chip)	Thousand tonnes	38	21	22
Paper	Thousand tonnes	27	23	22
Fans	Thousands	223	148	185
Electric bulbs	Millions	11	17	18
Gramophone records	Thousands	999	1,082	n.a.
Bicycles	Thousands	212	211	245
Sewing machines	Thousands	66	64	62
Cycle tyres	Thousands	2,542	3,180	3,392
Motor tyres	Thousands	100	166	182
Sea salt	Thousand tonnes	240	151	224
Sugar	Thousand tonnes	375	630	856
Cigarettes	Thousand millions	28	27	31
Fertilisers	Thousand tonnes	573	833*	810
Soda ash	Thousand tonnes	77	79	69
Caustic soda	Thousand tonnes	34	38	35
Sulphuric acid	Thousand tonnes	35	46	52
Paint	Thousand litres	5,983	7,128	7,924

*Urea 595, superphosphate 75, ammonium sulphate 96, ammonium nitrate 47 (all thousand tonnes)
Source: Monthly Statistical Bulletin, May–June 1977 *Pakistan Economic Survey*, 1978–79.

at that time, and subsequent development has been slight apart from the fertiliser industry. Denationalisation is now in train for some industries. An idea of the range and scale of industry is given in Table 13.3 which shows the latest production figures (1977–78).

The pattern of industrial distribution is bipolar (Fig. 13.3) with Karachi, supported by Hyderabad, very dominant at the southern end of the pole, and a more even spread of workers among the northern towns, where Lahore is the largest, Faisalabad not far behind, and Multan, Sialkot and Gujranwala each with more than 17,000 employees. Twelve other districts in the north have 5,000 or more while in Sind only four others exceed this level.

Karachi is by far the largest centre for manufacturing, heavily dominated by textiles but overshadowing the other cities in most fields, except engineering and electrical goods in which Lahore leads. The latter has the most balanced industrial structure of all seven cities tabulated in Table 13.2. The smaller cities tend to be dominated by one or two industries, textiles in Faisalabad and Multan, tobacco and textiles in Hyderabad, metal working

63   The village potter puts a finishing touch to bowls being sun-dried before firing. Photograph taken in a Rajput (Hindu) village at Chhor on the Pakistan side of the border with India on the edge of the Thar Desert.

64 Developing a natural gas well near Sui, Baluchistan. Petroleum gas is Pakistan's major mineral resource.
(Courtesy Govt. of Pakistan)

in Gujranwala (noted for agricultural machinery) and precision equipment (surgical instruments) in Sialkot.

Some of the major projects currently in hand merit mention. Several fertiliser plants are under construction, to use natural gas as raw material. Pak-Saudi Fertilisers at Mirpur Mathelo in Sind, and Pak-Arab Fertilisers in Multan are being financed with help from fellow Muslim countries in the Middle East. A Pak-Iran Cement factory at Kohat is being added to several already in production in the north, centre and south of the country. Iran is helping with two textile plants at Las Bela and Bolan in Baluchistan, and the Chinese with a yarn mill to be built at Tarbela. In heavy

industry Pakistan already has a machine tools factory at Taxila, where the Chinese are building a heavy foundry and forge. At Pipri, just east of Karachi, the USSR is building the Karachi Steel Mill to make over 1 million tonnes of steel by 1983–84 using imported ore and coal, the latter blended with coal from near Quetta.

Population distribution

Population distribution in 1972, based on tehsil data, is mapped in Figure 13.4. The highest densities are associated with the urbanised areas. Densities in excess of 200 per km² are found in the long established irrigated tracts of the Punjab, in a triangular region with its base on the piedmont border with Kashmir and its apex at Multan. Separated from it by one of lower density in the Potwar country of Jhelum District, a belt of similarly high density extends from Rawalpindi through to Peshawar. In Sind a few patches with over 200 per km² stand out along the Indus, but in general densities here are lower: less than 200 on the left bank and less than 100 or even 50 on the right bank. Towards the Thar Desert densities fall both here and in the Punjab. Similar deterioration occurs in Thal and in the trans-Indus piedmont. The extreme emptiness of Baluchistan is clearly indicated, the areas with over 6 per km² being associated with urban centres, mining development and better

Fig. 13.4

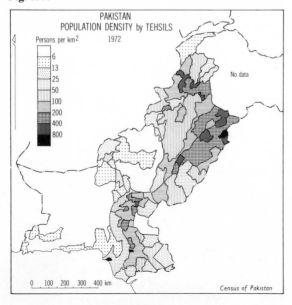

Fig. 13.5

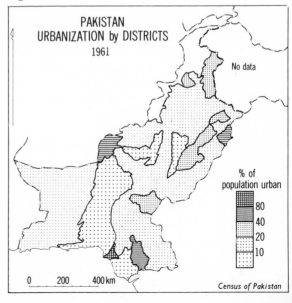

communications. Thus Las Bela lies in the economic sphere of Karachi, and the tehsils adjacent to Quetta are, relatively, better populated. The moderate densities of some tehsils in the Tribal Areas of NWFP are a reminder of that region's severe overpopulation in relation to its resources.

Urbanisation

Urbanisation by 1972 had brought 26.3 per cent of the population to be living in towns, a proportion well above that in India or Bangladesh. As Figure 13.5 shows, however, only 9 of the 45 districts mapped exceeded the average level for the country as a whole, indicating that a few large cities are responsible for the national level being as high as it is. Some data on urban centres are set out in Table 13.4.

The towns of over 100,000 are mapped and named in Figure 13.6. They all lie east of the Indus apart from Quetta, Mardan and Peshawar. The fortunes of the Wah and Rawalpindi – Islamabad group are tied to the latter's role as the country's capital city, still under construction. Karachi, the former capital and the only port, is the largest city, with 3.61 million people. The remaining cities are all associated with the canal irrigated Punjab and Sind and reflect the distribution of the population in general. Lahore (2.17 million) is the only other millionaire city and is studied in some detail in Chapter 24.

65 These girls in a refugee colony in Karachi are unlikely to appear in the occupational statistics. They are making paper bags for groceries out of old cement bags and glue.

Fig. 13.6

Table 13.4 Urban centres, 1972

Size class	Over 500,000	100,000– 499,999	50,000– 99,999	20,000– 49,999	Total
No. of towns	6	14	18	69	107
Population (millions)	8.379	2.253	1.274	2.136	14.042
Percentage of the urban population	60	16	9	15	100

Note: These data ignore the towns of less than 20,000 the total population of which exceeded that of the larger towns

Chapter 14

Bangladesh: A New Nation

Political Antecedents

The stresses and strains which in 1971 culminated in the failure and collapse of the political structure that was Pakistan were deep-seated. The appearance of a new country, Bangladesh, was one of a series of nationalistic ferments in the subcontinent. India also has been subject to several painful convulsions as the demand for self-determination by linguistic 'nations' has been conceded, with the establishment of States based upon a measure of linguistic homogeneity.

The tragedy of Bangladesh – the two dozen years of relative neglect which left the country at Independence as probably the poorest nation in the world – was that Muslim Bengalis were persuaded in the 1940s to seek independence of British rule and at the same time a guarantee of relief from Hindu Bengal economic domination, through the idea of a single Muslim nation, Pakistan. Religion in its negative aspects, specifically anti-Hindu prejudices, was the sole basis of unity in Pakistan.

Islam came to Bengal with the Moghuls who, in the process of establishing their political control over the Ganges* Plains, converted many Bengalis from both Hinduism and Buddhism. They also introduced Urdu, the language of the Delhi court, while Bengali continued as the vernacular. With the arrival of the East India Company, Moghul power declined and the commercially astute Hindus prospered in the new environment. To the poor peasant and Muslim tenant the Hindu landlord, merchant and moneylender, often combined in a single person, might well have been a man to fear and resent. It is not surprising therefore that as the prospects for self-determination

*In Bangladesh, the anglicised form Ganges is retained for the Ganga

and independence from British rule grew, the mass of the Muslim people could be persuaded that a complete break from India with its Hindu majority was the only acceptable answer.

The act of Partition in 1947 established the

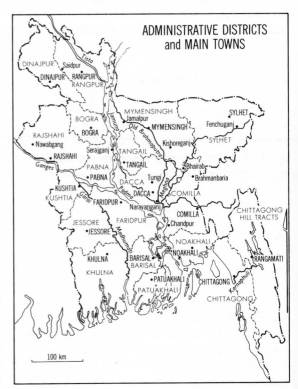

Fig. 14.1

frontiers of what is now Bangladesh (Fig. 14.1). The greater part of the old Province of Bengal, together with most of the Sylhet District, lying in the adjacent continuation of the delta plain into Assam to the northeast, became East Bengal, later

66 The interior of a jute mill making gunny for sacking.
(Courtesy Govt. of Pakistan).

called East Pakistan. In most of the area there was a clear Muslim majority, excepting Khulna (49.3 per cent) and Chittagong Hill Tracts (2.8 per cent Muslim). In the case of the Chittagong Hill Tracts the semi-tribal population was predominantly Buddhist, racially and culturally closer to the Burmese than to the plains Bengalis, and the area could hardly be administered effectively except through Chittagong.

Partition cut off Calcutta (23 per cent Muslim) from an important part of its economic hinterland, and when political relations became bad East Bengal was denied access to its traditional markets for raw jute. The population of the new East Bengal included almost 29 per cent Hindus, while 25 per cent of West Bengal's population was Muslim. It is some measure of the strength of the common Bengali cultural inheritance that partitioned Bengal saw relatively much less of the traumatic uprooting of refugees on either side that marked the partition of the Punjab.

One linguistic minority group that migrated to East Pakistan at the time of Partition were the Biharis, who by 1971 numbered about 400,000. As Urdu speakers many of them were understandably sympathetic to West Pakistani interests and were viewed with suspicion by the Bengali-speaking majority during the civil war that followed the declaration of Bangladeshi Independence in 1971.

From the start, disunity within Pakistan was apparent. The West Pakistani tended to look down on the Bengali as a 'second class Muslim', descendant of converts, and so not in the same direct line of religious purity as those who could look back to ancestors who brought Islam to the country. Furthermore the West Pakistanis, more specifically the Punjabi Muslims, could see themselves as direct heirs to the ruling tradition of the Moghul Empire in which of course Bengal had been a subjugated territory. Under the British, Punjabis formed the élite fighting troops of the Indian Army while Bengalis were regarded as a nonmartial people suitable at best for employment as clerks.

Thus there were deep-seated cultural prejudices current at the birth of Pakistan. The Bengalis were justly proud of a rich linguistic heritage. They were democratic in politics, resentful of oppression from landlord or government, and without any tradition of militant nationalism. To a considerable extent the Muslim Bengali maintained loyalty to a wider Bengali cultural nationalism that transcended the religious differences between Hindu and Muslim. At the village level there was much interweaving of the cultural strands and, usually, mutual respect for religious observances of others.

The Bengali's sense of democracy and pride in his culture was soon affronted by the manifestation of West Pakistani attitudes, which may be summed up in a determination not to allow the greater numbers of the population of East Pakistan ever to achieve political domination in the Pakistan state. The realities of the situation became evident within a year of independence when Punjabis promoted a policy to proclaim Urdu alone as the national language of Pakistan. The intention to implement his policy was announced in Dacca by Jinnah, the acknowledged father of the Pakistani nation, and provoked immediate hostile reaction from the Bengalis, and ultimately Bengali was accepted as a national language on an equal footing with Urdu.

However, although the Bengalis showed they could not be bullied into submission on cultural matters, they were to remain politically underprivileged and economically subservient in undivided Pakistan. This did not end the feelings of resentment on the part of Bengalis about the economic domination of their province by the West Pakistanis, and their feeling of colonial status. Repeated demands were made for measures of regional autonomy, and for a fairer share of investment in development. The standard of living in West Pakistan was estimated to be 60 per cent higher than in East Pakistan, largely on account of the much greater government expenditure in that wing. Bengalis felt discriminated against in job opportunities and training, and the long periods of quasimilitary dictatorship stopped up the safety valve of parliamentary democracy.

Despite the absence of truly democratic government in Pakistan the pressures for East Bengal autonomy grew, and the Central Government began belatedly to plan for a more equitable distribution of resources for development. After years of dictatorship and the experiment with 'basic democracy' which denied the public a direct vote except at the local government level, general elections on the basis of universal adult suffrage were held in December 1970. In East Pakistan the result of the elections was a landslide victory for the Awami League led by Sheikh Mujibur Rahman, whose party gained an absolute majority in the Pakistan National Assembly of 313 seats by winning 167 seats. Mujibur Rahman's election platform had been his 'six points' including: a federal system of government with the centre responsible only for foreign policy and defence; a separate economic policy for East Pakistan, allowing it to receive its proportionate share of foreign exchange earnings; its own militia, military academy and ordnance factory; and the establishment of the Pakistan Naval Headquarters in the East wing.

The fundamental issue from which stemmed the chain of events which produced the civil war and the mass migration of millions of refugees to India, and ultimately India's intervention to force a military settlement, was Mujibur Rahman's demand that his electoral victory entitled his party to confirm in the National Assembly his 'six points' as the basis for the new constitution which had been promised by the President. President Yahya Khan and Mr. Bhutto, leader of the majority party in West Pakistan, refused to accept this claim, saying that the constitution had to be agreed by the governments of each wing and not by a simple majority of the National Assembly. For Sheikh Mujibur Rahman this refusal could be seen as the last straw in a decade of denials of Bengali self-determination. On 26 March 1971, following the brutal 'crack-down' by the army at midnight on 25/26 March, the Independence of Bangladesh was proclaimed and the struggle became a civil war, terminating in victory in December, after the '14-day war', in which Indian military help was a decisive factor.

The People

The population was estimated at 89 million in 1980, increasing annually at more than 2.5 per cent. Muslims now account for 85.4 per cent of the total. Many of the Hindu refugees who fled to India in 1971 presumably decided not to return, with the result that the Hindu minority diminished from almost 20 per cent in 1961 to less than 14 per cent in 1974. Other religions make up only 1.1 per cent. Linguistically the population is overwhelmingly Bengali-speaking, 98.85 per cent. Tribal languages are spoken by 0.6 per cent, Urdu by 0.25 per cent.

The age structure of the population indicates a very high dependency ratio, 100 in the 15–64 age range supporting 106 below 15 and over 64. 48.6 per cent are under 15, and one-sixth under 5 years old. Despite a relatively high level of literacy, the birth rate has not yet been substantially affected by family planning propaganda. Literacy rates are shown in Table 14.1.

Table 14.1   Per cent literacy (in population aged 5 and over)

	Bangladesh	Urban	Rural
Both sexes	24.3	44.0	22.3
Males	32.9	52.0	30.8
Females	14.8	33.3	13.2

Note: Urban literacy rates are double rural, but as yet only 8.8 per cent live in towns.

Table 14.2   Occupations of the economically active (per cent of total)

Occupation	Bangladesh	Male	Female
Professional and technical	1.8	1.8	2.5
Administration, management	0.2	0.2	0.1
Clerical	1.0	1.0	0.3
Sales	4.6	4.7	1.3
Services	1.9	1.5	10.3
Agriculture	77.2	77.5	69.8
Production and transport	10.9	10.9	12.2
Not classified, out of work	2.4	2.4	3.6
Total	100	100	100
Millions	20.5	19.7	0.87

It is probable that the 1974 Census understates the number of women, for the same reason as reported in Pakistan. Overall, the number of women per 1,000 males is 925, in rural areas 943 and in urban 775. The larger cities where industry is concentrated, attracting male workers, have lower ratios still: Dacca 725, Chittagong 664, Khulna 748 and Narayanganj 760.

The occupational structure is given in Table 14.2. The very low figure for women should be noted, though many more will help their husbands informally.

Table 14.3 breaks the same totals down into more specific categories of employment.

Table 14.3 Categories of employment (per cent of total)

	Total	Male	Female
Agriculture	77.1	77.4	70.0
Mining	t	t	t
Manufacturing	4.6	4.6	4.2
Electricity, gas, water	t	t	t
Construction	0.02	0.02	–
Wholesale/retail	3.8	3.9	1.0
Transport, storage	1.6	1.6	0.2
Finance, commerce	0.3	0.3	0.1
Social services	10.0	9.6	20.9
Not classified, out of work	2.4	2.4	3.6

67 Farmers bring milk to be measured at a co-operative collecting centre near Tangail. Note the small quantities delivered: most farmers have only one or two cows. The milk goes to Dacca by truck.

Structure of the Economy

The strong predominance of agriculture is reflected in the structure of the Gross Domestic Product, though the value added by labour in non-agricultural activities is clearly higher per head than in agriculture. Table 14.4 shows the sectoral contribution to GDP in 1978–79 when the total value was Taka 63,360 million at 1972–73 factor cost. Per capita income at constant factor prices 1972–73 has been rising following the initial severe setback immediately following Independence. In Table 14.5 per capita income is based on Gross Domestic Product.

Table 14.4 Gross Domestic Product, 1978–79 (per cent of total)

Agriculture	55.2
Industry	8.8
Construction	5.0
Power, gas, water	0.8
Transport	5.4
Trade	7.4
House services	4.7
Public administration, defence	5.8
Banking, insurance	0.8
Professional, miscellaneous	6.2
Gross Domestic Product	100.0
Population	86.9 million
Per capita income	729.0 Taka

Source: Bangladesh Economic Survey 1978–79

Table 14.5 Per capita income (GDP)

1969–70	770
1972–73	612
1974–75	647
1976–77	682
1977–78	712
1978–79	729

Table 14.6 Exports, 1977–78 (million Taka and per cent of total)

Raw jute, mesta	1,454	19.6
Jute manufactures	3,735	50.4
Leather	693	9.4
Tea	679	9.2
Fish, etc.	296	4.0
Paper, board	110	1.5
Spices	21	0.3
Other	418	5.6
TOTAL	7,406	100.0

Source: Bangladesh Economic Survey 1978–79

68 The modern mosque in central Dacca epitomises the State religion of Muslim Bangladesh. Cycle rickshaws are still the most common means of public conveyance.

With both primary agricultural activity and the major industry – jute textile manufacture – linked to local factors, particularly flooding, the economy is liable to fluctuations quite apart from those due to the state of world markets. More than two-thirds of exports are of jute and jute goods, while imports are headed by food and petroleum, as Tables 14.6 and 14.7 shows.

It will be noted that exports fall short of imports by Tk 10,810 million, or 59 per cent of the cost of imports. Foreign aid is of vital importance. The excessive dependence on jute, a fibre for which there are competitive synthetic and natural substitutes, puts the economy of Bangladesh in jeopardy. While the land that grows jute might equally grow rice and so reduce the need to import foodgrains, there still remains the problem of what alternative there may be to jute in the export economy, without which the prospect of mere subsistence based on paddy is grim indeed.

The future for raw and manufactured jute on world markets is as problematical as that of natural rubber. Much will depend on the ability of producers to deliver high quality jute at low cost. In this, varietal research for high-yielding strains and agronomic research to establish the best ways of cultivating efficiently are necessary. If costs cannot be kept low, and if supplies of given quality cannot be guaranteed, the sophisticated industries now using the best jute will turn to synthetic alternatives. In 1966–68, before the rift with Pakistan, Bangladesh produced a third of the world's natural jute and allied fibres, and accounted for almost half of the world export trade in raw

and manufactured jute. India was close behind with 32 per cent production and 34 per cent of trade. About half of Bangladesh's jute production is exported raw after being sorted, baled and pressed at Narayanganj or Khulna.

The remainder goes to local industry which exports over 90 per cent of the goods manufactured. The upset of commerce during the war, followed by uncertainties and the nationalisation of trade, have hit the jute exports severely. In 1972–73, only 3.5 million bales of jute were exported of a total of 6.5 million produced, leaving an embarrassingly

Table 14.7 Imports, 1977–78 (million Taka and per cent of total)

			%
Food and live animals	4,728		26.0
Wheat		2,805	15.4
Rice		1,108	6.1
Other		816	4.5
Beverages and tobacco	48		0.3
Animal and vegetable oils and fats	999		5.5
Crude inedible materials	1,900		10.4
Petroleum, etc.	2,665		14.6
Chemical, drugs	1,241		6.8
Machinery, transport equipment	2,911		16.0
Other manufactured goods	3,626		19.9
Other	98		0.5
TOTAL	18,216		100.0

Source: Bangladesh Economic Survey 1978–79

large carry-over of stocks. Raw jute production has fallen because of these uncertainties, averaging over the five-year period 1972–73 to 1976–77, 68 per cent of the year before Independence, 1969–70. On the other hand, manufactured jute exports have held up comparatively well, at 86 per cent of the 1969–70 level by volume. Table 14.8 shows the

Table 14.8 Raw and manufactured jute exports (thousand tonnes)

	Raw jute and mesta	Manufactured jute
1973–74	482.9	445.1
1974–75	281.0	384.7
1975–76	425.7	444.9
1976–77	412.9	456.3
1977–78	302.4	525.3
1978–79	399.1	472.4

Source: Bangladesh Economic Survey 1978–79

variation in raw and manufactured jute exports over the past six years.

Tea is likely to make a modest contribution to earnings but as with jute it will be necessary to keep costs of production down in order to meet competition. Current exports are 29.7 million kg. A relatively recently developed resource is natural gas which may be capable of supplying the country's major energy demands and a surplus for export.

The high level of foodgrain imports is economically very serious in a country so predominantly agricultural as Bangladesh. In the four years 1975–76 to 1978–79 it has been necessary to import 1.48 million, 0.83, 1.66 and 1.16 million tonnes of foodgrains respectively – or more than one-tenth of the country's total needs in some years. As in the other countries of South Asia, the most urgent problem is for agricultural productivity to overtake population increase.

Chapter 15

Bangladesh: An Amphibious Environment

The geography of Bangladesh is in large measure a function of its rivers. The country is well watered by rain, by South Asian standards, and its problems are more often a result of super-abundance of water than of rainfall deficiency. More than 90 per cent of the country is lowland. With the exception of the hill country of Chittagong and Sylhet, on the borders of Burma and northeastern India, Bangladesh is the alluvial gift of two major rivers, the Ganges (the Indian Ganga) and the Brahmaputra, and of a number of lesser rivers, notably the Surma and Kusiyara which unite in the Meghna, and the Tista (Fig. 15.1). Unlike the rivers of the Punjab and the upper Ganges Valley, which can be controlled by headworks constructed in solid rock foundations, the courses of the great rivers within Bangladesh lie in deep alluvium and carry such enormous quantities of water when in spate as to defy economic control to protect the delta against floods. Examined in detail many aspects of life in Bangladesh – agriculture, settlement, communications – reflect man's adaptation to the delta's amphibious environment, and his acceptance of the inevitability of flooding and fluvial change. Granted minimal prospects of controlling water within his environment, man has had to make the most of what nature has to offer. That nature has offered much is testified by the extremely high densities of population the country supports.

Physiographic Evolution

A first step to an understanding of Bangladesh's geography is an appreciation of the variety of its relief and soils. A deltaic river flows on an alluvial ridge of its own making, the highest parts of which are the *levees* immediately adjacent to the river's channel. From the levee crest the land slopes away gently into the lowest areas, the *backswamp depressions*. When in full flood the river overtops its levee. The rate of flow of water away from the main channel diminishes rapidly, and with it, its capacity to carry its load of suspended sand, silt and mud. Consequently, the coarsest part of the load is deposited first, hence the building of a levee which is invariably of coarser material than will be found in the backswamp area. The load carried by one river may well differ from that of another, and so the range of textures of the alluvial material making up its levee –backswamp varies. The general principle holds however, for every river at every scale within the delta plain. Backswamp depressions are generally areas of clays and fine silt; levees of sand and coarse silt. The slope between levee and backswamp may be termed the *floodland slope*.

Fig. 15.1

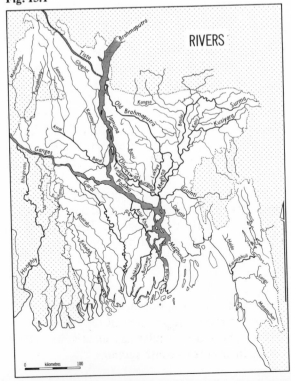

RIVERS

The whole delta plain is made up of these recurring elements, backswamp depressions and the levees forming their rims found at every scale, from a few metres across to tens of kilometres in extent. But not all such features in the present landscape are in a state of active evolution. Deltaic rivers flowing as they do on an alluvial ridge alter their courses from time to time, so gradually constructing their delta, and the surface details in any area may be in part the product of a past phase of river action. *Stabilised floodplains*, on which the meander belts of former channels can be picked out in old levees and whose courses and back-swamps may fill with water in the rainy season, are found particularly in the western part of the delta, in a region referred to as the Moribund Delta. The channels which traverse the Moribund Delta no longer carry much floodwater from the Ganges, which now discharges its main flow further east (Fig. 15.2).

Longer term geomorphological changes have also had a significant effect on the landscape. The Barind lying between the Ganges and the Jamuna (Brahmaputra), and the Madhupur Tract between the Jamuna and the Old Brahmaputra – Meghna, are usually referred to as areas of *old alluvium* and may be regarded as Pleistocene terraces of the present river systems. Smaller patches of similar age and material – lateritic, red, leached, silty clay-loams – occur in the Lalmai Hills close to Comilla and as a benchland formation fringing the hill country to the east of the plains.

If the old alluvial terraces may be regarded as corresponding to the *scalloped interfluves* of the plains of Pakistan, the *cover floodplain* has its equivalent in the Tippera Surface, intermediate in age between the Pleistocene and the present. Lying east of the Meghna, the Tippera Surface largely lacks the riverine morphological features such as abandoned meanders and levees that are clearly distinguishable in the younger parts of the delta plain.

Physiographic Regions

Physiographic regions provide a convenient and relevant framework within which to study agricultural development. Their boundaries are not always as clear cut, however, as Figure 15.2 suggests.

The hill country of Chittagong and the Chittagong Hill Tracts districts has its counterpart in Sylhet where the northern ends of hill ridges extending from the Indian area of Tripura project into the alluvial plain. In Sylhet the hills reach 336 m but ridges generally run at 60 – 90 m above sea level, and only 3 – 9 m above the plains. South and east the ranges are higher, culminating within Bangladesh in a peak of 955 m in the upper Sangu. The trend of the parallel ridges is roughly north – south and is picked out clearly in the pattern of subsequent drainage. A few major rivers traverse the ridges. Chief among them is the Karnaphuli which has headwaters in Mizoram and flows south-west across the grain of the country to enter the Bay of Bengal at Chittagong. The Feni River, Sangu, and Matamuhari have shorter transverse courses. All have important subsequent sections which make up a large proportion of their total length. Although the hill country is deeply dissected, and ridge-tops often stand 300 m above the valley bottoms, the gradient of the rivers is generally slight, and a meandering course is characteristic of their north – south sections.

Fig. 15.2

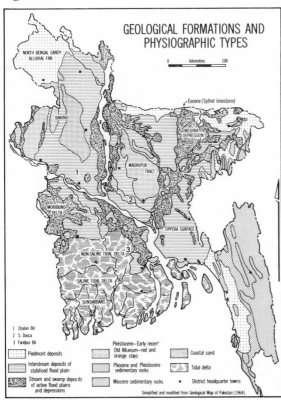

GEOLOGICAL FORMATIONS AND
PHYSIOGRAPHIC TYPES

0   kilometres   100

NORTH BENGAL SANDY
ALLUVIAL FAN

Eocene (Sylhet limestone)

BARIND

MEGHNA
DEPRESSION

MADHUPUR
TRACT

MORIBUND
DELTA

TIPPERA SURFACE

NON-SALINE TIDAL DELTA

SALINE TIDAL DELTA

SUNDARBANS

1 Chalan Bil
2 S. Dacca
3 Faridpur Bil

Piedmont deposits

Interstream deposits of
stabilised flood plain

Stream and swamp deposits
of active flood plains
and depressions

Pleistocene—Early recent
Old Alluvium—red and
orange clays

Pliocene and Pleistocene
sedimentary rocks

Miocene sedimentary rocks

Coastal sand

Tidal delta

District headquarter towns

Simplified and modified from Geological Map of Pakistan (1964)

The benchland features so important as sites for the tea plantations of Sylhet and Chittagong districts are found extensively in some of the longitudinal tributary valleys, standing as better drained but reasonably level (and so accessible) land above the floodplain alluvium. Some of the benchlands are under plantations of teak.

Generally speaking however, the hill-country slopes are clothed in bamboo jungle extensively used for *jhum* cultivation (shifting agriculture) while the narrow alluvial strips of the longitudinal valley floodplains support permanent fields. These aspects of the region, and its growing importance as Bangladesh's only source of hydro-electric power are discussed further below.

The *Chittagong Plains* form the southern part of the east Bangladesh coastlands referred to in Chapter 2. They are developed in the lower courses of the north – south aligned tributaries of the transverse rivers, the Karnaphuli, Sangu and Matamuhari. The rivers are distinctly tidal, and salinity during the dry seasons is a problem in low-lying tracts. From Cox's Bazar southwards a fine sandy beach backed by dunes stretches to the extremity of mainland Bangladesh in the Naaf Peninsula. Northwards, the coast consists often of tidal mudflats and mangroves up to the mouth of the Karnaphuli, beyond which a narrow coastal plain is backed by the Sitakund hills.

This plain merges with what geologists have called the *Tippera Surface*, in Noakhali and Comilla districts. Washed on the west by the Meghna, the surface is raised slightly above major flooding except from the occasionally turbulent Gumti and the lower Feni which flows across it from Tripura State in India.

The *Barind* and the *Madhupur Tract* of old alluvium have been slightly deformed by faulting and tilting which have had an influence on their drainage patterns and may also have been responsible for setting these areas a score or so feet above the adjacent younger floodplains. Perhaps it is this relative elevation that has prevented them from being covered by more recent alluvium and so allows their leached soils, lacking exotic sources of plant nutrient in the form of floodwater, to play a part in the areal differentiation of agriculture.

Rivers rising north of the Barind in the sub-Himalayan Piedmont Plain have cut channels through the old alluvium. It is probable that the

Tista, notorious for its changes of course, has flowed in several of the channels now occupied by lesser rivers such as the Atrai and Purnababha.

The Madhupur Tract is visually the more distinctive area since much of its surface is still covered with forest. Both terraces tilt perceptibly southwards with a gradient of 1m 2.6 km, and it is this that recent tectonic movements have contributed significantly to the country's physiography.

The *North Bengal Sandy Alluvial Fan* is part of the much more extensive submontane belt that stretches the length of the Himalayan foothills from Jhelum in Pakistan into the Assam Valley. Since most of its drainage is of local origin it is comparable to the *bhabar* and *terai* tracts (e.g. of Uttar Pradesh and Nepal) with the swampy terai element dominant. The plain slopes southeastwards with a gradient of 1 min 2.6 km, and it is this steeper slope (in comparison to those in the rest of the alluvial lowlands) that distinguishes this corner of Bangladesh.

Much of the sandy alluvium that makes up this very low-angled fan has been disgorged into the region by the River Tista. This river rises deep in the Himalaya, draining the Kanchenjunga massif, and from its point of entry into the plains at 168 m above sea level and 77 km north of the Bangladesh border, has varied its course from time to time to build up the fan. In the past the Tista has crossed the Barind to join the Ganges near the point where the latter enters Bangladesh. Its removal to the east of the Barind could have contributed to the decay of the Ganges's western distributaries. As recently as 1897 it used a channel more than 24 km south of its present course as a main distributary. An earthquake in 1897 appears to have reaffirmed the Tista's present channel, and contributed to the development of the Jamuna as the main course for Brahmaputra water. The Old Brahmaputra, which flows east of the Madhupur Tract, is now a much smaller river, carrying Jamuna water only at periods of high flood. The remaining regions may all be regarded as representative of the most recent phases in the evolution of the delta.

Representing the least active part of the meander floodplain, the *Moribund Delta* lies south of the Ganges and west of the Garai – Madhumati distributaries. Many of its channels are choked with water hyacinth or completely silted up, and its surface is no longer overrun by floodwaters from the Ganges. Watered only by direct rainfall the soils have become leached and badly need the rejuvenation by nutrient-bearing river water which the Ganges – Kobadak irrigation scheme is designed to achieve.

The *Stabilised Floodplain* is not so much a region as a widely distributed physiographic element. With the Moribund Delta it corresponds to the meander floodplain element in Pakistan, but is distinguished from the Moribund Delta on the grounds that it is still flooded periodically. The *Tidal Delta*, west of the Meghna estuary, is physiographically the continuation of the stabilised floodplain. The main channels are reasonably stable, and along the left bank of the Ganges and the Padma (formed by the Ganges – Jamuna confluence) a broad levee has developed. The stabilised floodplain is an extensive feature in the centre of Bangladesh, along the Ganges – Padma and surrounding the Madhupur Tract. Agriculturally it is the most productive region in the country.

Major *depressions* may be regarded as backswamp depressions to the main rivers, though tectonic subsidence is probably in some degree responsible for their persistence. Chalan Bil and the South Dacca depression are alike in being at once Ganges backswamps and apparently areas of subsidence related to the tilting of the Pleistocene terraces of Barind and the Madhupur Tract. The bil region of Faridpur District, 1800 km² of marsh, may be seen as a right bank backswamp of the Padma. (See Fig. 15.2) All these bils fluctuate greatly in area between a dry season minimum and a maximum late in the wet season. In the northeast, the sub-Garo and Meghna depressions are almost certainly regions of subsidence, but in a sense are also backswamps to the Old Brahmaputra. Compared with the Brahmaputra – Jamuna and the Ganges, the rivers flowing into the Meghna Depression from the Meghalaya Plateau and the Northeastern Hills carry only a small load of sediment, and have been unable to build up their floodplains to keep pace with the subsidence. Some bils in the depression are less than 3 m above sea level, yet almost 320 km from the sea. It is not surprising, therefore, that the Meghna Depression becomes a vast shallow lake for upwards of half the year, unable to discharge its waters southwards through the Meghna because of the higher level of the floodwaters in the Old Brahmaputra, flowing on its 'alluvial ridge'.

The *braided riverain charlands* are the active floodplains within which the major rivers are

69 Weaver at work on a handloom making a cotton sari. He pulls the cord in his right hand to move the shuttle, alternating the threads of the warp by means of a foot lever.

liable to change their channels frequently. The *chars* are the areas of fresh silt exposed at low water. In the case of the Jamuna, the river bed is as much as 30 km wide bounded by river cliffs as much as 8 m high and its charlands are very extensive. Those of the Lower Meghna are almost as wide at low water. The firmer levee banks of the Ganges – Padma seem to restrict the width of its charland belt somewhat. However, dramatic changes in course occur in both rivers, sweeping away villages and creating new charlands.

In the *Tidal Delta*, tidal flow in the distributaries has a marked influence on the pattern of channels and the distribution of sediment. Where alternating tidal and river flow is pronounced the distributaries make an elongated hexagonal pattern with their long axis normal to the sea coast. The tides also act to spread the fine sediment more evenly, so that the difference in height between levee and backswamp tends to be less than where river action alone is operative.

The effect of tides is measurable on the flow of the Padma to within 30 km of the confluence of the Ganges and the Brahmaputra – Jamuna, and on the Meghna system well into the heart of the Meghna Depression. Since so close to the sea the sediments are generally very fine, the channels are excavated in clay and tend to be deep and stable. For example, the Pusur south from Khulna takes ocean-going cargo liners 80 km from its mouth. Tidal scour assists in maintaining deep channels even where fresh-water flow in the rivers is minimal.

The extent to which salt-water penetrates the deltaic distributary channels varies seasonally and depends largely on the vigour of fresh-water flow from the landward side. The *Saline Delta* extends further inland in the west of the delta where the distributaries are more or less defunct as far as Ganges floodwater is concerned. Only in the wet season does fresh water gain the ascendancy in the tidal delta west of the Madhumati. East of this the Bishkhali and Burishwar distributaries remain fresh all the year, and salinity affects a much narrower zone at the sea face. The seaward fringes of the estuarine islands – Bhola, Hatia, and Sandwip – and the coasts south of Chittagong may be grouped with the Saline Tidal Delta.

Understandably the whole Tidal Delta, but particularly the estuarine islands, is very vulnerable to cyclones when wind force and low air pressure, sometimes coincident with high tides and river floods, may combine to devastate wide areas with great loss to human life and property.

In the southwest, the Saline Delta remains uncleared as the Sundarbans – a region of mangroves and swamp forest, the home of tiger, Chital deer and crocodiles.

Climate

It is not, of course, the geomorphological character of Bangladesh in itself that makes it an amphibious environment. It is rather its flatness and extreme liability to flood in the face of heavy monsoon rainfall not only within the country's borders but, more importantly, in the catchments of the rivers which pour into Bangladesh on their way to the Bay of Bengal. More than four times as much water flows *into* as falls *on* Bangladesh.

By South Asian standards, Bangladesh could be said to be moderately to excessively well watered, but such terms are coloured by one's comparative view or one's agricultural expectations. The mean annual rainfall ranges from less than 1,500 mm in the west to over 5,000 mm in Sylhet, but annual amount is of much less importance than seasonal distribution (Fig. 15.3). A distinguished Bengali wrote ' . . . rainfall in the months from March to May and again for September and October, rather than the total . . . determines the fortunes of the agriculturalist.'* In other words, he discounted entirely the sparse and unreliable rains of the dry season (November to February), and accepted as adequately reliable the rains of the wettest monsoon months (June, July and August). He underlined the decisive importance to the farmer of the pre-monsoon (*chota barsat* or 'little rains') and late monsoon rains.

The rainfall dispersion diagrams in Figure 15.3 show clearly the relative reliability of rainfall for the three mid-monsoon months. Sylhet, in the northeast corner of the country, can rely on an extra month of heavy rain in September. Another way of analysing the seasonality of rainfall is to examine the median value for monthly rainfall at stations representative of the four corners and the centre of Bangladesh (Table 15.1.)

Three seasons are clearly seen: dry, little rains and monsoon rains, through their duration is not

Fig. 15.3

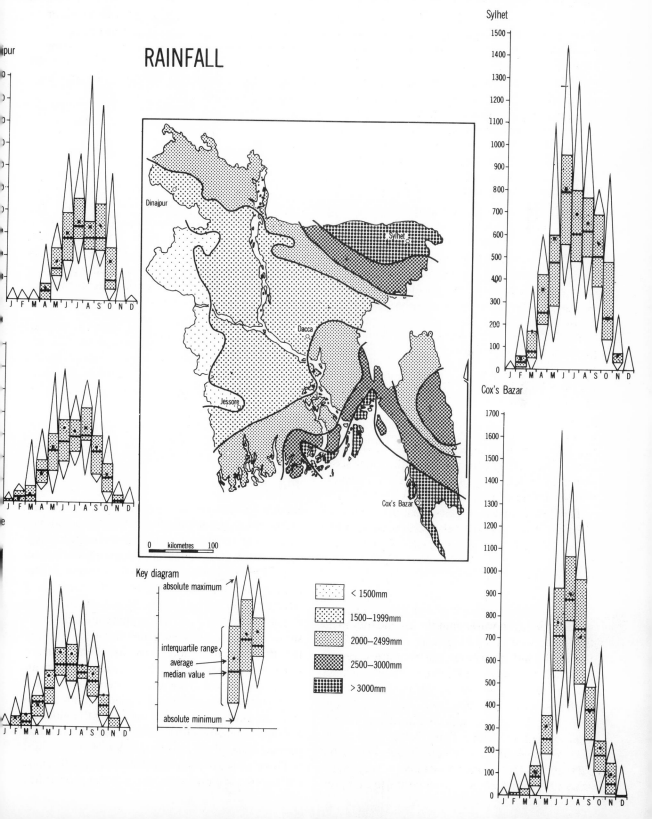

RAINFALL

Sylhet

Cox's Bazar

Dinajpur

Dacca

Jessore

Sylhet

Cox's Bazar

Key diagram

absolute maximum

interquartile range
average
median value

absolute minimum

< 1500mm

1500–1999mm

2000–2499mm

2500–3000mm

> 3000mm

0   kilometres   100

Table 15.1 Monthly rainfall medians (in mm)

| | Dry season | | | | | 'Chota Barsat' | | Rainy season | | | | | | | |
	Nov	Dec	Jan	Feb	March	April	May	June	July	Aug	Sept	Oct	Nov	Dec
Dinajpur	0	0	3	51	3	51	165	279	330	279	279	76	0	0
Jessore	0	0	0	13	23	102	152	279	279	241	203	76	0	0
Dacca	3	0	3	28	36	142	229	279	304	304	229	102	3	0
Sylhet	8	0	0	20	64	254	292	762	610	635	508	229	8	0
Cox's Bazar	51	0	0	5	3	102	241	711	889	762	381	178	51	0

*Mukerjee, Radhakamal, *Changing Face of Bengal* (Calcutta, 1938), p. 51.

Table 15.2 Monthly rainfall variability

	Nov	Dec	Jan	Feb	March	April	May	June	July	Aug	Sept	Oct	Nov	Dec
Dinajpur	∞	∞	200	275	275	60	45	38	34	29	40	113	∞	∞
Jessore	∞	∞	∞	150	122	45	51	23	29	13	38	50	∞	∞
Dacca	575	∞	250	91	102	36	36	32	23	25	39	62	575	∞
Sylhet	333	∞	100	94	100	41	32	29	25	21	33	72	333	∞
Cox's Bazar	175	∞	∞	150	430	55	39	28	16	31	32	150	175	∞

everywhere identical. The eastern stations have shorter dry seasons, Sylhet with an earlier opening to the 'little rains' in late February – March, Cox's Bazar a later conclusion to the monsoon rains which trail on with decreasing reliability into November.

The relative unreliability of rainfall outside the monsoon rainy season is seen in Table 15.2 in which monthly variability for the same five stations is calculated as the proportion expressed as a percentage of half the interquartile range to the median value.

Tables 15.1 and 15.2 taken together indicate the negligible value of dry season rainfall, and the high degree of unreliability of rains everywhere from November to March inclusive. Although more reliable, the range of variation within the low values of April rainfall (in all stations but Sylhet) is high enough to embarrass farmers. Similarly, towards the end of the rainy season in October, reliability decreases sharply.

Floods

In most countries floods are regarded as hazards with which the population have to contend from time to time as with other disasters, natural and man-made. In Bangladesh, flooding is very much a part of the normal cycle of the seasons. A delta cannot develop physically without flooding, and it is to floodwaters bearing plant nutrients in the form of dissolved and suspended solids that much of a delta's fertility can be attributed. Man has therefore been attracted to the sometimes hazardous environment of the delta because of the returns in terms of food crops that it is able to give him. Traditional agriculture in Bangladesh is an adaptation to a regime of annual deluge by the monsoon rains and floods both from this rain and from the overspilling of the rivers. Modernisation of agriculture requires that man be less directly at the mercy of natural events, and better able to control

70 Pulling and bundling paddy seedlings for the transplanted *boro* crop at Demra near Dacca.

all the factors of production. The Bangladeshi farmer, hopefully moving towards a more scientific agriculture, has still to adapt the modern technology of which he is becoming aware, to the same vagaries of nature that faced his father. In the case of flood control, the scale of the problem is generally beyond the individual's power to attempt to do anything about it and he looks to the greater financial and technical resources of his government and of richer, more advanced countries to seek a solution. So in considering floods in Bangladesh, we have to strike a balanced appraisal between floods as a hazard and floods as an asset, between floods drowning crops and livestock, and damaging property, and floods which water and fertilise the land.

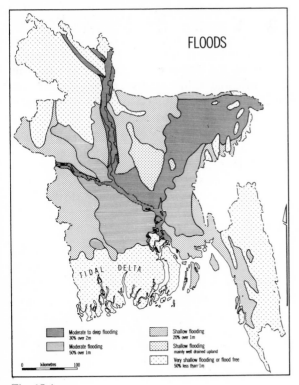

FLOODS

	Moderate to deep flooding 30% over 2m		Shallow flooding 20% over 1m
	Moderate flooding 50% over 1m		Shallow flooding mainly well drained upland
			Very shallow flooding or flood free 50% less than 1m

0   kilometres   100

Fig. 15.4

The map of flooded areas (Fig. 15.4) should be compared with that of the generalised physiographic types. It will be seen that the areas generally free from annual floods (except of course those due to occasional local downpours) are the hill country of Chittagong and Sylhet, the North Bengal Sandy Alluvial Fan and the Barind. In a sense, the Tidal Delta is free of deep-standing floods, but it certainly experiences widespread shallow flooding and infrequent but devastating cyclonic storm surges. Much the same is true of the Noakhali–Chittagong plains though in many places floods exceed 1 m in depth. Flooding of only moderate depth occurs in the Ganges left-bank levee plains in Rajshahi and the Moribund Delta in the southwest. Other regions of moderate flooding flank the Brahmaputra–Jamuna and extend into the Madhupur Tract and the Old Brahmaputra floodplain.

In most of these areas effective flood protection can probably be achieved and is indeed being provided in several instances, such as the Brahmaputra Right Bank Embankment Project. The same is probably true of the areas in which more than half the land floods to the 'moderate' depth of over 1 m. These are of two kinds. Between the Barind and the Ganges' left-bank levees, the Atrai River follows what is possibly a tectonic depression, but which also has the nature of a back-swamp zone. South of the Ganges–Padma this zone continues in the Stabilised Floodplain and Faridpur Bil, which floods in part from the Ganges. The Tippera Surface floods in some measure from the Meghna, but more hazardous are the flash-floods from the Gumti that drains from the hills of Indian Tripura.

The regions of severe flooding are most extensive in the Meghna Depression of Sylhet and Mymensingh, and along the Meghna floodplain from Bhairab Bazar to the confluence with the Padma. Here, this deeply flooded zone is continuous with another paralleling the Padma along the Dhaleswari which carries Brahmaputra–Jamuna water past Dacca to the Meghna. In the case of the Megna Depression, probably no general amelioration can be sought since the scale of the problem is so great. For some parts of the area it may be worthwhile to construct 'submersible' embankments, designed to be overtopped by maximum floods, but capable of delaying the onset of deep water in the fields – so guaranteeing to the farmer a longer growing season.

The regimes of the Ganges, Brahmaputra–Jamuna and Meghna are basically similar since they show a rapid rise to a peak and a somewhat gentler fall to a pre-monsoon minimum, but there are significant minor differences. The Meghna flow

71 As roads are constructed across the delta, bridge building is generally in arrears, and ferries such as this one near Dacca delay communications.

rises early to a maximum in late May and June. (This is partly explained by the comparatively short distance the river has to flow compared with the other larger rivers and partly by the earlier rainfall in the Northeastern Hills.) Consequently, the Meghna Depression fills with water by May and remains a great lake until October. The Brahmaputra–Jamuna rises more gradually to a July peak, while the Ganges reaches its peak in August from a minimum in April–May, differences that reflect the later onset of the monsoon rains in the Ganges catchment.

A very much more dangerous and less predictable hazard are *cyclones* which can cause enormous damage and loss of life in the coastal areas.

Cyclones occur in the Bay of Bengal chiefly in two seasons: April–May and October–November. They originate as depressions in sea areas to the east, and intensify into tropical cyclones as they progress into the Bay of Bengal. Some strike across Peninsular India to cause havoc in the Arabian Sea. Many adopt a curvilinear path within the Bay, developing from a westerly to a more northerly track (Fig. 15.5). Andhra Pradesh and Orissa receive frequent cyclones from the southeast quarter. Those that menace Bangladesh approach the estuary of the Meghna from the south-southwest and the Chittagong coast from the southwest. Over land, cyclones are soon dissipated as they move away from the water body which is their energy source.

Great damage to flimsy structures is caused by the strong winds associated with cyclones. Wind velocities in excess of 160 km/h are not unusual. The most devastating cyclone in living memory, on 12 November 1970, may have devel-oped winds of 241 km/h (150 miles/h). However, the greater destructive force of cyclones in Bangladesh comes from the storm surge engendered by the strong winds. A wave of up to 9 m high was produced by the cyclone of November 1970. Its devastating effect was very greatly increased by the fact that the storm swept up the gently shelving shores of the estuarine channels at a period of high tide. Maybe half a million people were drowned along with many thousands of work animals.

Fig. 15.5

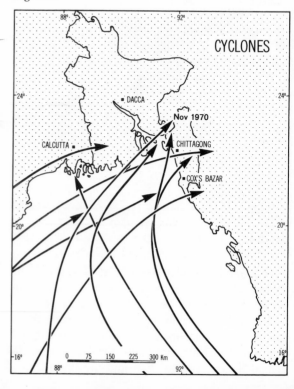

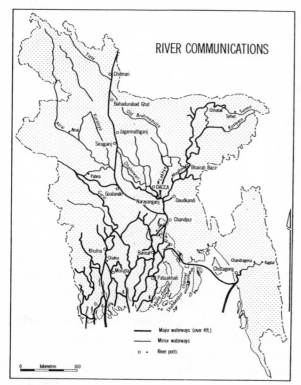

Fig. 15.6

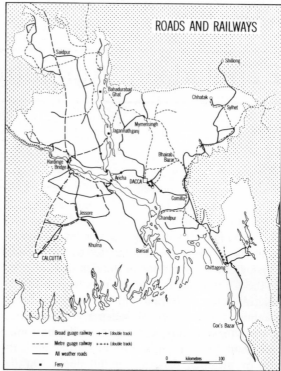

Fig. 15.7

Communications

With its huge rivers – the Brahmaputra–Jamuna has no bridge – and extensive flooding, Bangladesh's amphibious environment presents peculiar problems for communications.

For most farmers a small boat takes the place of the farm cart and a large part of the traffic in farm products moves to market and processing plant by country boat. These are sail driven, sometimes rowed and even hauled by man-power against adverse winds. From the larger agricultural collecting centres cargoes may move by motorised launches or paddle steamers. In the wet season boats can ply in almost any direction across country, but are limited to the deeper channels in the dry season. The navigable channels of commercial importance are shown in Figure 15.6.

The railway system (Fig. 15.7) is cut in two by the Brahmaputra–Jamuna–Padma. On the west, a broad gauge system (formerly terminating at Calcutta) crosses the Ganges by the Hardinge Bridge, and has spur lines to river ferries. Its southern limit is Khulna, and prospectively its outport of Chalna on the Pusur River, through which most of the bulk jute exports go. There are also metre gauge lines in the north. East of the river barrier the metre gauge system, based on the major port of Chittagong, bridges the Meghna to serve Dacca and Mymensingh and follows the edge of the hill country to Sylhet.

A road network, punctuated by ferries, is developing slowly. Ferries make travelling tedious and slow, but the cost of alternative bridges is enormous in a region with so many rivers.

Chapter 16

Bangladesh: Agriculture

Human ingenuity spurred on by the pressure of population on the land has brought almost all the surface of Bangladesh into productive use. The mainly self-sufficient farmer has evolved methods of cropping well adapted to the diverse physiographic conditions of the deltaic lowlands. In the Chittagong Hill Tracts people akin to the hill tribesmen of Burma and Northeastern India combine the practice of sedentary agriculture, in the Bangladeshi style, along the valley bottoms, with jhum cultivation, a form of shifting agriculture or 'swidden' farming, on hill slopes. On the benchlands between, fringing the hill country in Chittagong but more particularly in Sylhet, tea plantations represent a third distinct type of agricultural development.

Farming in the Lowlands

The basic factors influencing the Bangladeshi farmer in his choice of crop from season to season and from one type of land to another may conveniently be discussed in the context of the chart of agricultural activities (Fig. 16.1). The chart is adapted from the actual cultivation calendar in Iswarganj, a *thana* of Mymensingh District, but it may be taken as a representative model for average conditions in Bangladesh.

Corresponding to the three seasons, determined by rainfall incidence and amount, three cropping seasons are recognised:

(a) The *rabi* season corresponds to the dry season, from the end of October to March or April, during which, although only 28 per cent of the cultivated land is cropped, a great variety of crops is grown both 'dry' (dependent on moisture remaining in the soil from the wet season) and by irrigation. 'Dry' *rabi* crops include wheat, oilseeds, pulses, vegetables and tobacco, while *boro* paddy is by far the most important crop irrigated.

(b) The *bhadoi* season, during which aus paddy and jute are the main crops cultivated, literally means the rainy season, but in agricultural terms it lasts from the 'little rains' (*chota barsat*) of the pre-monsoon period from March or April to May until these crops are harvested in July or August, at the height of the rainy seasons.

(c) The *Aghani* season, more conveniently called the *aman* season is that of the main rice crops, transplanted and broadcast *aman*, which may be in the ground from June to November–December. The *aman* season thus overlaps with both *rabi* and *bhadoi* cropping seasons. Little else besides *aman* paddy is grown.

In any part of the delta (with the exception of the old alluvial terraces) soils differ in texture as between the levee crests (the 'highest land' in the chart) and the backswamp depressions ('lowest land'), often ranging from light sandy loams to heavy clay loams in the space of a few hundred metres and an altitudinal range of six metres or so. The lighter higher soils are easier to work than those of the heavier lower land, and can often be tilled dry or with the minimum of moistening from early rains in March. Close to the homesteads, for which sites are selected on the highest parts of the levee in order to avoid most floods, vegetables and spices may be grown in kitchen fields all the year round, and a small area of sugar cane cultivated under fairly close supervision. Seed beds of tobacco and *aman* paddy may also be planted here if water is available from a tank or well nearby. These lands receive most of what little there is to spare in the way of animal manure after domestic needs for fuel have been satisfied, and their crops are usually fenced to protect them from stray cattle and goats looking for forage. Fruit trees, mangoes, jack fruit, betel nut and

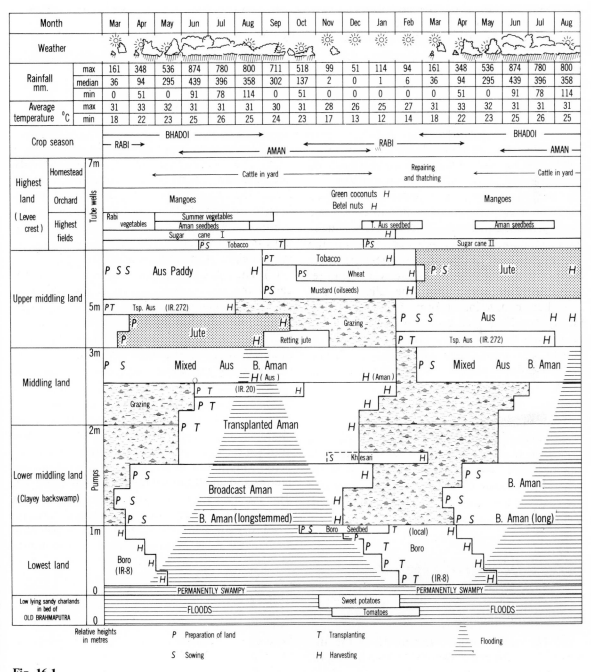

Fig. 16.1

coconut palms shade the homesteads and provide a supplement to the farmer's diet and to his income. Apart from the fields immediately around the homestead, most of the agricultural land is unfenced, and the farmer has little choice but to cultivate his scattered fields in the same way as do his neighbours. So although the village lands may be farmed by a number of individuals, there is little apparent variety to distinguish one plot from another. Normally a farmer holds his lands in a number of separate parcels in different parts of the village, some high, some low.

The highest 'open fields' carry *aus* and jute in the *bhadoi* season, crops which both rely on direct rainfall for moisture and which prefer not to grow in standing water. *Aus* paddy is an 'upland' variety, sown broadcast in non-flooded land. It is harvested in August, when the weather is wet, hot and very humid. Because of its poor keeping qualities, partly related to these conditions, *aus* rarely enters into trade. Jute is more tolerant of floods, but deteriorates in quality if left long to grow in water. However, the farmer may have to harvest it in water waist-deep if the monsoon rains are exceptionally heavy. After cutting, the jute is retted by soaking in water until the fibres can be stripped from the stem, washed and bundled in skeins for baling in hydraulic presses at collecting centres.

Some of the land that has carried one of the two *bhadoi* crops may be ploughed during September and sown with mustard to produce seed for cooking oil before being cultivated in readiness for the next *bhadoi* season. Tobacco can also be fitted into this period, the seedlings being planted out from the plots nearer the homestead.

On some of the land sown to *aus*, *aman* paddy may be broadcast with the *aus* seed, to mature after the *aus* has been harvested. This practice is regarded as an insurance against either crop failing, but does not get the best yields of either. *Aman* paddy may also occasionally be intersown with jute.

In any village, the greater part of the land will probably be 'middling' land or lower. Here, *aman* paddy is the main crop. These lands are generally too heavy for early ploughing, and have first to be thoroughly soaked by the 'little rains'. The best yields come from paddy which is transplanted from seed beds into rain-flooded fields early in the monsoon. The paddy fields are kept thoroughly wet by heavy rains and sometimes river floods, and the latter introduce soluble plant nutrients as well as essential moisture. Later transplanted crops may need rain in October for best results, after which the fields dry out and the crop ripens to be harvested in the clear sunny days of November–December. A common practice is to sow a pulse, *khesari*, among the ripening *aman* so obtaining a useful 'catch' crop for food and fodder early in the dry season.

On lower land the risk of flooding is naturally greater, and consequently broadcast varieties of *aman* are sown, among them long-stemmed types. Preparation of land for broadcasting *aman* can be more cursory than for transplanting, and the object is to get the *aman* plant well established before the onset of floods, so that the plant can grow quickly when the floods come, keeping its head above the rising water. *Aman* can grow at the rate of at least an inch a day, some varieties as much as 30 cm in

72   Raising irrigation water by bucket swinging in the dry season. The pond is covered with water hyacinth. The boys sit on a bamboo frame and throw the water into a channel protected from erosion by banana leaves.

24 hours. The long-stemmed variety can produce a stalk 7 m long, and often has to float in water 4.5 m deep.

Where the combined 'little' and monsoon rains last long enough, it is sometimes possible to follow aus with *aman* on the same land, but the presence of both crops in a farming system usually means they are grown on different fields.

The lowest land of all, in the backswamp depressions, may flood too soon for *aman* to be grown, but in some areas it is cultivated as soon as the floodwaters (or accumulated local rain-water) have receded sufficiently to allow a plough team to work knee-deep in water and mud. The dry season *boro* paddy is transplanted before the fields dry out, and has to be irrigated throughout the rainless months of January and February. Water scoops operated on the cantilever principle, water shovels, and baskets swung on ropes are used to raise water from the dwindling backswamp lake, into which the *boro* fields advance as the water recedes. Low-lift diesel pumps are becoming widely used to increase the efficiency of *boro* production, and it may be advantageous to speed the initial cultivation by tractor ploughing since the secret of success is to make the most of the water left over after the end of the rains before it evaporates. Although it is nutritious and yields well, growing in the clear dry season sunshine, *boro* paddy is relatively coarse and not popular in trade.

A final element in the chart is grazing. Cattle and water buffalo are used in ploughing, and to a small extent as milking animals. During the dry season the beasts of the village graze together on the paddy stubble, but while *aus* or *aman* crops are in the open fields they have to be fed near the homesteads on rice-straw or grass cut and carried by the children.

Crops and Agricultural Regions

Table 16.1 lists the area and production of the major crops averaged over the five years 1973–74 to 1977–78, with the immediate pre-independence year, 1969–70 for comparison.

Of the *aman* crop, 68 per cent of area and 76 per cent of production is attributable to transplanted *aman*, the rest being broadcast. Traditional transplanted varieties can tolerate moderate flooding once they reach 30 cm in height and provided the water level rises slowly, no more than 2.5 cm per day. Broadcast varieties are better able to cope with fast rising and deep flooding.

In addition to wheat, rape and mustard listed below, there are other valuable 'dry' *rabi* crops. Pulses, mainly gram, average about 314,000 ha, potatoes 85,400, chillies 77,000 ha, and tobacco 57,000 ha.

The map of agricultural regions (Fig. 16.2), based on crop associations, indicates the close relationship between agricultural practices and physiographic conditions. The regions may be summarised thus:

1. The Barind: near monoculture of transplanted *aman*. Some diversity occurs along the Atrai terraces, and two low-lying thanas with *boro* as an associated crop may also be linked with the Barind.

Table 16.1 Major crops

Crop	Area (thousand ha)		Production (thousand tonnes)	
	1969–70	1973–74 to 1977–78 average	1969–70	1973–74 to 1977–78 average
Rice				
aus	3,424	3,219	3,010	3,049
aman	6,006	5,705	7,061	6,923
boro	883	1,062	1,933	2,163
Wheat	120	147	105	201
Sugar cane	161	147	7,537	6,473
Rape and mustard	217	193	128	115
Jute	989	672	1,340	856
Tea	43	43	30	32

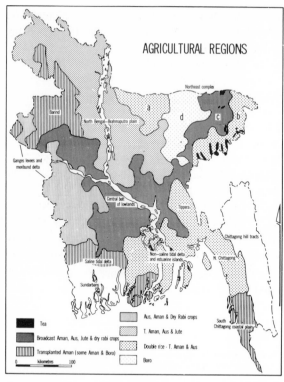

Fig. 16.2

3. The Central Belt of Lowlands linking the Atrai–Chalan Bil depression, the Dhaleswari depression in South Dacca, Lower Meghna, Faridpur Bil and the floodlands of the Padma: broadcast *aman*, sometimes monocultural, often in association with *aus*, and sometimes also with jute, and dry *rabi* crops.

4. The Moribund Delta and adjacent Ganges levees: *aus*, widely with broadcast and less commonly transplanted *aman*, and with significantly high percentages of dry *rabi* crops.

5. The Saline Tidal Delta: approaching absolute monoculture of transplanted *aman* which cannot be planted until the rains have leached accumulated salt out of the surface soil.

6. The southeast region of the Non-saline Tidal Delta, the Estuarine Islands, the charlands of Noakhali and the Tippera–North Chittagong Plain: double rice cropping with transplanted *aman* and *aus*. *Aus* is generally secondary in importance to transplanted *aman*. Jute is insignificant nor does the dry *rabi* crop group feature prominently. *Boro* is of growing importance in Chittagong particularly, but of small significance in the Tidal Delta and Estuary because of dry season salinity.

7. The South Chittagong Coastal Plain: transplanted *aman* and, in areas not affected by tides, *boro* paddy and dry *rabi* crops as minor associations with *aman*.

2. The North Bengal–Brahmaputra Plain, including the North Bengal Sandy Alluvial Fan, the stabilised floodplains of the Tista and Old Brahmaputra, the Brahmaputra–Jamuna active floodplain and the Madhupur Tract: transplanted *aman* and *aus* vie for primacy in a consistent combination, which generally includes jute.

73 To strip retted jute stalks men stand waist deep in water all day. The skeins of fibre can be seen piled beside each worker. In the background unstripped jute is piled on the left and the stripped stalks on the right. These are used for fuel or for building light screens. Jute is growing in the distance. This view is in Tangail district west of Dacca.

8. The northeast region lying between the Old Brahmaputra and the edge of the Meghalaya plateau: a complex of sub-regions, forming an irregular saucer-like basin unified by a common drainage outlet, via the Meghna.

(a) North of Mymensingh the western rim of the basin is an area of transplanted *aman* with *aus* which might alternatively be regarded as part of region 2, above.

(b) Skirting the hill country in South Sylhet the edge of the basin is a similar region of transplanted *aman* with *aus*, characterised on its hill margin by tea gardens established on benchlands above the several lakes which fluctuate in size according to season.

(c) A slightly lower plain adjoins this piedmont, extending from the foot of the Meghalaya plateau, to the south of Sylhet District. Here, floods spread early in the rains but not generally to excessive depth. Broadcast *aman* is followed by *boro*, utilising the abundant standing water remaining in the dry season.

(d) At the heart of the Meghna Depression deep extensive flooding persists through the rainy season, and very little land can be cropped at all until the dry season. *Boro* paddy is then cultivated as a transplanted irrigated crop and attains near monocultural status. Much of the region's cultivation is done by seasonal migrants who come from neighbouring districts by boat to grow *boro* and graze their cattle on the lush pastures.

9. The Chittagong Hill Tracts: *aus* with some transplanted *aman* and *boro* on the valley floors, shifting cultivation on the slopes.

Shifting Cultivation

The people of the Chittagong Hill Tracts, although possessed of a culture quite different from that of the plains Bangladeshi, have added permanent field cultivation in the Bangladeshi style to their traditional swidden or jhum agriculture. Jhum farming involves clearing slopes covered in a three- or four-year growth of bamboo, burning the dried rubbish, and planting mixed crops of upland rice, maize, millets, cotton, bananas, and vegetables. Sowing takes place during the little rains, and the crops are harvested as they mature. After a single season's cropping the slope reverts to bamboo jungle for three years or more. The jhum land is not owned by the individual cultivator, but is distributed by the village head-man among applicants who pay a capitation fee.

Along the valley bottoms a narrow strip of paddy land is cleared and generally carries *aus* paddy though transplanted *aman* may also be grown. Some light lands have a *rabi* crop of mustard, tobacco or vegetables. Permanent fields such as these are held as individual property. Jhum cultivation is often the occupation of the younger families, who inherit permanent fields later in life. Some tribes in more rugged parts of the region have little land other than jhum. The map in Figure 16.3 shows a typical valley in the Chittagong Hill Tracts.

Fig. 16.3

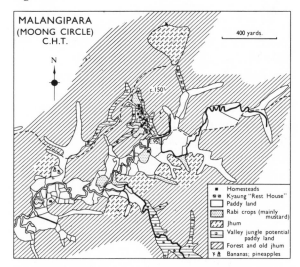

The tribal population supported by this mixed system in the Hill Tracts numbers about 400,000, mostly Chakma, Maghs, Tipra and Tenchungya. It is a population now facing considerable difficulties. The Hill Tracts contain the only sites for hydro-electric power development in Bangladesh, and are also the principal source of hardwoods, including teak and garjan. The establishment of the Kaptai Power Station on the Karnaphuli created a lake which flooded the valley lands of about 90,000 tribal people. This put increased pressure on the remaining areas available for jhum clearing outside the catchment of the dam, and no thoroughly satisfactory answer has been found for resettling the displaced tribesmen. Intensive horticulture of pineapples may be a part solution for some, for they have a tradition of good husbandry on permanent village gardens of spices such as ginger and turmeric and vegetables and a liking for rearing pigs and chickens.

Plantation Agriculture

Tea planting was begun in the 1870s when British (largely Scottish) entrepreneurs established gardens using labour brought in from Orissa and West Bengal. The descendants of this labour force still work the plantations, picking being done by women, and other tasks by the men. As yet, the local Bangladeshi Muslim has shown little liking for the idea of his womenfolk working in public, and the job is left in the hands of a Hindu minority group. Management has, however, been taken over progressively by non-Europeans.

About 43,000 ha are under tea in 153 gardens, mostly in Sylhet, with a few in Chittagong, the Hill Tracts and Comilla. Small experimental acres are under coffee and rubber. While the best estates in the Bangladesh tea industry were among the most efficient in the world in terms of yield per acre, ageing of the gardens and the failure to replant and to modernise has been harmful to the industry's economic position. Until 1965, tea was a valuable export from the then undivided Pakistan, but increased internal demand kept all production for home consumption. Bangladesh's Independence meant a sudden loss of the Pakistan market and the problem of disposing of more than half the potential crop of about 30 million kg. Unfortunately, in terms of cost efficiency, Bangladesh is in a poor competitive position in the world

market, though new outlets in the Middle East are being developed.

The tea produced is 'lowland tea', suitable for bulking by overseas blenders with more flavoured leaf from elsewhere. The gardens produce heavily for nine months of the year, January to April being a period of shut-down of the tea factories, and the time for pruning and maintaining the gardens. The cessation of the rains is the principal cause of stoppage, and there are prospects of introducing spray irrigation to extend the producing season. The more urgent need is to replant old tea with high-yielding clones.

The possibility of substituting home-grown rubber and coffee for imports has prompted experimental planting. Temperature and rainfall conditions are suitable for rubber in southern Chittagong, but the risk of cyclones uprooting the trees is a major deterrent. Coffee planting might succeed in Sylhet.

Agricultural Change

The Bangladeshi farmer is characteristically a small-scale entrepreneur, achieving a very low return for the minimal amount of capital and the long hours of labour he and his family invest. To bring his standard of living above its present bare subsistence level requires at the very least that his working capital and the efficiency of his farming operations be increased and so the return from the total family investment. He has to be educated towards a scientific approach to farming, so that he can adapt to his particular situation whatever modern knowledge and know-how is applicable.

Traditionally, much of his land has lain fallow through the dry season or has carried a low-yielding *rabi* crop. If he has a source of water available he has used the technique of irrigation known to

74 Representative of Bangladesh's hill tribe minority are this Mro woman and child, ginning cotton on the verandah of their bamboo home in the Chittagong Hill Tracts. Note carrying baskets and cooking pots behind. The woman has large silver ear-rings, beads and bangles, and a diminuitive homewoven skirt.

75 Jute-loaded country boats and the sidewheeler 'Rocket' steamer that plies to Khulna, on the Buriganga at Dacca.

him to grow *boro* paddy, raising the water by wearisome human effort. Only in the hills can farmers train the natural flow of streams to water their fields. Government at one level or another has recognised the farmer's situation as being capable of change by methods beyond his means as a private individual and has undertaken large-scale projects to divert rivers into channels by gravity or power pumping and to bring about conventional canal irrigation. There is, however, only limited scope in Bangladesh for irrigation by gravity canal. The nature of the terrain and the widely dispersed resources of water in the dry season call for a dispersed system of water delivery units such as small capacity low-lift pumps drawing on surface water, and tube wells. Initially government has to provide pumps and wells and help farmers organise themselves effectively to use them, but much initiative remains at the village level.

At other times of the year it is superfluity of water that bedevils the farmer, drowning his crops and deterring him from investing capital and effort in the face of the risk of loss. Here, government necessarily plays the major role in surveying the extent and origin of floods and in designing and executing the flood protection works. Guaranteed some known level of protection against the hazard, the individual farmer can replan his enterprise to take advantage of the new conditions in his environment.

The provision of a guaranteed supply of water in the dry season and the assurance of flood protection in the rains are preconditions for an increase in productivity on the farm in many areas, but do not of themselves ensure optimum levels of yield per ha or output per man. These can only be achieved by changing the nature of the inputs at the farm level, changes that require a conscious commitment on the part of the cultivator to an improved system of farming. The technological changes that have had greatest impact in recent years are the introduction of high-yielding varieties of rice, the extended use of irrigation principally through low-lift pumps, and the use of fertilisers. Improvements in the control of pests, diseases and weeds have also been initiated. Obviously these several changes are in considerable degree interdependent. There is no use changing to HYV of *boro* paddy if water or the essential fertilisers are not going to be available.

While the distribution of pumps for dry season cropping had been progressing earlier, the real impetus to modernisation (using this word to encompass the acceptance by the farmer of the need for the whole gamut of technological changes) seems to have come in the wake of the 'green revolution' which began in Bangladesh in the mid-1960s.

A brief review of rice production in Bangladesh since the Partition of India in 1947 shows how area and output have increased over the years before the introduction of HYV, and puts in perspective the recent, remarkable, but still relatively modest advances of the years since their introduction. Figure 16.4 shows the upward trend in total rice area and production. From a mean of 7.9 million ha in the late 1940s, the rice area has increased through a range of 7.9 – 8.9 million ha in the 1950s to between 8.5 – 10.4 million ha in the 1960s, to settle to an average of 10.0 million ha in the last five-year period. Fluctuations are mainly due to seasonal variations in flooding. Change in area and output has not been evenly spread over the three rice types, as Figure 16.5 demonstrates. *Aman* has shown least change, *boro* the most dramatic rise. The impact of the 'green revolution' is best seen in the graph of yield per ha in Figure 16.6.

The New Rice Varieties

The fundamental objective of research at the International Rice Research Institute, at Los Baños in the Philippines and at the Bangladesh Rice Research Institute is to discover and to breed fertiliser-responsive varieties of rice which are adapted to the wide range of conditions found in the rice-growing tropical countries of South and Southeast Asia. Among the characteristics which the BRRI is endeavouring to produce in HYV are:

1. Shortness of stem to give strength and prevent the crop lodging or flattening when the head is formed. However, shortness is a disadvantage in areas subject to flood.

2. An appropriate degree of sensitivity to photo-

Fig. 16.4

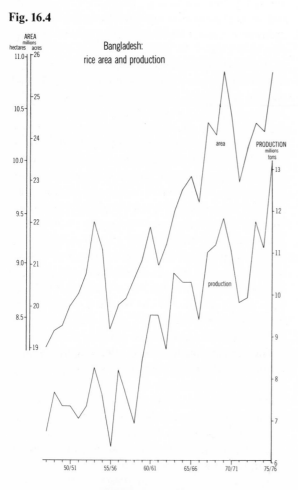

Fig. 16.5

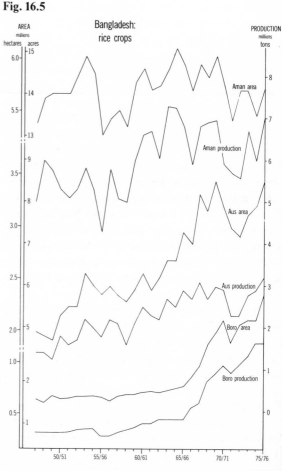

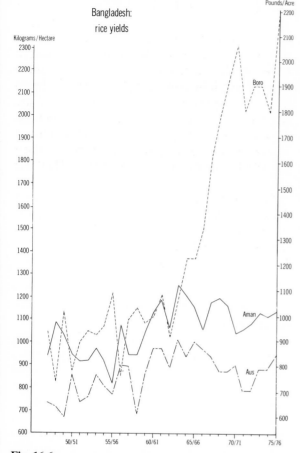

Bangladesh: rice yields

Kilograms/Hectare

Pounds/Acre

Fig. 16.6

5. Resistance to pests and diseases.

The first HYV to be introduced into Bangladesh was the one metre high dwarf, IR-8, from **IRRI**. As a *boro* crop it requires 170 or more days to mature owing to its sensitivity to cold. As an *aus* crop IR-8 needs only 130–135 days.

An alternative to IR-8 for cool season use is the dwarf variety Chandina, IR-532 (now BR-1), similarly non-sensitive to photoperiod, but having better resistance to cold as well as to pests and diseases. It matures a month sooner than IR-8. The local *boro* varieties are relatively short season types but tend to respond to fertiliser by growing too tall and lodging badly. Thanks to its better resistance to disease, Biplap, BR-3, is replacing IR-8 and can be grown at any season.

A new variety Mala, IR-272 (BR-2), which grows 1.2 m (*c.* 4 ft.) tall, may be used as a *boro* crop in low-lying land where there is an early risk of flooding, though it is more specifically an *aus* type. In the cool season it needs 150 days; as an *aus* crop only 110 days.

During the hotter and more humid seasons when *aus* and *aman* are traditionally grown, a different and more difficult set of problems faces the plant breeder. The contrast between the crops with regard to photosensitivity is utilised by the farmer who broadcasts mixed *aus* and *aman*, harvesting the first before the second has responded to the reducing day length of July and after. Sensitivity to photoperiod can be an advantage. Without it, a short season variety planted in, say, early June might come to maturity in August when floodwaters are still too deep to allow harvesting. A photosensitive type will not mature for at least another month. Most *aman* rices are well adapted to growing in floodwaters more than a metre deep, and on many sites cannot be replaced by short-stemmed varieties. *Aus* and *aman* rices need to be resistant to diseases and insect pests.

The prospects for using IRRI high-yielding varieties in the rainy season are best in the case of

(a) *aus*, traditionally a fairly short-stemmed rice that cannot tolerate flooding; (however, *aus* is usually broadcast and rain-fed, not irrigated) and

(b) *aman*, grown on land which only floods to a shallow extent.

period. Many varieties, such as those grown in the *aman* season, are triggered to mature by a reduced ratio of day to night, i.e. by the onset of autumn. This characteristic is highly desirable in a crop that may have to endure a spell of inundation during the summer and which cannot be harvested conveniently until late autumn when the floods have subsided and the dry season has begun. On the other hand, for *boro* and *aus* varieties grown in winter and springtime, photoperiod insensitivity is preferred so that they will mature as early as possible irrespective of day length.

3. Responsiveness to nitrogenous fertiliser. The crop needs to be well watered to make use of the nitrogen applied.

4. Relatively short growing season to enable more than one rice crop to be taken during the year. Cold tolerance is sought in *boro* varieties particularly, to reduce their growing season.

76 During the monsoon rains some parts of Bangladesh are deeply flooded every year as this village on the edge of the Meghna Depression. Typical of the Bangladeshi homestead family huts are grouped around a central court. Rice straw stacks and cattle shelters can be seen, and the canoes which make the amphibious existence of the villagers tolerable.

For a while the most successful new rice in the *aman* season was IR-20, a short season (120–135 day) variety, short-stemmed, disease resistant, slightly photoperiod sensitive and of good eating quality. By 1971–72, IR-20 occupied 253,000 ha, 14 per cent of the transplanted *aman* area. Subsequently Brrisail, BR-4 was evolved from an IR-20 cross and possesses a distinct advantage as an *aman* crop in producing taller seedlings which can be transplanted into deeper water. BR-4 and Pajam, the latter a non-photoperiod sensitive variety from outside the IRRI/BRRI catalogue, have largely displaced IR-20. Perhaps as much as 4.0 million ha of land which floods normally to a depth of no more than one metre could carry a HYV crop – effectively the whole of the transplanted *aman* area.

The 1.7m ha of low-lying land that carries a crop of broadcast *aman* floods too early and generally too deeply for a transplanted *aman* crop to be possible, and presents the rice breeder with a considerable problem. Some of the basic principles of the 'green revolution' cannot be applied. Long-stemmed varieties are essential and regular effective applications of fertiliser are impossible. The researchers have however been able to identify some better yielding traditional varieties suited to deep water. Several of these growing 2.7–3.7 m in height and yielding 2,300–2,500 kg/ha have been named. They compare favourably with the average yield of about 1,000 kg/ha for broadcast *aman*.

Although the introduction of several high-yielding varieties will give the country a chance to achieve self-sufficiency in the short run, the longer term prospects for increasing rice production in Bangladesh are subject to a number of constraints. Water resources in the dry season may permit the cultivation of about 1.2 million ha of *boro* paddy, provided pumps and tube wells are installed. It may prove a more productive use of part of these resources to concentrate them on ensuring a more extensive early *aus* crop which can come to maturity on the basis of rainfall in May–June and be followed on the same land by an *aman* crop.

The first HYV to be distributed in Bangladesh was IR-8 which was suitable as a *boro* paddy. By 1968–69, 18 per cent of the *boro* crop (then 884,000 ha) was under HYV, and this rose to 62 per cent of the larger total of 1,072,210 ha by 1978–9. On the *aman* crop the impact of HYV came later with IR-20, and has affected only areas of shallow flooding. By 1973–74, 38 per cent of the transplanted *aman* crop (3,886,000 ha) was in HYV, but increasingly high costs of fertiliser caused a setback to 10 per cent in 1976–77 from which there has been a recovery to 17 per cent of the total of 4,125,100 ha by 1978–79. The *aus* crop has proved least suitable for the introduction of HYV, only 13 per cent of the 1978–79 crop of 3,235,600 ha being HYV. A probable development will be the use of BR-2 or BR-3 (Chandina) as a late *boro* – early *aus* season crop, where irrigation is available, thus avoiding the cold weather which delays maturity in the *boro* crop, and harvesting the crop before the monsoon sets in. Unfortunately, surface water is most scarce at this time of year, but tube well supplies might be developed to compensate for this.

Changing the Agricultural Environment

The past and continuing efforts by government agencies to assist the farmer by intervening in the natural environment may be stated as being projects

(a) to redistribute available surface water;
(b) to exploit groundwater resources;
(c) to protect cultivated land from floods;
(d) to prevent the ingress of saline water.

Surface Water

It is of vital interest for Bangladesh to utilise its main resource — land — to the utmost. In order to do this, as much land as possible has to be under productive use at all times. With only 28 per cent cultivated during the dry season and 50 per cent during the *bhadoi* season there remains considerable scope for increasing the total cropped area, *if water can be made available.* By reducing the growing period, the breeding of fast maturing HYV rices much improves the prospect of multiple cropping, but puts greater demands on water resources for crops grown out of the rainy season.

Impressive advances have been made in dry season irrigation of rice since low-lift diesel-driven pumps were introduced. It is estimated that 1.2 million ha can be irrigated by pumps from existing water bodies, and a further 2.8 million ha if available river water could be better distributed by canals to areas of need.

The only major diversion of water undertaken to date is in the Ganges-Kobadak Scheme which draws heavily on the Ganges at Bheramara to irrigate a projected 89,000 ha, half of which is currently serviced, in Kushtia District (Fig. 16.7). Technical problems have bedevilled the project since its inception in the 1950s. In concept, the scheme proposes pumping Ganges water into a canal system which would command areas of the Moribund Delta where a perennial supply of nutrient-rich Ganges water would upgrade the region's agricultural activity. A further objective is to bring fresh water to the Saline Tidal Delta in Khulna, which has deteriorated agriculturally with the decay of the Ganges' distributaries – allowing salt water to penetrate further inland, and so restricting cropping effectively to a single *aman* planting. Poldering of the saline-affected area and the supply of fresh water could reverse the present wasting of these lands. It now seems unlikely that the low-level flow of the Ganges when India completes the Farakka Barrage to divert water to keep clear the Hooghly at Calcutta, will

Fig. 16.7

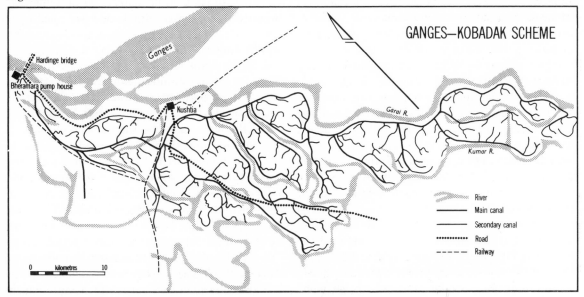

GANGES–KOBADAK SCHEME

Hardinge bridge
Bheramara pump house
Ganges
Kushtia
Garai R.
Kumar R.

River
Main canal
Secondary canal
Road
Railway

0   kilometres   10

77 In the Chittagong Hill Tracts near Rangamati. Dissected Tertiary sandstones and shales. The near slopes carry mixed crops of upland rice, millets, beans, cotton, etc. planted by shifting (jhum) cultivators. A patch of bananas can be seen near the bamboo hut. The hillsides are cleared of bamboo and shrub in rotation every three or four years. The valley floors are under permanent cultivation for paddy: a farmer is seen pulling seedling rice for transplantation.

allow the earlier targets of the Ganges–Kobadak Scheme to be achieved. The irrigation of polders in the Saline Delta will now depend on the prospects of diverting Brahmaputra–Jamuna water into the Garai and thence into Khulna. The most important impact of the scheme has been in promoting transplanted *aman* through guaranteeing irrigation to supplement rainfall particularly towards the end of the growing season. Dry season cropping has changed very little and there has been a slight decrease in the *bhadoi* crops, which may be cancelled out when HYV transplanted *aus* becomes more generally adopted.

Groundwater

Groundwater exploitation has revolutionised agriculture in the northernmost district of Dinajpur, and appears to have considerable potential over most of the lowlands of Bangladesh wherever salinity is absent. The hill margins where alluvium tends to be coarser and so provides more easily managed aquifers, give most promise. Coarse textured soils tend also to be thirsty soils, not retentive of rainfall or irrigation water, and their irrigation is apt to be relatively expensive compared with low-lift pump irrigation. In Dinajpur cement-lined distribution channels are used to minimise wastage. From being a district with the lowest cropping intensities in Bangladesh, the tube well irrigated areas of Dinajpur now carry two crops a year on almost all the area commanded.

Flood Protection

Flood protection can seldom be absolute in Bangladesh except at prohibitive cost. The problem is to assure the farmers protection while at the same time not denying them sufficient water. The most ambitious scheme so far undertaken was the Brahmaputra Right Bank Embankment extending 217 km south from the Tista almost as far as the Ganges confluence, to protect an area chronically and deeply inundated. Relief from flooding has allowed farmers to increase their area of HYV transplanted *aman* by 35 per cent, and although the total area under rice has decreased in the short run, production has been higher. Adequate maintenance and supervision of the long embankment and its irrigation regulators is a problem.

In a smaller scheme near Dacca 6,000 ha of once seasonally flooded land has been completely surrounded with an embankment to keep out the waters of the Lakhya and Buriganga Rivers. Rainfall that accumulates inside the embankment has to be removed by pumping, but the same pumps can be reversed in the dry season to bring in irrigation water from the rivers. The close control of water thus achieved has led to a substantial increase in *rabi* and *bhadoi* cropping, and a switch from broadcast to transplanted *aman*. Cropping intensity has risen from 100 to 188 per cent.

Salinity Control

Coastal Embankment Projects have been undertaken for several decades and now over 3,000 km of bank with sluice gates protect 760,000 ha from salt water ingress throughout the Saline Tidal Delta, the main estuarine islands of Bhola, Hatia and Sandwip and the coast south of Chittagong. For optimum use of the land it is not sufficient merely to keep out saline water. Excess rain floodwater may have to be removed from the polder if controlled irrigation of transplanted HYV *aman* is to succeed, and ideally fresh water should be introduced to support a *rabi* or a *bhadoi* crop. This may be very costly to achieve in many parts of the delta. The embankments are not an adequate defence against cyclonic surge which from time to time salinifies the lands normally protected against tidal ingress.

The Cultivators' Socio-economic Environment

As important to agricultural development as the physical conditions in the farmer's fields is the socio-economic system within which he operates. To the extent that this system is rooted in tradition, it proves more difficult to change than the physical and material aspects of agriculture.

Holdings are small and generally fragmented. According to a recent estimate 80 per cent of the land is in holdings of less than 4 ha and 99 per cent of agricultural families hold less than this figure. A ceiling of 100 *bighas* (13.4 ha) has been set to a family's holding and the excess is to be acquired for distribution to landless agricultural workers and to small holders.

Many cultivators rent some or all of the land they farm, either on a regular renewable basis or under an annual share cropping arrangement by which the owner gets one-half of the crop (except on charland where the risks are high and only one-third of the crop is taken).

For this reason the size of the area constituting an agricultural enterprise is probably impossible to estimate accurately. The agricultural Census of 1960 gave the following data:

	Per cent of total	Cumulative per cent
Holdings under 0.2 ha	13	13
Holdings 0.2 – 1 ha	39	52
Holdings 1 – 2 ha	26	78
Holdings over 2 ha	22	100

Districts where holdings over 2 ha much exceed the national average of 22 per cent of the total are Dinajpur (49 per cent) where agricultural colonisation by clearing of *terai* jungle has been proceeding in recent decades, Kushtia (46 per cent), Rajshahi (37 per cent) and Jessore (34 per cent). All are border districts to India and the figure may reflect the effects of out-migration by Hindu landowners after partition.

At the other end of the scale, while an average 13 per cent of holdings are under 0.2 ha, high proportions are found in Chittagong (28 per cent), Comilla (23 per cent), Faridpur (26 per cent) and Noakhali (24 per cent).

Landless labourers numbered 2.6 million, and formed as much as 32 per cent of all workers in Barisal District, and as little as 10 per cent in Comilla. In 1977, 5.7 million households with 28.2 million persons (41 per cent of the rural population) owned less than 0.2 ha.

Fragmentation of holdings into a number of non-contiguous plots is the rule. In 1960 more than half of the holdings were divided into six or more fragments. Unfortunately Muslim customary law entitles every heir to a share of an estate, and it is difficult to prevent holdings becoming uneconomically small and increasingly fragmented.

Some of these disadvantages of the land-holding system are being overcome under various types of cooperative schemes. The low-lift and tube well irrigation projects have encouraged farmers to cooperate to be able to obtain a share of the water. At Comilla, the Rural Academy specialises in research into cooperative farming and systems to provide rural credit. Modernised farming is providing the incentive for experimentation in new forms of cooperative management.

Chapter 17

Bangladesh: Population, Urbanisation and Industrialisation

Population Density

Bangladesh is among the most crowded corners of the world by any criterion, and among the nations dependent on agriculture it is probably the most densely populated. While agriculture remains very largely a subsistence activity the population density distribution reflects the capacity of the land to support cultivators using traditional skills. The existence of industrial cities undoubtedly affects the pattern since these represent concentrations of job opportunities which attract population to themselves and to their immediate vicinity, and which create economic demands for food, other goods and services, stimulating the development of surrounding areas and so increasing their carrying capacity.

Figure 17.1 shows the distribution of population at the 1974 Census.

In terms of carrying capacity the heaviest burden is carried by the southeastern deltaic quadrant of the country, centring on a Dacca–Comilla axis. The region extends along the Old Brahmaputra and Dhaleswari distributaries as far as the Jamuna floodplain to the northwest, with an outlier developing in Faridpur–Bakarganj. Soils regularly rejuvenated by flooding in the western half of this quadrant, and a sufficiently prolonged rainy season to permit double cropping of rice in the eastern part, are significant advantages, quite apart from the stimulus of urbanisation at a number of points. The areas around Chittagong may be associated with this quadrant. The industrial concentration of Khulna in the heart of the Saline Delta is a pocket of high density little related to agricultural development.

West of the Jamuna floodplain and the line of the Garai–Madhumati, the most westerly of the

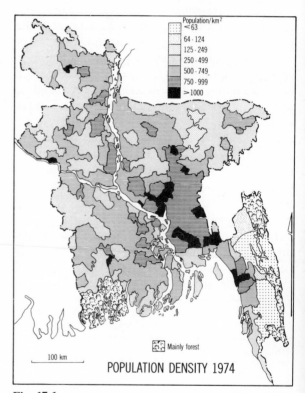

Fig. 17.1

POPULATION DENSITY 1974

Population/km²
<63
64 - 124
125 - 249
250 - 499
500 - 749
750 - 999
>1000

Mainly forest

100 km

more or less active distributaries of the Ganges, agriculture faces more difficult problems of water supply than in the eastern regions of Bangladesh: lower rainfall and a longer dry season; poorer access to surface water for dry season irrigation since they are denied the widespread floods of the Ganges and Brahmaputra; heavy soils on the Pleistocene terraces of the Barind, workable only in the rains; and, in the tidal reaches of the delta, seasonal salinity limiting farmers to a single wet season crop. The core of the Barind and the Saline Delta are clearly areas of difficulty, and the areas close to the Indian border have never recovered from the out-migration of non-Muslim population, firstly after Partition in 1947 and again during the civil war of 1971.

The portion of Bangladesh northeast of the Old Brahmaputra floodplain contains the Meghna Depression and other low-lying swampy lands along the Sub Garo Fosse and the Sylhet Hills. Persistently low densities underscore the difficulties facing rural development over much of the region where deep seasonal flooding for upwards of four months every year converts several *thanas* into a vast lake. Industrial development at Fenchuganj in the centre of Sylhet District accounts for the single *thana* with over 750 per km².

Low densities are the rule also in the ever changing islands and charlands in the Meghna estuary and the adjacent coast of Noakhali, where cyclones periodically frustrate man's efforts to sustain himself. In the Chittagong Hill Tracts densities reach their lowest in overall terms, on account of the extensive practice of shifting cultivation.

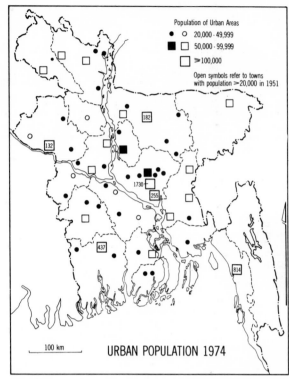

Fig. 17.2

Urbanisation

For its size, Bangladesh is probably the least urbanised of countries. In 1974, 8.8 per cent of the population was urban, 240 per cent more than in 1951 when the urban proportion was 4.4 per cent. The number of towns in different size classes is shown in Table 17.1. Urban centres are located in Figure 17.2.

Table 17.1   Urban centres

Size	1951	1974
Over 500,000	—	2
100,000 – 499,999	2	4
50,000–99,999	3	14
20,000 – 49,999	19	35

Dacca's population is estimated at 1,730,253. Nearby, Narayanganj with its three industrial satellites totals 255,583. In effect, then, one can talk of a Dacca–Narayanganj conurbation of about two million people. The conventional idea of a conurbation as a continuously built-up area interconnected by roads is not simply transferable to a deltaic environment where rivers simultaneously separate dry point settlements and unite

them by water-borne transport, where ferries are more frequent than bridges.

Dacca is typical of the primate city. Even without Narayanganj and its satellites, Dacca has more than double the population of 'greater' Chittagong (814,000) whose growth (176 per cent between 1951 and 1974) has been much less spectacular than that of its rival industrial port city of Khulna (936 per cent). The other centres over 100,000, Mymensingh and Rajshahi, both achieve that size by inclusion of their environs. Three others are little short of this level: Barisal (98,127), Comilla with the adjacent cantonment (96,500), and the railway town of Saidpur (90,132).

Of the 14 centres between 50,000 and 99,999, eight are district headquarter towns and the remainder share outstanding importance as communications and collecting centres with considerable industry. The five towns exceeding 50,000 in 1951 have burgeoned into 20 in 1974, while those in the lowest category have hardly doubled their number.

In terms of the geographical distribution of towns, the poorest showing is in Sylhet and Bogra Districts, which have but one urban centre each,

78 Setting up the warp for a hand loom, in Pabna District

and Dinajpur which, by the withering of the railway town of Parbatipur (more important before Partition, on the Calcutta–Darjiling route) has lost its second centre. Generally, the pattern is one of significant growth in the major cities, accompanied by the appearance of minor regional centres in the lowest category. In Dacca District, the growth of the Dacca–Narayanganj conurbation has not prevented the establishment of one town in the third and five in the fourth category. Chittagong District reveals a different, more centralised pattern, in that urban growth has been restricted to *thanas* close enough to Chittagong itself to become extensions of its conurbation.

Industrialisation

Bangladesh has a superabundance of unskilled labour. In most other necessities for modern industry the country is grossly deficient. Its major raw material, jute, is a product of agriculture, and much of its industry is directed to processing the output of its farms, forests and fisheries. There is a considerable small-scale craft industry in cotton textiles, metal work, leather and wood, representing the survival of traditional cottage industries. Almost all large-scale manufacturing industry has been established since Partition in 1947, most of it in jute and cotton textiles.

Until the early 1950s it looked as if the country's sole indigenous source of power would be in the hydro-electric potential of the rivers of the Chittagong Hill Tracts. With the construction of the Kaptai Hydel Project on the Karnaphuli, 80,000 kW capacity was harnessed, later to be increased to 120,000 kW. All other power generated was then on the basis of imported fuels. However, the picture changed dramatically, certainly as far as potential is concerned, with the discovery of

natural gas in several localities. Known reserves could maintain a consumption of 22.7 million m³ per day for 20 years. With consumption at about 2.6 million m³ daily in 1977–78 some export trade can be contemplated. The gas fields are mainly in Sylhet District and the adjacent corner of Comilla, the latter conveniently located for linkage by pipeline to Dacca. The principal industries based directly on natural gas are the nitrogenous fertiliser factories at Fenchuganj (Sylhet) and Ghorasal (Dacca) which produced 212,039 tonnes of urea in 1977–78, accounting for 41 per cent of gas consumed. The Chhatak cement works, using limestone from just over the border in India, is now powered by local natural gas. Power generation used 36 per cent, industry 16 per cent, domestic uses 3.6 per cent and commerce 1.6 per cent.

Mention may be made of two potential resources for fuel, neither likely to attract urgent exploitation while natural gas is so abundantly available.

Table 17.2   Industrial output, 1977–78

Jute looms installed	23,800
Jute looms utilised (per cent)	90
Raw jute consumed (tonnes)	557,349
Hessian (tonnes)	179,439
Sacking (tonnes)	269,697
Carpet backing (tonnes)	77,377
Total jute manufactures (tonnes)	555,102
Cotton cloth, (million m)	75.5
Paper (tonnes)	32,055
Newsprint (tonnes)	28,074
Sugar (tonnes)	178,071
Fertiliser, urea, (tonnes)	212,039
Mild steel (tonnes)	148,144
Cement (tonnes)	346,456
Cigarettes (millions)	11,974

Coal of high grade, similar to that of the Damodar Valley in West Bengal, has been proved in quantity and at workable depth, between 850 and 1160 m, in Bogra District. Reserves are estimated at 560 million tonnes. Peat deposits in swamps in Faridpur and Khulna and extensively in the Meghna Depression are a vast reserve of low grade fuel.

Natural gas now accounts for almost 40 per cent of the power consumed, hydro-electricity for 36 per cent and imported oil for the remainder. The main centres for power generation and consumption are Kaptai (supplying Chittagong), Dacca–Narayanganj, Khulna and Fenchuganj. The Bheramara thermal station powers the Ganges–Kobadak pump house, while small independent units feed the small towns throughout the country. A power grid between Kaptai, Chittagong and Dacca's major thermal station at Siddirganj has been established but has proved vulnerable to cyclone damage. By 1979 installed capacity was about 660,000 kW, one-fifth of it being at the Kaptai HEP station. For the vast majority of the population electricity is still an unimagined luxury enjoyed by the wealthy few who live in cities.

The inventory of modern industry is all too short. Before 1947 the country was an economic tributary of Calcutta, and had a few cotton textile mills, a cement works and factories processing its raw agricultural produce for export: tea factories and jute presses. Now there are 77 jute mills, in Dacca-Narayanganj, Khulna and Chittagong, and 49 cotton textile mills. There is now a steel rolling mill of 254,000 tonnes capacity at Chittagong, based on all-imported materials. There is also an oil refinery to process 1.52 million tonnes annually. A paper mill at Chandraghona on the Karnaphuli River, using bamboo cut in the Chittagong Hills and rafted down river, has a capacity of about 30,000 tonnes. Another at Khulna uses softwood from the Sundarbans Forest to make newsprint and hardboard, while a third – at Ishurdi in Pabna District – uses bagasse, the fibrous residue of sugar crushing as a basis for high grade paper. A further mill at Chhatak, Sylhet, is designed to use bamboo, swamp reeds and jute waste. The 15 sugar mills are mostly in the northwest, and most of the 114 tea factories are in Sylhet. Leather tanning is important at Dacca and Chittagong, which exports hides, skins and finished leather. Narayanganj has a shoe factory, but footwear is mostly a domestic craft industry; so too is woodworking. Plywood factories at Chandraghona make tea chests.

Sophisticated industries such as mechanical engineering are little developed as yet but have tremendous potential to service the market for agricultural pumps and other machinery needed for modernisation, as well as the expanding transport industries.

Output in some major industries is shown in Table 17.2.

Government policy towards industrial development is based on the socialist philosophy of the new nation. Large-scale enterprise is State owned and managed, while the private investor is encouraged to invest in development areas away from Dacca, Chittagong, Khulna and Jessore. Foreign private investment will be permitted only in enterprises in which government holds at least 51 per cent equity. For small and cottage industries, private enterprise will be encouraged and their production integrated with large-scale industry.

79 A jute mill near Narayanganj, showing the bungalows of supervisory staff in the foreground.
(Courtesy Govt. of Bangladesh).

Chapter 18

Sri Lanka: The Heritage of the Past

The island republic of Sri Lanka, or Ceylon,* could be regarded as the most fortunate of the countries of South Asia in its overall level of development. On obtaining its independence within the British Commonwealth in 1948, Sri Lanka inherited a well developed plantation industry whose exports paid for the import of half its requirements of food and almost all its manufactured goods. The country's major problems are associated with the need in a changing world to adjust its economy, based upon rather limited natural resources, to the ever increasing demands of a fast growing population.

It was probably in Sri Lanka that the demographic impact of the insecticide DDT as a killer of the malaria-bearing *Anopheles* mosquito became first apparent. Prior to 1947 the island's population had been increasing at the relatively moderate rate of 1.6 per cent per annum. Immediately following World War II an extensive scheme of spraying with DDT was undertaken which, along with other measures to improve health, led to a rapid reduction of the death rate and to an increased birth rate, and so to an upsurge in the rate of population increase.

At the latest Census in 1971 the population was 12.7 millions and is projected to reach between 15.3 and 15.9 millions by 1981. Table 18.1 summarises the demographic history of Sri Lanka over the past hundred years.

Unlike the rest of South Asia, migration has played a major role, accounting for up to two-thirds of the population increase in the decades up to World War I. Up to 1953 some 1.2 million immigrants from South India (in excess of those

returning) came to work on plantations and so to contribute to the country's productivity. It is only since Independence that the balance of migrant flow has been reversed. The trends in birth and death rates are characteristic of the demographic transition. There has been a steep decline in the death rate, particularly since World War II, while the birth rate has only started to fall over the past 15 years. There are signs that the intercensal rate of 2.5 per cent per annum between 1963–71 (which would, if sustained, double the population in 20 years) has begun to fall appreciably; in 1976 registrations revealed a crude birth rate of 27.6 compared with a death rate of 8.0 and a resultant rate of natural increase of under 2 per cent.

This rapidly expanding population is in itself a major problem, aggravated on the one hand by a relative lack of developable physical resources, and on the other by political tensions and instability which militate against effective internal economic advancement. The tensions stem in part from the complicated cultural make-up of the population. There have been problems, too, arising from 'decolonialisation' of the country's economy and the attempt to follow a neutral line in foreign policy.

To understand the present-day geography of Sri Lanka, it is necessary to appreciate the various phases in man's occupation of the island, and how, through past ages, the physical environment interacted with man's changing aspirations. As is the case with every country, there are features of Sri Lanka's distant past which permeate strongly into the fabric of its present social and political life, and perhaps even to bias judgements in favour of following lines of development which might resuscitate memories of glories long past. This study cannot attempt to examine every facet of its complicated 'human' environment, but will

Sri Lanka replaced *Ceylon* as the official name of the State in 1972, but seemingly without prejudice to the earlier title. For trade purposes, notably for tea, the name Ceylon is retained, as also in that of the Central Bank and of many institutes, as well as in popular usage.

Table 18.1   Population of Sri Lanka

Census year	Millions	Average annual growth rate (per cent)	Percentage of increase due to migration	Birth rate per thousand	Death rate per thousand	Natural increase (per cent)
1871	2.4					
1881	2.8	1.4	67	27	23	0.5
1891	3.0	0.9	42	29	24	0.5
1901	3.6	1.7	60	34	28	0.7
1911	4.1	1.4	34	38	29	0.9
1921	4.5	0.9	18	38	30	0.7
1931	5.3	1.7	19	40	27	1.3
1946	6.7	1.5	5	37	23	1.4
1953	8.1	2.8	5	38	17	2.1
1963	10.6	2.7	−1	37	10	2.7
1971	12.7	2.2	−5	33	8	2.5

seek to explain the more significant aspects of its modern human geography.

The People

The origins of the people of Sri Lanka are somewhat obscure. The earliest inhabitants were probably the ancestors of the present Veddahs, a once relatively primitive group now no longer recognised separately in the census, who have lost their identity by physical and cultural absorption into the Sinhalese population. Anthropologists find affinities between the Veddahs and some hill tribes of Peninsular India and it is probable that, like the latter, they were in part absorbed and in part driven into the less attractive highlands by invading peoples. As a separate ethnic entity, the Veddahs can be said already to have disappeared.

There are two distinctive cultural groups forming the bulk of the population, the Sinhalese and the Tamils. The role of migration in the genesis of the Sinhalese people, much the larger of the two groups, is uncertain, but tradition holds that they entered Sri Lanka from India at an early date. Possibly through continued contact with their homeland, they received Buddhist missionaries sent by Asoka, ruler of northern India in the third century BC. Thus the Sinhalese acquired their Buddhist religion and its associated Aryan language of Pali with its Brahmi script. The Sinhalese language as it has since developed has been much modified by the fusion of Dravidian linguistic

80   Buddhist *dagoba* at Mahiyangana, one of the Sri Lanka's three most important places of pilgrimage. (Courtesy Margaret Scrivenor).

elements, derived from the other major group in Sri Lanka, the Tamils.

The Sinhalese established an advanced civilisation in northern Ceylon during the first millennium of the Christian era. Close proximity to the Tamil country of Southern India ensured some degree of cultural contact and physical mixture, probably from the very earliest days. It was customary for Sinhalese kings to seek brides from Southern India. Ludowyk suggests that for several centuries after the introduction of Buddhism into Ceylon 'over large tracts of the northern plain Tamil and Sinhalese must have been indistinguishable from each other. In these years there were Tamil rulers who had been patrons of Buddhism, then flourishing in South India. (Hindu) Brahmins were officials in the court of Sinhala kings, and the gods of the Hindu pantheon were respected by Hindu and Buddhist alike.'* These idyllic conditions must have been strained and ultimately shattered by the more aggressive turn taken in Tamil relations with Sri Lanka from about the tenth century AD. As so often today the threat of political and economic competition between differing cultural groups led to the exaggeration of their differences and the more fierce 'protection' of their respective cultural badges, of language, religion, and social custom. From this early phase of Sri Lanka's history derives the continuing mutual antipathy of Sinhalese and Tamil: the Sinhalese, with his Buddhism coloured by fervent nationalism, views the Tamil as the political and economic aggressor from overseas. Prejudices built up over a millennium or more cannot be expected to disperse overnight, and in fact have become accentuated since Independence.

The early Sinhalese colonists were attracted to the drier parts of the island. The principal focus of settlement was the north central lowlands, where the Buddhist kingdom of Rajarata was established by the third century BC, and from which Buddhism probably spread to other 'kingdoms' such as Ruhuna in the southeast and to parts of the lowland west. It seems that the 'wet zone' in general, forming the southwest quadrant of the island, and the highlands over 1,000 m within that zone in particular, were rather neglected by these colonists who perhaps found in the dry

zone a region more readily cleared for irrigated paddy cultivation. Both tank-fed irrigated paddy farming in valley floors and *chena*, a form of shifting cultivation on interfluves, were practised by the Sinhalese. In common with many parts of Asia, agricultural methods have changed surprisingly little in the course of two thousand years.

By the eleventh century AD pressures from the Tamil Chola kingdom on the mainland reached the level of military invasion, and there began a period of progressive 'Tamilisation' of northern Ceylon, as a result of which the Sinhalese were eventually pushed southwards. Thus in AD 1017 the south Indian Cholas captured the ancient and glorious Sinhalese capital of Anuradhapura, compelling the Sinhalese to move their capital to Polonnaruwa, 80 km to the southeast, where there developed a civilisation more strongly influenced by the Dravidian culture of the Tamils. Invasion and migration from India persisted in the twelfth century, resulting in the establishment of a strong Tamil kingdom in the north, based on Jaffna. The Tamils were, and are still, mainly Hindu by religion and their language belongs to the Dravidian linguistic family.

The two cultural characteristics have persisted, keeping Tamil and Sinhalese apart throughout the centuries by discouraging intermarriage and minimising close social contact between the groups, except recently among the élites educated in and customarily using English. The persisting separateness of the Sinhalese (constituting 72 per cent of the population) and the Sri Lanka Tamils (11 per cent) remains the most potent of the country's political problems.

By the thirteenth century the old Rajarata kingdom of north central Ceylon had decayed, and with it many of its splendid feats of irrigation engineering. From this time until the arrival of the Portuguese early in the sixteenth century there were three principal political foci in Sri Lanka: the Tamil kingdom of Jaffna in the far north, centring on the Jaffna Peninsula and separated by what is now a somewhat desolate and extensive region in the northern third of the island from the Kandyan kingdom of Udarata, extending eastwards across the island from the lower hill country in the north of the wet zone, and the kingdom of Kotte, inland and northeast from Colombo on the west coast (see Fig. 18.1).

*Ludowyk, E. F. C., *The Story of Ceylon* (London, 1962), p. 58

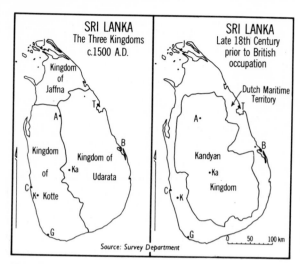

Fig. 18.1

The Country

It is appropriate to pause here to consider what kind of country it was that the Sinhalese and Tamils were striving to colonise, and by what techniques of land exploitation they were able to support themselves. The present-day map of population distribution probably bears very little similarity to the situation that obtained in AD 1500 immediately prior to the establishment of European contacts with the island, and still less to that of AD 1000 when the Sinhalese kingdom based on Anuradhapura was at its height. The early Sinhalese colonists and after them the Tamils, who established their civilisations in the northern half of the island did not occupy the areas which we today would regard as the most favourable to settlement. We can only speculate as to why the better watered southwest quadrant of the country was for so long neglected. In so small an island, measuring very roughly 400 km by 240 km, it is unlikely that people in one part remained long in ignorance of conditions in another. A more likely explanation is that the agricultural techniques available to the colonist and which probably originated in India were found to be adequately effective in supporting, within the dry zone, the population attained within the first millennium AD. The heavy forest cover of the wet zone deterred settlement at this stage.

The fundamental limiting factor in Sri Lanka, as far as agricultural activity is concerned, is rain-fall (Fig. 18.2). The island lies between 6 and 10° latitude north of the equator and is exposed to the open ocean on all sides except the northwest, where along for perhaps one-fifth of its circumference its shores may be said to be lapped by the 'enclosed' sea areas of Palk Strait and the Gulf of Mannar. Proximity to the equator combined with insularity are important influences in the island's climate and account for Sri Lanka's rather more complex rainfall regimes compared with those of South India.

The southwest monsoon – that most dominant of climatic phenomena throughout western India and the eastern shores of the Bay of Bengal – brings heavy rainfall to the southwest coastal lowlands from Negombo through Colombo to beyond Matara, and deluges the west-facing hill country in May and June. From July to September the rain-giving force of the monsoon airstream slackens somewhat as the wind dies down to make way for the doldrum conditions of October to

81 Hindu temple in the Pettah commercial area of Colombo where there is a large Tamil community. Beggars sit by the entrance to obtain alms. The vertical stripes of orange and white signify the building is sacred. Gods of the Hindu pantheon are depicted in gaily painted plaster statuettes.

December.* During the months of the southwest monsoon, two-thirds to three-quarters of Sri Lanka is experiencing its dry season, during which some rainfall occurs, but of an extremely unreliable character. The rainfall dispersion diagrams for Colombo and Trincomalee (see Fig. 3.8) epitomise the two types of regime in Sri Lanka. Figure 20.3 depicts the contrast between the two conventional crop seasons, *Maha* (October to March) and *Yala* (April to September).

the word monsoon generally conjures up impressions of strong winds, it may be better to think of this rainfall as coming from unstable air masses stagnating over Sri Lanka as it lies temporarily becalmed in the doldrum belt. Crowe's studies† of the consistency of the trade wind systems indicate that the northeast monsoon does not firmly establish itself over Sri Lanka until January, by which time the period of maximum precipitation has passed (see Fig. 3.8). In the southwest of the

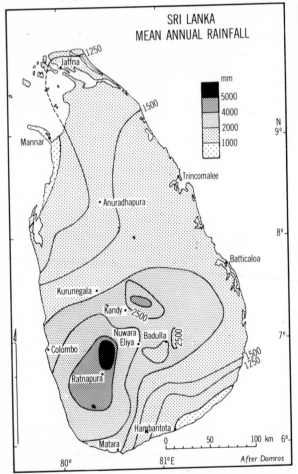

Fig. 18.2

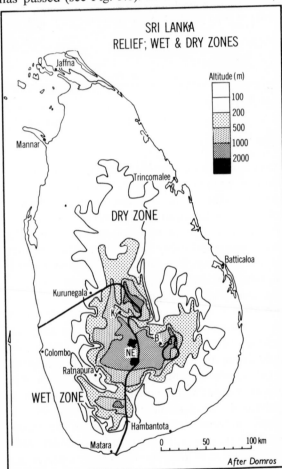

Fig. 18.3

In common with much of the Indian States of Tamilnadu and Kerala, most of Sri Lanka enjoys an important rainy season from October to December. This rain has been attributed to what is called the 'retreating monsoon' but, in so far as

island, most sheltered from the northeast trades, January and February are the months of lowest rainfall, but even so precipitation is far from negligible in quantity and is reasonably reliable (Colombo averages 88 and 96 mm in these months).

With the return of doldrum conditions in March and April the relative importance of inter-monsoonal rainfall to many parts of the island is again demonstrated. At several stations in the dry zone

* Crowe, P. R., 'The Trade Wind Circulation of the World', Trans. Inst. Brit. Geographers (1949), p. 37
† Ibid., 'Wind and Weather in the Equatorial Zone', Trans. Brit. Geographers (1951), p. 23

82 Aerial view of the lowlands in Colombo District showing the distinct separation of paddy cultivation on the flood plains from coconut and mixed homestead gardens on the low interfluves. Drainage of the paddy land is more necessary here than is irrigation; drainage channels follow the centre line of the flood plains. For the most part the paddy has only recently been planted and the fields are under water.

(e.g. Mannar) there is a secondary maximum in April — the 'little monsoon' — after which monthly totals *decline* as the southwest monsoon establishes itself in May.

These several factors affecting rainfall may be seen resolved in Figure 18.2 showing mean annual isohyets. The boundary between wet and dry zones into which Sri Lanka is conventionally and conveniently divided (Fig. 18.3), is based on the occurrence of an 'effective dry period' of three consecutive months, each with less than 102 mm of actual rainfall, more often than not. This boundary can be seen to approximate to the 2,000 mm annual isohyet as it runs inland from Negombo to Kurunegala, and also northwards from the coast near Matara. Within the highlands, however, the boundary runs close to Nuwara Eliya, approximating to the limit of dominance of the southwest over the northeast monsoon. An outlier of the wet zone surrounds the Namunu-kula massif near Badulla in the Uva basin.

The wet zone is, then, a region of generally abundant rainfall, reaching in some highland areas a mean total of over 5,000 mm per year. Characteristically there are two maxima, the greatest in the southwest monsoon in May–June, and a lesser peak in the doldrum season of October–November. As the run of the annual isohyets suggests, the wet zone gives place rather abruptly northwards and southeastwards to the dry zone. Indeed, there is a transitional zone which now and then is invaded by dry zone conditions.

To the traveller from Pakistan or even from the driest parts of Tamilnadu, 'dry' might seem an inappropriate epithet to apply to regions that receive mainly over 1,250 mm of rain, and only rarely below 1,000 mm. The driest parts of Sri Lanka are the northwest coast near Mannar which receives an average of 964 mm, and the south coast east of Hambantota, where *Yala* averages 923 mm. However, the general tendency for areas of lower rainfall to experience greater variability holds here, and it is the occasionally high annual (or monthly) rainfall that tends to raise the average above the median figure which represents the balance of probability. (Trincomalee, for example, with a mean annual rainfall of 1,646 mm had totals ranging from between 873 mm and 2,416 mm.) Flying over or driving through the north central parts of the dry zone, one is struck by the apparent luxuriance of the woodland vegetation. Trees and shrubs with their deep root systems are able to withstand periods of drought better than shallower rooted field crops, and so cannot be taken as an entirely reliable index of the agricultural potentialities of the climate. For agriculture, the big problem is the unreliability of a rainfall which fluctuates from year to year about the point at which a farmer, trying to grow crops without the added insurance of irrigation, would regard as inadequate.

In the dry zone, rainfall comes mainly from October to December, this wet season being extended particularly on the east coast with January's trade winds. The secondary 'little monsoon' rains of April are more marked away from the east coast. June to September, when the southwest monsoon is blowing, are here the months of lowest and least reliable rainfall, conditions which are aggravated, as far as crop growth is concerned, by the desiccating effect of the winds.

Rainfall, through its influence on the growth of natural vegetation and as a limiting factor in agricultural activity, has been the dominant, but not the sole climatic factor affecting man's occupance of the land. Sri Lanka rises to 2,524 m in Pidurutalagala and there are 13 peaks exceeding 2,000 m. In the south centre of the island, the highlands rise to above 1,000 m over a roughly elliptical area measuring 80 km from east to west by 55 km north to south. In addition to this continuous upland there are substantial areas northeast of Kandy, east of Badulla, and in the south of Ratnapura district, which exceed this altitude. (Fig. 18.4 shows the location of districts and their headquarter towns.) Temperatures in these highlands are, of course, 6 degrees and more below those in the surrounding low country, but whether it was the cooler climate, the high rainfall, or the heavy forest cover that discouraged them, the Sinhalese had not settled there except in the lower valleys, and the region awaited development by British plantation owners in the mid-nineteenth century.

The early colonists of Sri Lanka were concerned principally with the lowlands, and with the dry zone lowlands at that. Their staple food, rice, was grown in irrigated fields in valley bottoms. In the dry zone, tank storage of water was essential to guarantee a paddy crop, while in the wet zone the perennial streams had simply to be diverted to water the fields, and floods rather than drought would have been the problem, as they are today. Over many centuries the Sinhalese and Tamils built thousands of tanks and some elaborate and finely executed irrigation systems. Today, tanks are found throughout the dry zone. Many of them have been abandoned, being silted up or in a state of disrepair. Others have been restored. The greatest concentration of tanks, and some of the largest, – the inheritance from the ancient kingdom of Rajarata – are to be seen in Kurunegala, Anuradhapura and Vavuniya Districts. Batticaloa, Amparai and Badulla have relatively few tanks, but they are concentrated again in the south of Monaragala and adjacent parts of Hambamtota, in what must have been a most populous district of the southern kingdom of Ruhuna. A few large tanks are in the nature of dams in the upper and middle reaches of fair-sized rivers such as the Kala Oya (Kala Wewa) and Malwatu Oya (Nachchaduwa Tank). Some, like the Giant's Tank in Mannar District and many small storage systems, derive their water from rivers by means of diversion weirs or *anicuts*, but the vast majority are small storage reservoirs tapping minor catchment areas in the tributary valleys of the major rivers. In the Jaffna Peninsula the low relief and limestone rock, lacking surface streams, are not conducive to tank construction. There are ponds but many of the larger water bodies are saline and the Jaffna Tamils still sink wells for drinking water and to supply intensively cultivated cash crops, while relying on rains for rice growing. Supplementary to paddy farming in the dry zone (and in a few areas independent of it) the early cultivators, like their modern counterparts, utilised wooded interfluve areas for *chena*

Fig. 18.4

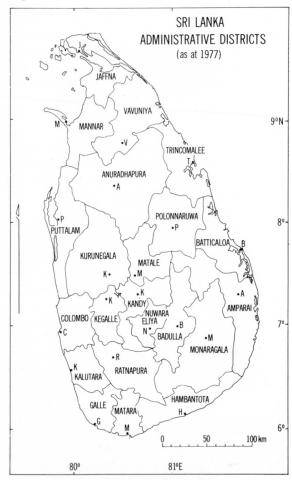

SRI LANKA
ADMINISTRATIVE DISTRICTS
(as at 1977)

83 Old colonial style upper class residence in Cinnamon Gardens, Colombo. Many such houses are now used as offices for government departments, foreign legations, etc.

(shifting) cultivation, growing dry crops such as millets and oilseeds. In their homestead gardens they no doubt cultivated — as is the practice today throughout Sri Lanka — fruit trees, spices, and vegetables, but their economy was one of local self-sufficiency. What trade there was had little direct effect on the peasant. The export of gemstones, pearls, and elephants through Arab and Chinese traders helped enrich the king and his officials in the capital but, to quote Ludowyk, 'the kingdom's prosperity was based on the prosperity of its rice fields'. He suggests that the kingdoms stagnated through the progressive imposition on the cultivator, whose techniques did not develop, of too great a burden of supporting the state and its religious institutions.

Irrigation schemes on the scale developed in the north central lowlands by the twelfth century AD depended for their continued success on an efficient and centralised administration. The proper maintenance of tank bunds, weirs, and canals would have been beyond the means of simple villagers. In the wet zone, however, where paddy fields can be watered by diverting streams and impounding rainfall, there would be no such complex administrative problems. The centuries of political disintegration which followed the relative stability of the Anuradhapura (250 BC – AD 1029) and Polonnaruwa (AD 1111–1215) periods saw the decay of many of the irrigation schemes and the impoverishment and probably the partial depopulation of what are now the districts of Anuradhapura and Polonnaruwa. From what must have been a quite highly centralised and unified island State, Sri Lanka lapsed into the three weaker kingdoms and an unnumbered array of 'war-lordships' under local leaders. It is perhaps significant that the three kingdoms were based on areas where subsistence agriculture could be pursued without State initiative or control: Jaffna had its wells and rain-fed paddies; the foci of the kingdoms of Kotte and Kandy (Udarata) lay mainly in the wet zone (Fig. 18.1).

For perhaps three centuries there was little change in the situation, but in 1505 a new factor appeared on the scene. Up to this time the island's overseas contacts had been primarily Asian. Arabs, Moslem Indians, Malays (probably) and Chinese had used the island as an entrepôt, conveniently sited midway between the Red Sea and the Persian Gulf, gateways to European trade, and the Straits of Malacca leading to China's sphere of trading influence. With the sixteenth century Europe ceased to be content to leave this profitable commerce in Asian (especially Arab) hands and, following exploratory voyages in the late fifteenth century, the Portuguese were quick to establish a chain of trading centres around the shores of the Indian Ocean. Their acquisition of Colombo in 1505 must be viewed in the wider context of other bases in Ormuz, Diu, Goa, Cochin, Madras, Hooghly, Chittagong, Bassein, Malacca and elsewhere, which formed the foundation of one hundred years of trading monopoly. The arrival of the Portuguese to trade in the high grade wild cinnamon that flourished in the west coastal lowlands saw the beginnings of a commercial agricultural economy that was to reach its culmination in the nineteenth century under the British. The cinnamon trade, which predated the Portuguese in Sri Lanka, probably brought to the fore a sociological phenomenon which is only now beginning to weaken in the face of economic necessity. Cinnamon grew wild on the royal estates, and a labour force had to be found to peel the cinnamon twigs to obtain the commercially valuable bark. The Sinhalese Buddhist of whatever social level, while willing enough to labour on the land for himself and his family, has always tended to regard toil for another as distasteful. Whether or not this was the major reason, from the fourteenth and fifteenth centuries South Indian labourers were imported to peel cinnamon.*

A continuing feature of the political geography of Sri Lanka from the medieval period until 1815 was the independence of the Sinhalese kingdom based upon Kandy. The Portuguese failed to establish unified political control over the island, though they set up fortified ports in Jaffna and Galle in addition to Colombo, and effectively dominated trade. By the early seventeenth century European trade rivalry showed itself, when the Dutch treated with the Kandyan king on how to rid the island of the Portuguese. By 1640 the Dutch were in Galle, by 1656 in Colombo and in Jaffna by 1658. Furthermore, they built forts on the east coast at Trincomalee and Batticaloa in their efforts to monopolise the trade of the Indian Ocean. With the Dutch came (as in the East Indies) the embryonic plantation system. Gardens of cinnamon were planted, and this, with arecanuts, dominated trade. Pepper and coffee trees were introduced, coconut planting increased, and commercially valuable field crops such as sugar cane and tobacco were encouraged. Under the Dutch, the idea of commercial plantation agriculture blossomed with their Sinhalese official class, the Mudaliyars, becoming wealthy land-holders in the process. The problem of feeding a partly non-subsistent agricultural population made itself apparent. Rice had to be imported from India, and slave labour was introduced from Tanjore (Southern India) in an effort to reclaim some of the land which had been lost to paddy cultivation during the Portuguese period.

By the end of the eighteenth century the effect of many decades of commercial activity and peace could be seen in the prosperity of the west coastal lowlands, though the Kandyan kingdom remained relatively poor, backward and aloof, with a traditional economy. It was this dichotomy that led to the separate identification of Kandy and Low Country Sinhalese, the latter being much more affected by contact with European culture and commerce than the more traditionally minded

*Ludowyk, E. F. C., *op. cit.*, p. 195

84   Tea picking on an upcountry estate is done by Indian Tamil women. The small shade trees are *Dadap* the largest trunks, *Grevillea*.

and independent Kandyans. Today the distinction has little or no political significance.

The events which led to the Dutch abandoning their possessions in Malaya were paralleled in Sri Lanka. The British, strongly established in Madras, were at war with France at the end of the eighteenth century and intense rivalry for the naval bases essential to trading nations existed between them in the Indian Ocean. Trincomalee first attracted the attention of the British, who after losing it to the French regained control and returned it to the Dutch in 1784. With the overrunning of Holland by the French, the British (in the form of the Madras Presidency of the East India Company) stepped in as a 'caretaker' of Dutch interests in Sri Lanka, as in Malaya and the East Indies, and remained in possession thereafter. The Dutch territories, effectively the former Jaffna Kingdom and the coastal belt, became a crown colony in 1802, and thus began the last volume of the trilogy of domination by a European power (Fig. 18.1).

The British accomplishment in Sri Lanka has been described as a modernisation of the structure laid down by the Dutch. Against the wishes of the home authorities the Governor in Sri Lanka proceeded to 'tidy up' the political situation by bringing to an end the independent existence of the Kandyan kingdom. By building roads as a means to political control the economic possibilities of the interior of the island could begin to be realised. British colonial rule heralded a new era of plantation development, in which the mixed economy of wild cinnamon collecting and the cultivation of export tree crops such as coffee, pepper, and coconuts alongside traditional subsistence agriculture gave place to a more specialised and commercial economy for much of the wet zone. Coffee was the prop of the new economy and was grown on Sinhalese small-holdings as well as European-owned estates. Booming in the 1840s it reached a peak of exports in 1875 (43,514 tonnes from 101,200 ha) but was hit by blight which ruined most of the trees in the late 1870s and brought production down to less than 9,144 tonnes by 1886. Botanists had long been active, however, and were ready first with cinchona and then tea to replace coffee and so enable the whole complex structure of the economy, including roads, railways and ports, to continue in use. Tea planting,

begun commercially in 1867, went ahead apace on both lowland plateaux and in the high country where (from 1840 with the passing of the Crown Lands Encroachment Ordinance) much land was alienated to British private ownership, in some cases certainly depriving the Kandyan villagers of their traditional common woodland — in which they could pasture animals, cultivate *chenas* and, when population pressure compelled, build and cultivate paddy terraces. Rubber joined tea towards the end of the century to compete for the lower hill country and to add to the demand for plantation labour. Unlike tea and rubber, the coffee harvest is seasonal and temporary labour was generally recruited in South India to work under extremely poor and unhealthy conditions. Thousands succumbed to malaria. For tea a more permanent workforce was needed and, since the Sinhalese prejudice against wage labouring was still strong, the planters had to create villages of Indian Tamils on their estates. These 'Indian Tamil' immigrants, separated by a thousand years of history from the 'Sri Lanka Tamils' of Jaffna, are even more distinct than the latter, from their Sinhalese neighbours. For five generations now they have lived on their estates, remote from their ancestral homeland yet largely out of contact with Sri Lanka also.

In overseas trade, Sri Lanka tea and rubber have held dominant positions since World War I, but in a worthy third place has stood another tree crop – coconuts. Of greater seniority than tea or rubber in Sri Lanka's economic history, coconut growing is mainly the preserve of Sinhalese estate owners and small-holders, and is extensively grown in the sandier coastal lowlands, especially in the 'coconut triangle' northwards from Colombo to Chilaw and east to Kurunagela. Profits in coconut plantations have never compared with those to be gained in tea or rubber, with the result that European interest therein was slight.

Soon after the end of World War II the British voluntarily relinquished their colonial rule and Sri Lanka achieved once more the state of unified independence that history suggests may have prevailed a millennium ago. While superficially it may appear that independence has brought little change in the economy, which is still dominated by the fluctuating fortunes of plantation commodities on the world market, there has been considerable movement away from the rigidly dual economy of colonial times. Whereas formerly British capital and Indian Tamil labour generated profits and earnings which were in part repatriated and in part invested in the infrastructure of the plantation sector, since the nationalisation of all but the small estates and the virtual disappearance of the British interest at the production level, the economy is becoming gradually more integrated. It is also expanding in sectors previously neglected, specifically the cultivation of the staple foodgrain rice, and the manufacture of goods for local consumption. As in many developing countries it is the outcome of the struggle by production to overtake population increase that will determine the nation's welfare.

Chapter 19

Sri Lanka: The People and the Economy

Ethnic Structure

Not least among Sri Lanka's problems is that of welding into a national unity the several more or less distinct ethnic groups. Their population strength is shown in Table 19.1 and their distribution by districts in Figure 19.1.

Grouped together, the Kandyan and Low Country Sinhalese constitute 72 per cent of the total population, a level exceeded over the lowland wet zone and in the dry zone in all but the three northern and three eastern districts. Nuwara Eliya, the highest tea growing district, has only 41 per cent Sinhalese, and the neighbouring districts of Kandy and Badulla, 62 and 59 per cent respectively.

Sri Lanka or 'Jaffna' Tamils with 11.2 per cent of the total are in an overall majority in the three northernmost districts (reaching 92 per cent in Jaffna), and in the east coast district of Batticaloa.

Trincomalee and Amparai, adjoining Batticaloa to its north and south respectively, have 35 and 22 per cent Sri Lanka Tamils. In no other district do they exceed 6.5 per cent of the total.

Indian Tamils are mainly where they can find work on plantations. They have little in common with the Sri Lanka Tamils, and are mainly unenfranchised non-citizens. They reach 52 per cent of the total in Nuwara Eliya and 25 and 34 per cent in Kandy and Badulla respectively. The dry zone district of Mannar (18 per cent) has very small absolute numbers, related to proximity to the rail ferry entry from India at Talaimannar.

The other community with substantial numbers is the Sri Lanka Moors with 6.5 per cent of the total. As a group descended from sea-going Arabs arriving in the eleventh century, and with strong fishing interests, they exceed 23 per cent in the east coast districts of Trincomalee, Batticaloa and

Amparai (45 per cent) and in Mannar. The small number of Indian Moors came to Sri Lanka in the nineteenth century in search of work, and the Malays were brought in earlier to serve under the Dutch. The Burghers and Eurasians are the descendants of mixed marriages of Portuguese, Dutch, or British colonists mainly with Low Country Sinhalese.

Fig. 19.1

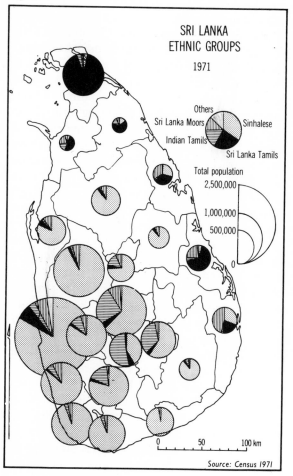

Source: Census 1971

Table 19.1   Population by ethnic groups, 1971

Ethnic group		Number (thousands)	Per cent
Low Country Sinhalese	5,426; 42.8%	9,131	72.0
Kandyan Sinhalese	3,705; 29.2%		
Sri Lanka Tamils		1,424	11.2
Indian Tamils		1,175	9.3
Sri Lanka Moors		828	6.5
Indian Moors		27	0.2
Burghers and Eurasians		45	0.4
Malays		43	0.3
Others		16	0.1

Source: Statistical Pocket Book of Sri Lanka, 1977

Religion

While the majority of the major groups adhere to their traditional religions, the Sinhalese to Buddhism, the Tamils to Hinduism, the European colonial contact can be seen in almost 8 per cent of the population professing Christianity (over 80 per cent of these being Roman Catholics). Buddhism is the religion of over two-thirds of the total population, a proportion that has been rising with the revival of this faith following Independence. Hinduism, following with 18 per cent, has been declining with the repatriation of Indian Tamils, while Islam with 7 per cent shows a recent fractional advance though the percentage has varied only between 6.6 and 7.2 since 1881.

Both Buddhist and Hindu communities are stratified by caste. Among the Sinhalese there are five major castes which, although deriving from pre-Buddhist Hinduism, now carry no religious sanctions but are merely functional in origin, and now have some connotation in terms of traditional social status especially as affecting marriage and social mobility. At the top are the Goyigamas (the cultivators) followed by the Salagamas (the cinnamon–peelers, coming from the Chaliyas or weavers), the Karavas (fishermen) and Duravas (toddy tappers). There are many other minor castes like tailors, barbers, domestic servants, etc. The Tamils have castes similar to those of South India, ranging from the priestly Brahmin through superior and inferior cultivating castes, Vellala and Koviyar, and numerous others to the 'Untouchables' at the lowest rank of the system.

The Ethnic Problem

No study of Sri Lanka today can ignore the issue of ethnic disharmony which has become increasingly acute since Independence. Under the British, the Sinhalese and Sri Lanka Tamil élites, educated in English, lived and worked together amicably while preserving their respective cultural identities. The British, by introducing Indian Tamil labour to work the plantations, created a new community which until World War II had been fairly transitory, a fact that was recognised in early measures towards representative government which denied most of them the franchise. However, 225,000 had been granted the vote as domiciled Indians by 1939, though more than half of these were disenfranchised and many rendered stateless by an act passed in 1949 soon after Independence. The fate of the Indian Tamils has been the subject of Indo-Sri Lanka discussions culminating in the so-called Srimavo-Shastri Pact of 1964 under which Sri Lanka was to grant citizenship to 300,000 Indians and India was to accept 525,000 as repatriated workers. They were subsequently granted Indian citizenship. In 1974 the numbers were adjusted to 375,000 and 600,000 respectively, and 1982 was set as the date by which the whole transaction would be completed.

The fate of the Indian Tamils and the question of their enfranchisement are minor issues compared with those that confound relations between Sinhalese and Sri Lanka Tamils. Since Independence the resurgence of Sinhala-Buddhist nationalism, seeking for the majority group in the population a larger share of power and influence than had been theirs under British rule, has resulted in discriminatory legislation and administrative action to the detriment of Sri Lanka Tamils. Language and education have been the areas in which Tamils have suffered most overt discrimination. In the 1972 Constitution, Sinhala was made the official language thus denying to the Tamils the use of their language for official purposes. Although the 1978 Constitution removed or moderated some of the earlier legislation, it will take a generation of constructive tolerance to disperse the bitter memories of intercommunal violence and the insidious slights handed out by petty bureaucrats infected by the attitudes engendered by public opinion unmoderated by political opportunists.

Employment in the public service under the British had disproportionately favoured the Tamils who had earned a reputation for scholastic achievement and success in open competition. Insistence on proficiency in Sinhala severely reduced this area of employment for Tamils. They were also discriminated against by the 'standardisation' procedures adopted to ensure that a higher proportion of Sinhala speakers obtained places in the University, even though their academic results were below those of Tamil applicants.

The 1978 Constitution makes some amends in recognising Tamil as a language permissible for legal uses in the Northern and Eastern Provinces, i.e. Jaffna, Mannar and Vavuniya, Batticaloa, Amparai and Trincomalee Districts, and by assuring all domiciled non-Sinhalese of 'civil rights', but not including the right to vote. President Jayewardene also announced that the optional use of English was to be re-introduced generally in secondary and tertiary education, in which it had been progressively replaced by Sinhala and Tamil.

Many educated people in Sri Lanka from all communities see a return to English as a way of overcoming the divisiveness of education in one or other of the majority languages by restoring a common language for communication, and at the same time re-opening to scholars the resources in human knowledge, not available in Sinhala or Tamil.

It is somewhat ironic that education, so often regarded as the panacea for the ills of underdevelopment, itself becomes a bone of contention in

85 Traditional outrigger fishing boats at the Fisheries harbour, Colombo. The grain store of the flour mill near the docks can be seen behind.

this, the best-educated of the countries of South Asia. The 1971 Census showed 72 per cent of the males and 67 per cent of the females aged 10–14 were at school, levels that compare very favourably with standards elsewhere in South Asia. The figure for both sexes was 71 per cent for Sri Lanka as a whole, ranging from 85 per cent in Jaffna to 58 per cent in Batticaloa. The high proportion of girls in school is particularly noteworthy. That 78 per cent of the population 10 years old and over are literate (86 per cent of the males, 71 per cent of the females) bears witness to the long-held respect in which education is held in the country. Colombo District (with 88 per cent literate) leads the field, in which again Batticaloa trails on 57 per cent.

86. Finishing pots made and fired near Trincomalee.

Occupations

The occupations of the employed population according to the 1971 Census are shown in Table 19.2.

Half the total are engaged in primary production, 20 per cent being cultivators of the three major export tree crops — tea, rubber and coconuts. In tea growing there are slightly more women than men, but in no other activity do they approach equality. Manufacturing industry is relatively poorly developed with 9 per cent of all employed, mostly in textiles, the food, drink and tobacco group, and working in wood etc. Metal and mechanical industries are quite small employers. Wholesaling and retailing engage as many as does manufacturing, not a surprising fact when one sees the great numbers of tiny 'boutiques' along the roads, many with quite minuscule stock and

turnover. Unemployment is high and underemployment also is rife. In 1971, 437,400 were registered as seeking employment, compared with the Census total of 3.6 million employed. In the first quarter of 1977, the figure had increased to over 567,000 though these numbers include those seeking to change their employment as well as those out of work.

Gross National Product

Table 19.3 shows the sectoral composition of the GNP in 1978.

GNP per head of population was Rs 2,543, approximating to US$ 164, which represents a 50 per cent increase since 1959. Had population growth been at half the rate, the increase would have been 78 per cent. The sectoral values differ somewhat from the proportions of the workforce

Table 19.2   Major occupations, 1971 (thousands and per cent of total employed)

	Total*	%	Males	%	Females	%
Total employed	**3,649**	**100**	**2,838**	**78**	**810**	**22**
Agriculture, hunting, forestry, fishing†	**1,829**	**50**	**1,328**	**36**	**501**	**14**
Agriculture, paddy cultivation	803	22	689	19	114	3.1
Agriculture, tea cultivation	559	15	266	7	294	8
Agriculture, rubber cultivation	138	3.8	87	2.4	51	1.4
Agriculture, coconut cultivation	43	1.2	36	1.0	7	0.2
Agriculture, fishing	54	1.5	54	1.5	0.7	—
Mining and quarrying	**13**	**0.4**	**12**	**0.3**	**1**	—
Manufacturing†	**339**	**9**	**240**	**7**	**99**	**2.7**
Manufacturing, food and drink and tobacco	72	2	59	1.6	13	0.4
Manufacturing, textiles	99	2.7	30	0.8	70	1.9
Manufacturing, clothing	19	0.5	12	0.3	6	0.2
Manufacturing, wood, cork, furniture	71	1.9	70	1.9	2	—
Manufacturing, pottery, etc.	5	0.1	3	0.1	2	—
Manufacturing, iron, sheet and fabricated metal	11	0.3	11	0.3	—	—
Manufacturing jewellery	8	0.2	8	0.2	—	—
Electricity, gas, water	**10**	**0.3**	**10**	**0.3**	—	—
Construction	**104**	**2.8**	**103**	**2.8**	**1**	—
Wholesale, retail trade etc.	**344**	**9**	**320**	**9**	**23**	**0.6**
Transport, storage, commerce	**179**	**4.9**	**176**	**4.8**	**3**	**0.1**
Finance, business	**25**	**0.7**	**23**	**0.6**	**2**	—
Community, social, personal services	**493**	**14**	**361**	**10**	**132**	**4**
Other	**314**	**9**	**267**	**7**	**47**	**1.3**

*Totals across columns may not tally due to rounding
†Only major sub-heads to agriculture etc. and manufacturing are shown

employed therein, mining, manufacturing and transport and communications showing a relatively higher contribution to national product than their workforce would suggest, presumably because of greater capital investment permitting higher productivity per capita. How vital the plantation sector is to the economy is clearly seen in the export and import trade statistics, set out in Tables 19.4 and 19.5.

It is noteworthy that there was a positive balance of trade in favour of Sri Lanka. As revised by Customs the balance was Rs 631 million in 1977. Apart from the previous year when the surplus was Rs 170 million, the decade since 1968 showed a trade deficit in every year.

The heavy dependence on plantation products for earning foreign exchange is very apparent, these making up 78 per cent of the total. Such commodities are notoriously subject to fluctuations in the world market price. Tea is a non-essential beverage for which substitutes exist – particularly coffee – which is subject to more variation in world production and price than is tea. The world shortage of coffee in 1977 helped Sri Lanka, through a rise in tea prices.

Table 19.6 and Figure 19.2 show the trends in tea and rubber exports by volume and value since 1967, indexing the latter at 100. The value of imports is also shown similarly and the terms of trade, i.e. the export price index as a percentage of the import price index. While the volume of export trade has fluctuated relatively slightly in the case of tea (between 100 and 81) and rubber (between 97 and 122) their value has increased more or less marching with inflation in the case of tea, but more erratically in the case of rubber. The volume of imports shows more variation than that of exports, from 108 down to 56, but in terms of value imports have been rather erratic so that despite a substantial drop in volume in 1974–75–76, their rising value (largely due to the escalation in the price of oil and related products like fertilisers) depressed the terms of trade. The table and figures illustrate how difficult it is for rubber producers, for example, to foresee the market trends. Since they provide less than 5 per cent of the world's natural rubber they are hardly likely to have much impact on its price. Sri Lanka's fluctuating income from rubber in the mid 1970s ran inversely to its exports, rising as exports fell and vice versa.

Table 19.3 Gross National Product 1978 (percentage of total provisional value Rs 36,139 million, current cost)

Sector	Per cent of total
Agriculture, forestry, hunting, fishing	31.8
Mining and quarrying	1.8
Manufacturing	20.7
Construction	4.9
Electricity, gas, water, sanitation	0.6
Transport, storage, communications	8.1
Wholesale and retail trade	17.4
Banking, insurance, real estate	2.1
Ownership of dwellings	1.3
Public administration and defence	3.8
Services	8.1

Source: Central Bank of Ceylon, *Annual Report for 1978*

Table 19.4 Export trade, 1978 (current value and per cent of total)

	Rs million	Per cent
Tea	6,401	48
Rubber	2,021	15
Coconut products	1,259	10
Minor crops	371	3
Gemstones	531	4
Industrial products	1,891	14
Others	733	6
TOTAL	13,207	100

Source: Central Bank of Ceylon *Bulletin*, Feb. 1979

Table 19.5 Import trade, 1978 (current value and per cent of total)

	Rs. million	Per cent
Food and drink	4,249	29
flour	2,095	14
rice	698	5
sugar	553	4
other foodstuffs	912	6
Textiles and clothing	1,228	8
Petroleum	2,499	17
Fertiliser, chemicals	1,292	9
Other intermediate goods	1,424	10
Machinery, equipment	1,800	12
Transport equipment	1,682	12
Unclassified	376	3
TOTAL	14,500	100

Source: Central Bank of Ceylon *Bulletin*, Feb. 1979

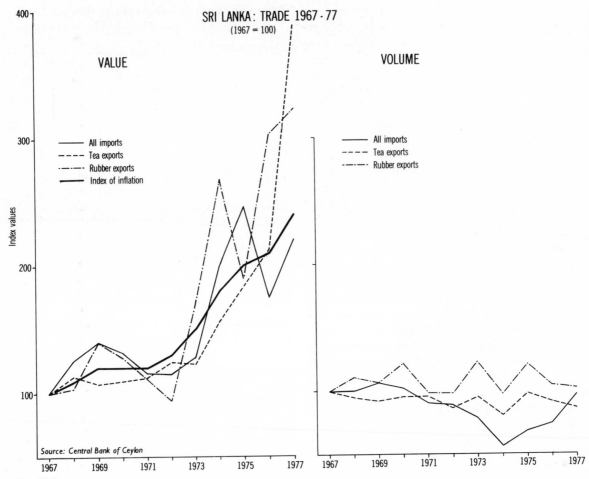

SRI LANKA : TRADE 1967 - 77
(1967 = 100)

VALUE

VOLUME

— All imports
--- Tea exports
-·-· Rubber exports
▬▬ Index of inflation

— All imports
--- Tea exports
-·-· Rubber exports

Source: Central Bank of Ceylon

Fig. 19.2

Table 19.6   Indices of export and import volumes and values, 1967–78
(1967 = 100)

Price index	*Export volume (kg million)*	*TEA Export volume (index)*	*Export prices*	*Export volume (kg million)*	*RUBBER Export volume (index)*	*Export prices (index)*	*All imports price index*	*All exports price index*	*Terms of trade price index*
1967	218	100	100	132	100	100	100	100	100
1968	209	96	114	150	113	104	126	101	93
1969	202	93	108	143	108	141	140	108	88
1970	208	96	110	161	122	128	131	102	84
1971	208	96	113	129	98	111	115	90	78
1972	190	87	125	130	98	96	115	88	75
1973	206	95	124	161	122	172	128	79	65
1974	175	81	158	128	97	269	201	56	58
1975	213	98	185	161	121	191	246	69	46
1976	200	92	214	137	104	304	175	75	62
1977	186	86	389	136	102	324	221	97	81
1978	193	89	680	138	104	686	877	698	80

Source: Central Bank of Ceylon

87 Minipe *anicut* on the Maha-weli Ganga, an ancient scheme now modernised. A canal (left background) leads the water for several kilometres to paddy fields. In flood the river overflows the anicut without damaging it.

88 A craftsman at work on a brass tray at Kundasale, a village near Kandy, specializing in brass work.

89 An elephant working timber on the outskirts of Colombo. The wood has been floated down the Kelani Ganga to the saw mill.

Chapter 20

Sri Lanka: Agriculture for National Subsistence and for Export

The Food Supply

Sri Lanka's basic agricultural problem is indicated in the tables of exports and imports. As an agricultural country, how is it to reduce the need to import foodstuffs (and so leave more of the earned foreign exchange for the purchase of manufactured goods) and at the same time to maximise the production at low cost of the exportable plantation commodities? The long-elusive target of self-sufficiency in rice seems at last to be in sight, and maybe flour imports will be substantially reduced

Table 20.1 Paddy area harvested 1949–50 to 1977–78

	Sri Lanka 1949–50[1]	1977–78[2]	Percentage increase	Wet Zone 1949–50[1]	1977–78[2]	Percentage increase	Dry zone 1949–50[1]	1977–78[2]	Percentage increase
	(a) Paddy: Area harvested (thousand hectares and percentage increase)								
Maha crop	247	553	124	117	157	34	130	396	205
Yala crop	149	277	86	95	129	36	54	148	174
TOTAL	396	830	110	212	286	35	185	544	194
	(b) Paddy: Maha and Yala crops as percentage of total by Zone								
Maha crop	62	67		55	55		71	73	
Yala crop	38	33		45	45		29	27	
TOTAL	100	100		100	100		100	100	
	(c) Paddy: area irrigated (thousand hectares and percentage increase)								
Maha crop	100	342	242	24	58	142	76	284	274
Yala crop	67	162	142	21	43	105	47	119	153
TOTAL	167	504	202	45	101	124	122	403	230
	(d) Paddy: area irrigated as percentage of Maha, Yala and total								
Maha crop	41	62		21	37		58	72	
Yala crop	45	59		22	33		87	80	
TOTAL	42	61		21	35		66	74	
	(e) Paddy: Wet and Dry Zone crops as percentage of Sri Lanka total by season								
Maha crop	100	100		47	28		53	72	
Yala crop	100	100		64	47		36	53	
TOTAL	100	100		53	34		47	66	

Source: [1]Department of Census and Statistics, *Abstract of Statistics*, Colombo, 1951;
[2]Department of Census and Statistics, unpublished mimeographed tables; courtesy of Mr. H. Jayasinghe

Notes: (1) The data refer to the crop seasons (i) *Maha* 1949–50 and *Yala* 1950, and (ii) *Yala* 1977 and *Maha* 1977–78
(2) Rounding off accounts for some apparent errors in addition
(3) The allocation of Districts to Wet or Dry Zones follows the practice of the Central Bank of Ceylon. The following are Wet Zone Districts:
Colombo, Kalutara, Galle, Matara, Kegalle, Ratnapura, Kandy, Nuwara Eliya and Badulla

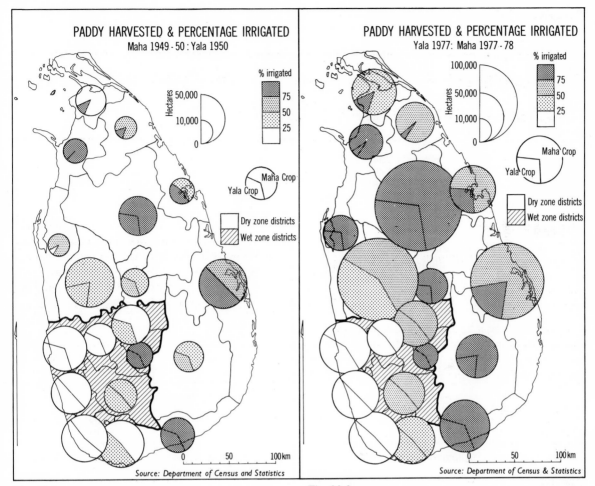

Fig. 20.1

Fig. 20.2

as more rice becomes available to meet the demands for this, the traditional staple. The main trends in paddy cultivation are summarised in Figures 20.1 and 20.2 showing by districts the area harvested in each season in 1949–50 and 1977–78 respectively. Table 20.1 sets out the salient facts in terms of the wet and dry zones and the country as a whole.

Two cropping seasons are recognised traditionally in Sri Lanka; the *Maha* season from October to March, covering the period of the 'retreating' monsoon, the northeast monsoon and the beginning of the inter-monsoonal doldrum phase that follows, and the *Yala* season from April to September, including the southwest monsoon. As shown in Figure 20.3 of the distribution of rainfall in these two seasons, *Maha* is the more generally wet season, while in *Yala* the distinction between a wet zone and a dry zone is quite marked.

In Figures 20.1 and 20.2. the circles representing the total area harvested by districts are divided proportionately for *Yala* and *Maha* crops and are shaded to indicate the percentage irrigated. The sector representing the *Yala* harvest is oriented to the southwest and *Maha* to the northeast, the quarters from which the relevant rainfall comes. As three of the 1949–50 districts i.e. Anuradhapura, Batticaloa and Badulla were subsequently subdivided, each into two, the 1977–78 data are shown for the directly comparable areas.

Since 1949–50 the area harvested has increased by 110 per cent, 434,000 ha; most of this in the dry zone – (194 per cent of 359,000 ha) with only 35 per cent increase in the wet zone. (Table 5.3.1a) It follows that more of the increase has been in the area harvested in *Maha* (124 per cent increase) than in *Yala* (77 per cent). *Maha* now accounts for two

Table 20.2   Paddy yields, 1949–50 and 1977–78

| | *(Kilograms per hectare)* | | | | *Per cent increase* | |
	Maha 1949–50	*Yala* 1950	*Maha* 1977–78	*Yala* 1977	*Maha*	*Yala*
Sri Lanka	794	712	2,279	1,908	187	168
Rain-fed	732	598	1,738	1,537	137	157
Irrigated	892	846	2,599	2,171	191	157
Wet Zone	773	619	1,949	1,712	152	177
Rain-fed	763	593	1,666	1,537	118	159
Irrigated	810	696	2,341	2,021	189	190
Dry Zone	835	918	2,491	2,248	198	145
Rain-fed	598	773	1,851	1,568	210	103
Irrigated	954	928	2,692	2,264	182	144

thirds of the total crop area. (Table 5.3.1b) Much of the increase has been made possible by extension of irrigation. In the dry zone 281,000 ha or 230 per cent more land is irrigated than in 1949–50, and in the wet zone 124 per cent. (Table 5.3.1c).

The percentage irrigated in the dry zone is about double that in the wet zone, even during *Maha*, the most generally wet season (Table 5.3.1d.). In the dry zone, the proportion irrigated ranges from 72

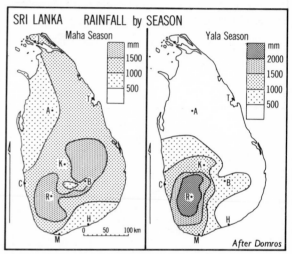

Fig. 20.3

90   Processing high grade crepe rubber in a large mill near Avissawela, Colombo District.

per cent in *Maha* to 80 per cent in *Yala*, compared with 37 and 33 per cent respectively in the wet zone. In the driest districts of the dry zone (Jaffna, Vavuniya and Mannar) the whole *Yala* crop has to be irrigated if any harvest is to be reaped, and in these same districts 80, 96 and 94 per cent respectively are irrigated in *Maha*, and in Batticaloa, Monaragala and Amparai, over 80 per cent. In the wet zone on the other hand irrigation is often a more casual procedure, valuable as a standby when rains are erratic, but rarely absolutely essential to the harvesting of a crop.

Yields of paddy per ha by seasons and regions are given in Table 20.2: rice yields would be 68 per cent of the figure for paddy, i.e. unhusked rice.

The very considerable improvement in yields is attributable to the introduction of HYV and the better cultivation methods that have been associated with the 'green revolution': fertiliser use, the chemical control of pests and diseases, etc. The dry zone, especially where irrigated in *Maha*, shows the highest yields of all – at 2,692 kg/ha. Overall, it is the irrigated crops that are generally better yielding since they are most likely to benefit from the 'green revolution package'.

The basic contrasts in paddy cultivation are between wet zone and dry zone: the wet zone has abundant moisture but a shortage of land, while in the dry zone the position is reversed, there being a shortage of water but available land. Figure 20.4 shows the percentage of the total land area used for agriculture by districts, and points to the greater problem of land availability in the wet zone.

Fig. 20.4

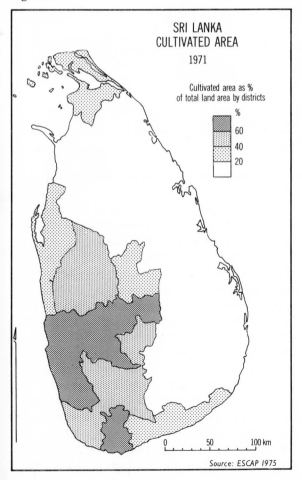

SRI LANKA
CULTIVATED AREA
1971

Cultivated area as %
of total land area by districts

%
60
40
20

0   50   100 km

Source: ESCAP 1975

Paddy in the Wet Zone

It can be seen in Figure 20.2 that there is a near balance in paddy acreage between *Maha* and *Yala* seasons in the wet zone. Overall the *Maha* crop makes up 55 per cent of the annual total, and yields are higher, despite the low rainfall of this season. In fact, the higher rainfall of the *Yala* season, often producing floods, and the cloudier weather associated with it which promotes the development of plant diseases and pests, combine to make it a less favourable period for paddy cultivation. Sown in April, the *Yala* crop comes to maturity in July – August when conditions are seldom ideal for ripening, cutting, threshing, drying and storing the grain. The terrain of the wet zone lowlands consists largely of low plateau closely dissected and interfingered by the narrow floodplains of many short but occasionally vigorous rivers, whose profiles are prematurely flattened from their middle courses. Consequently, in their lower reaches, lagoons and marshes are common, and the river mouths are usually obstructed by sand bars built up by waves driven by the dominant southwesterly winds. Flooding is a regular occurrence, tending to affect not only the plains of the main river but also those of its tributaries which become ponded back.

In the south, behind Matara, the coastal lowland is 25 km wide but it narrows north of Galle to as little as 5 km, to widen again through Kalutara and Colombo districts to almost 50 km inland of Negombo, and even wider in the wet zone – dry zone transition in Kurunegala.

Figure 20.5 shows the land-use of a characteristic portion of the wet zone lowland in Colombo District. Rice growing occurs in a similar fashion above the regularly flooded areas on the lowland valley floors throughout the wet zone, and penetrates the 'ridge and valley' region of Ratnapura and the lower valleys of the hill country generally.

Paddy relies largely on direct rainfall supplemented by water led from the streams in small channels known as *elas*. Although the rainfall is over 2,000 mm per annum, and is normally well distributed throughout the year, occasional dry spells occur, more often in January – February but sometimes also in August, which make the maintenance of the *elas* a worthwhile insurance. By Asian standards, paddy cultivation techniques are still at a mediocre level. Apart from the environmental

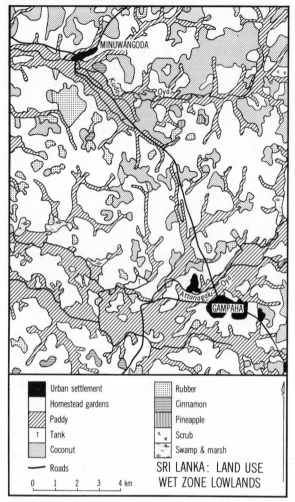

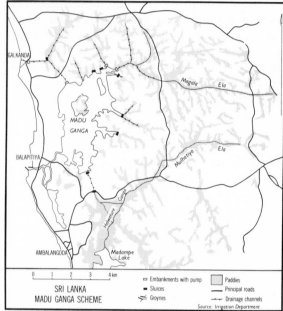

plains of the major rivers and the areas around the coastal lagoons. In the case of rivers like the Bentota Ganga, Gin Ganga and Nilwala Ganga, flood protection involves building levees to restrict the flood current to the main channel, expediting its discharge to the sea, and preventing floodwater entering the tributary basins. Sluices allow the tributary drainage to enter the main river when its level is low.

Fig. 20.5 (based on a map of the Sri Lanka Survey Department with the sanction of the Surveyor General).

Fig. 20.6

difficulties part of the blame for low yields must be placed on the field practices which are not intensive. Transplantation is exceptional, to some extent because the high organic content of the marsh soils renders them too weak to support transplanted seedlings. Normally pre-germinated seed is broadcast on to the puddled land.

Investment in long-term improvements in paddy production is inhibited by the common land-holding practice of *thattumaru* under which the partition of ownership in land is achieved by sharing its use over time rather than by subdividing the fields. While this helps to avoid reducing holdings to uneconomic levels, the man who uses the land for one year in five, for example, will limit his inputs to those giving immediate returns.

The problem of flooding differs between the

The Madu Ganga Salt Water Exclusion Scheme (Fig. 20.6) illustrates the approach to the problem of the coastal lagoons. The Madu Ganga, on the borders of Kalutara and Galle Districts, forms a lake 8 km² in extent which drains to the sea about a kilometre distant at Balapitiya, through a natural channel the depth of which is restricted by rock and whose mouth is constrained by the longshore drift of beach sand building up a bar. This effectively dams the river during dry periods, and while the lake deepens when the river is in spate there is some delay before the river waters breach the bar so releasing the impounded floodwaters. Much of the 810 ha of paddy land in the tributary valleys draining into the lake is low-lying; one-third of it lies between −0.3 and +0.6 m relative to mean sea level and another third between +0.6 and 1.5 m. Works have been undertaken to reduce the frequency of flooding the paddy lands. Rock groynes were first built, 140 m out to sea at the mouth of the river, to reduce longshore drifting, but a sand bar still forms occasionally and villagers with the help of the Irrigation Department clear it from time to time. Subsequently, several of the tributary valleys were separated from the lake by embankments incorporating sluices (and in three cases pumps) to enable excess water to be evacuated. The embankments also serve to prevent salt water intruding under tidal flow during dry weather. An additional exit for the lake was cut 5 km, north of Balapitiya, discharging into the sea through a channel dug in the rock. The drainage channels entering the lake have been cleared and some of them shored up with timber revêtments of bamboo or coconut logs, to prevent blockage by slumping of the banks, while the river bed under the railway and road bridges has been deepened by blasting.

That the wet zone districts have over 71 per cent of the population of Sri Lanka but only 47 per cent of the paddy area with yields considerably lower than those in the dry zone, suggests that paddy cultivation plays a subsidiary role to other agricultural enterprises.

Homestead gardens and plantations particularly, and economic activities in different fields outside agriculture are more important here and will be examined later.

91   A youngster breaking coconut at a factory making desiccated coconut for export, near Kurunegala.

Paddy in the Dry Zone

The maps (Fig. 20.1 and 20.2) and the data in Table 20.1 show clearly the greatly increased importance of the dry zone in paddy cultivation, and the heavy dependence of virtually the whole *Yala* crop and over three-quarters of the *Maha* crop on irrigation. The latter crop predominates strongly in every district, reaching 96 and 94 per cent of the annual total in Vavuniya and Mannar respectively, and 80 per cent or more in Jaffna, Batticaloa, Monaragala and Amparai.

Almost everywhere, annual rainfall is less than 2,000 mm and extensive areas receive less than 1,500 mm. The marked seasonality in rainfall distribution has been noted (Fig. 20.3) and its notorious variability from year to year (see Fig. 3.8). From time immemorial paddy has been irrigated by channels led either directly from anicuts across rivers (and so liable to fail in periods of extreme drought), or, more usually, from tanks or storage dams. The dry zone is dotted liberally with the relics of ancient tanks, and many others still in use, some of them restored by modern engineers. The traditional tank is an earth dam with a masonry spillway to carry floodwaters and a control and distribution system. Early engineering techniques could not build structures on major rivers strong enough to withstand peak floods, so the tanks were located in the shallow valleys of minor rivers whose flood surges could be contained. Some of the most elegant irrigation engineering of pre-industrial times is seen in the channels cut to lead water from the submersible generally flood-proof anicuts on perennial rivers to maintain supplies in large tanks in marginal tributary basins. The Yoda Ela, a part of which is seen in Figure 20.11, is the best known example of a finely engineered channel, built in the fifth century AD to supply the tanks at Anuradhapura and many others en route from the Kala Wewa, 87 km distant in the head waters of the Kala Oya catchment. Its overall gradient averages less than 1:5,000. Figure 20.7 shows how a restored anicut across the Mahaweli Ganga (first built in the sixth century AD) supplies water for double cropping paddy in the 8,7000 ha of the Minipe scheme. Another ancient anicut on the Amban Ganga, a major tributary of the Mahaweli, was first constructed in the twelfth century AD to feed the Parakrama Samudra, the tank system upon which

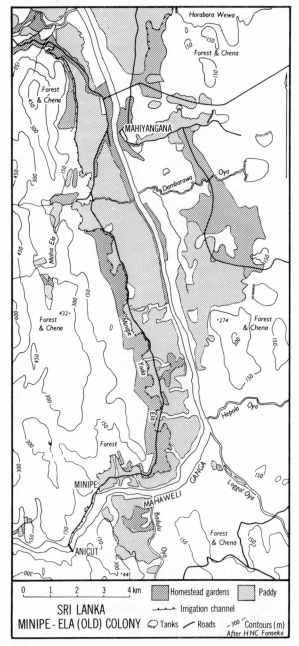

Fig. 20.7

the one time capital city Polonnaruwa depended.

Since Independence the reconditioning of dry zone tanks has been greatly accelerated, and with foreign aid in finance and modern technology, much more ambitious schemes for regional water management have been designed and are in the process of implementation. First completed was the Gal Oya scheme which created a 1,000 km²

reservoir (the Senanayaka Samudra, in Amparai District) to command a potential irrigated area of 48,600 ha and form the basis for settling a substantial new colony in formerly jungle country. A 10,000 kW power station was incorporated to utilise the 33 m head of water provided by the dam. The Gal Oya Basin is wholly within the dry zone and its regime is strongly seasonal, 91 per cent of the flow being in *Maha* (Fig. 20.8). The catchment supplying the Uda Walawe Reservoir on the Walawe Ganga, the next major scheme, in the extreme south of the island, is partly in the wet zone and the seasonal supply is rather better balanced (63 per cent in *Maha*). The dam commands 28,700 ha, and is still being actively developed for paddy and sugar cane cultivation. By far the largest and most ambitious scheme is that using the diverted waters of the Mahaweli Ganga, now under development.

Fig. 20.8

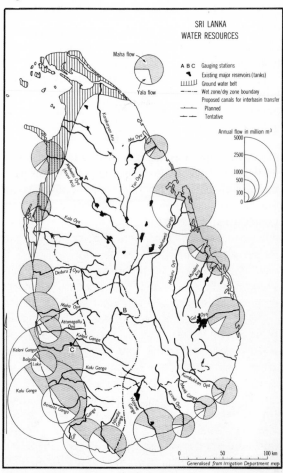

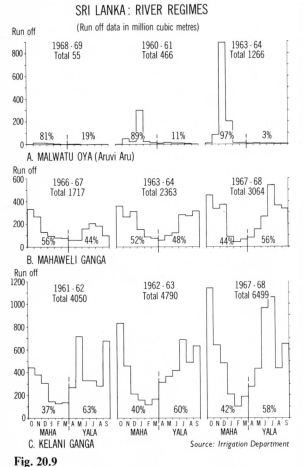

SRI LANKA: RIVER REGIMES

A. MALWATU OYA (Aruvi Aru)

B. MAHAWELI GANGA

C. KELANI GANGA

Source: Irrigation Department

Fig. 20.9

Most of the rivers with courses in the dry zone have regimes which are seasonally unbalanced as well as being highly variable. The general pattern of seasonality can be gauged from Figure 20.8 from which it can be seen that most dry zone rivers discharge more than 80 per cent, and six of them over 90 per cent of their flow in the *Maha* season. The wet zone rivers generally show a balance only slightly in favour of the *Yala* season, on average 46 per cent in *Maha*, 54 in *Yala*.

Figure 20.9 shows the regimes of three characteristic rivers. The location of the gauging points is shown on Figure 20.8. The Kelani Ganga is a wet zone river with minimum flow during the *Maha* season, a peak in May, June or July during the southwest monsoon, and a secondary peak at the time of the 'retreating monsoon' in September – October. The three years chosen illustrate a dry, an average and a wet year. Over 27 years the Kelani Ganga's average flow is $4,627 \times 10^6$ m³. The

Malwatu Oya, known better perhaps as the Aruvi Aru, is entirely a dry zone river, and shows great extremes of flood and drought. In a dry year when the *Maha* rains failed (1968–69) the river scarcely flowed at all and the total discharge amounted to 54.5×10^6 m³ compared with $1,266.1 \times 10^6$ m³ in a year of heavy flood, 1963–64. The average is 414×10^6 m³. The dry season is always dry in the north.

Mahaweli Ganga

Fortunately for the dry zone, the country's largest river, the Mahaweli Ganga, which accounts for one-fifth of the island's total run-off, has its headwaters in the wet zone highlands. It has an intermediate type of regime, 66 per cent of the flow being in *Maha*, 33 per cent in *Yala*. Its average flow, $2,462 \times 10^6$ m³ from a catchment of 1,417 km² is little more than half that of the Kelani Ganga from a similar sized area. As the river flows from wet zone to dry zone, very substantial quantities of water are brought to regions that need it. In fact, the flow is well in excess of the capacity of lowlands within the Mahaweli basin to utilise. It is the challenge of putting this surplus flow to work that has produced the Mahaweli Development Scheme. In essence, the scheme is to harness the resources of the Mahaweli and its tributaries for irrigation and hydro-electric power generation, to develop to the full the irrigation possibilities within the basin and that of the adjacent Maduru Oya, and to transfer surplus water into the upper reaches of the Kala Oya, Malwatu Oya (Aruvi Aru), Yan Oya, Ma Oya, Karakaryan Aru, Parangi Aru and Pali Aru – all of them dry zone rivers. Existing tanks and new reservoirs will be used to store water locally, thus modernising the ancient system of irrigation and making possible double cropping of rice and the cultivation of other crops over large areas of land both presently used and yet to be cleared. Ultimately (optimistically by 1982) 364,200 ha (26,500 ha of it new land) will be commanded, and 507 mW of HEP installed. Of the total land, 174,000 ha is outside the Mahaweli – Maduru Oya basins, in the north central region. The principal features of the project are mapped in Figure 20.10. In Phase I, Project I, completed in 1978, a barrage across the Mahaweli at Polgolla near Kandy diverts 56.6 m³ per second of water through a 8 km tunnel to a power station (40 mW) on a tributary of the Amban

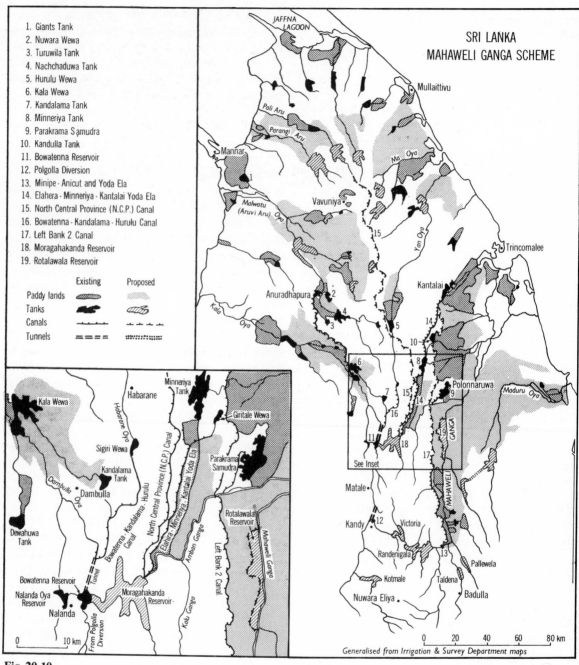

Legend:

1. Giants Tank
2. Nuwara Wewa
3. Turuwila Tank
4. Nachchaduwa Tank
5. Hurulu Wewa
6. Kala Wewa
7. Kandalama Tank
8. Minneriya Tank
9. Parakrama Samudra
10. Kandulla Tank
11. Bowatenna Reservoir
12. Polgolla Diversion
13. Minipe - Anicut and Yoda Ela
14. Elahera - Minneriya - Kantalai Yoda Ela
15. North Central Province (N.C.P.) Canal
16. Bowatenna - Kandalama - Hurulu Canal
17. Left Bank 2 Canal
18. Moragahakanda Reservoir
19. Rotalawala Reservoir

	Existing	Proposed
Paddy lands		
Tanks		
Canals		
Tunnels		

**SRI LANKA
MAHAWELI GANGA SCHEME**

Generalised from Irrigation & Survey Department maps

Fig. 20.10

Ganga. A reservoir at Bowatenna diverts some flow through a 6.4 km tunnel and canals lead it into branches of the Kala Oya, (and thus into existing tanks like the Kala Wewa and Kandelama Tank) and into the Habarane Oya and so to the Hurulu Wewa. Downstream of Bowatenna Reservoir established canals, the Elahera and Kantalai Yoda Ela, carry the increased flow to improve supplies to the irrigated tract west of the Mahaweli between Polonnaruwa and Trincomalee.

The Mahaweli Development Scheme and others of lesser scale will go far to change the face of the dry zone as a relatively empty region as represented in Figure 20.4. Quite apart from the irrigation

92 Cattle treading out the paddy harvest near Colombo. In some areas the task is performed by human feet.

Fig. 20.11 (based on a map of the Sri Lanka Survey Department with the sanction of the Surveyor General).

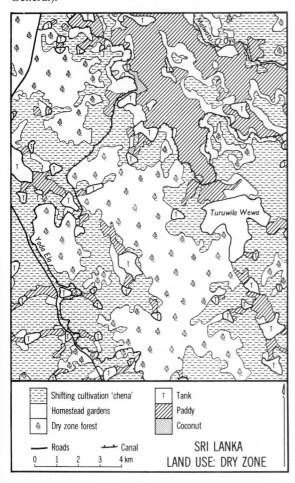

engineering works described, the fulfilment of the scheme involves the establishment of colonies of farmers and the services to support them, a considerable exercise in social engineering, but one in which the authorities now have long experience upon which to draw.

The radical concept of interbasin transfer of water, now transformed into reality in the Mahaweli Scheme, is spawning ambitious proposals elsewhere for bringing the surplus water from the wet zone rivers to the dry zone. The Kelani Ganga may some day be tapped to water areas in northern Puttalam, and the Kalu Ganga water may be channelled eastwards as far as the Kumbukkan Oya basin.

Groundwater Resources

The exploration of Sri Lanka's groundwater resources is still in its early stages. Compared with the alluvial plains of mainland South Asia, Sri Lanka has only modest prospects of finding productive aquifers. The Miocene limestone formation of the coastal belt from Puttalam through Mannar to Jaffna has some potential, the more important in view of the comparatively low rainfall of this region. A number of tube wells are operating, most of them non-artesian and requiring power pumps to raise water. In some cases, fresh water is known to overlie salt water, indicating a risk that overpumping could lead to saline contamination. It seems unlikely that groundwater will prove of more than local and small-scale importance compared with surface resources. In the Jaffna Peninsula however, groundwater is the basis of an intensive traditional agriculture.

Lacking rivers and suffering a long season of drought, Jaffna supports its prosperous and intensive agriculture – in some respects more properly termed horticulture – by a great number of wells sunk into the Miocene limestone. Pumps and hand watering are used to irrigate the fields which man has made fertile by adding leaf mould, green manure crops like sunnhemp, and by penning livestock on the stubble and fallow weeds. The agricultural scene is an epitome of conditions in Tamilnadu: dry fields above the reach of water carry kurakkan and manioc; low ground with grey soils is bunded to hold water for paddy cultivation during the rains, and vegetables where water can be brought in the dry season, while red soils served by wells are used for multistoried high value garden crops – tobacco, chillies, onions and potatoes as ground crops, plantains or cassava as an upper storey, with betel vines, grown for their aromatic leaf, as climbers in shade structures.

Homestead Gardens, Chena, and Dry Farming

Such is the strength of tradition that it is rare to find Sinhalese farmers using paddy lands for crops other than paddy. Within the drier margins of the hill country vegetable crops may alternate with paddy if water is too scarce for a second paddy crop in the dry season. Diversification of agricultural production for subsistence takes place on different land.

In the mind of the small farmer everywhere the homestead garden holds an important place and every family aspires to a degree of self-sufficiency in the fruits, nuts, spices and vegetables that can be grown around the house. There is hardly a plant in the close vicinity of the Sri Lanka homestead that cannot be identified as kept for its productive or decorative function. In the wet zone particularly, where moisture is abundant, the homestead garden may play a major role in the household subsistence, since paddy land is often scarce, and alternative activities like tending tea or rubber small-holdings are for cash. Where garden ends and smallholding begins may be difficult to gauge. Areca nut, coconut, kapok, jak, breadfruit, mangoes and cashew nut trees may be seen singly or in clumps, with coffee, cocoa papaya (pawpaw) and plantain as a lower storey, underplanted casually

with manioc and pineapple, and with pepper vines climbing among the palms. In the traditional dry zone village the homesteads are sited close enough to water for household and garden watering needs to be met. The homestead gardens of some of the more recently settled colonies are often sad dusty affairs, too far from water for horticulture to be practical without excessive labour carrying it in, and so denying the colonists this traditional source of subsistence. As the maps of the two land-use samples suggest, homestead gardens are a much more significant element of the rural landscape of the wet zone than they are of the dry zone.

The other traditional supplement to paddy farming is *chena* or shifting cultivation which is still of some importance in all but the driest parts of the dry zone and its transition to the wet zone. *Chena* is practical on the 'highland', the interfluves between the paddy lands of the river valley floors. Forest or secondary growth of woodland is cut and burnt from June onwards, and the ash-enriched soil is dibbled with seeds in September. The millet kurakkan (*Eleusine corcaran*), sorghum, maize, chillies and various vegetables are the popular *Maha* crops, and these may be followed in *Yala* by the oilseed gingelly if moisture conditions allow. In the past, a farmer would move on to another plot after two or three years when weeds made cultivation difficult, and the jungle would be allowed to recolonise for 15–20 years. Under pressure of population the period of rotation has fallen to 5–8 years or even less, and market factors have converted some *chena* to a commercial business producing chillies, tobacco, pulses, papaya, pumpkin and sorghum organised sometimes by absentee entrepreneurs using hired labour. The cash returns now allow fertilisers to be applied, thus compensating for the reduction of the fallow period and effectively changing *chena* into a permanent dry farming system in some areas.

Much research has been undertaken to try to evolve stable systems of rain-fed agriculture for the dry zone. The risk of drought and low yields were for long the major handicaps. Increased market demand permitting fertiliser use and improved, less expensive techniques for watering dry-field crops from wells using small power pumps have changed the situation radically. Valuable cash crops like tobacco, grown under quota for the Ceylon Tobacco Company which provides all

93 Small motor pumps are commonly used to irrigate chillies and other cash crops from wells or rivers.

the inputs, are now grown on permanent dry fields in many dry zone districts where there used to be *chena* or forest. Chillies (much favoured because wild pigs do not take them) and other transportable cash crops like brinjals may be found growing on isolated river bank plots near to roads linking them to distant markets. Another speciality is papaya grown for the extract papain which is used as a tenderiser for meat and in pharmaceutical preparations. Gardens of papaya and tobacco are widespread on steep slopes on the margins of the wet zone in Matale and Kandy Districts.

The cultivation of sugar cane by temporary occupiers of cleared forest is a further example of opportunist enterprise. When the price is favourable, sugar cane is a profitable crop which can be ratooned (grown without re-planting) for several years in succession in quite rough country. It is crushed and the juice is boiled down to crude sugar or jaggery in small plants requiring little capital. Refined white sugar is produced by State owned factories from cane grown on large irrigated monocultural estates at Kantalai in Trincomalee District and near Amparai under the Gal Oya scheme.

Thus it is clear that subsistence is giving way to a largely commercial economy.

Agriculture for Export

The perennial so-called plantation crops which have been the basis of Sri Lanka's prosperity for a century and which accounted for 78 per cent of the exports in 1978 are mainly produced in the wet zone.

These perennial crops, which occupy almost twice the area used for paddy, have not altered significantly in distribution over the past 50 years. The area under the principal perennial crops is shown in Table 20.3.

Table 20.3 Area under principal perennial crops, 1978

Crop	Area
Coconuts	451,472
Tea	242,903
Rubber	226,328
Cinnamon	21,926
Cocoa	8,567
Pepper	7,449
Coffee	6,438*
Cardamom	4,508
Citronella	4,498

*1976
Source: Department of Census and Statistics *Statistical Pocket Book*, 1979

A major change in direction in the ownership and organisation of the plantation industry took place in the mid 1970s when estates exceeding 50 acres (20 ha) were nationalised. The tea and rubber industries, for example, which had been dominated by British capital and management, were taken over by Sri Lanka government corporations, as were the larger estates owned by Sri Lanka nationals. Individuals and companies were restricted to a maximum of 20 ha. Parts of some estates were broken up into minuscule holdings of 0.2 – 0.4 ha in response to the political pressures for the distribution of property among the landless.

94 Tea factory on an estate near Hatton. The tea on the right is recently planted VP tea; on the left is older more heterogeneous tea.

Tea

Table 20.4 shows the size distribution of tea holdings.

Economies of scale restrict the factory manufacture of tea to estates of over 40 ha, and the tendency is for small factories to close. Thus the factory side of the industry is now effectively in the hands of the nationalised corporations which process in factories on the larger estates the leaf collected from nearby small-holdings and private estates along with that plucked on their own.

The areal distribution of tea estates is shown in Figure 20.12. In order to help quality control in the market the tea trade distinguishes three types of estate by altitudinal range: *high tea*, on estates at elevations averaging 1,220 m or more, accounted for 41 per cent of the estate area and 39 per cent of estate production in 1976; *medium tea*, on estates averaging 610–1,220 m, with 38 per cent of the area and 33 per cent of production; and *low tea*, below 610 m, with 21 per cent of the area and 29 per cent of production. These figures exclude small-holder tea which is mainly from medium and low

country areas. Average total production over the five-year period 1971–75 was in the ratio 38:34:27 (high:medium:low). Thus tea is grown in Sri Lanka through a wide range of altitudes, from almost sea level up to 2,250 m, where its yield is limited by frost. Rainfall is the major determinant of the distribution of estates. Production is seriously affected by drought, though quality or 'flavour' teas are obtained where the plant is under slight stress rather than when regular rains are stimulating heavy leaf growth. Most of the tea region lies within the wet zone including its small outlier east of Badulla, but there are quite extensive high and medium estates in the centre of the Uva Basin and around its margins which lie within the dry zone as delineated in Figure 18.3.

The seasonality of rainfall controls production, there being a clear differentiation of estates receiving most rain from the northeast monsoon, from those more exposed to the southwest monsoon. In terms of maintaining supply to a fairly constant market the complementarity of the seasonal growth is a great advantage for Sri Lanka

Table 20.4 Tea holdings, 1976

Size class	No. of holdings	Total area (ha)	Percentage of total
Small-holdings (< 4.05 ha)	122,804	47,924	20
Estates 4.05 to < 40.5 ha	3,089	32,574	14
Estates 40.5 ha to < 202.3 ha	536	56,386	23
Estates 202.3 ha and over	286	103,691	43
Total	126,715	240,575	100

Source: Sri Lanka Yearbook, 1977

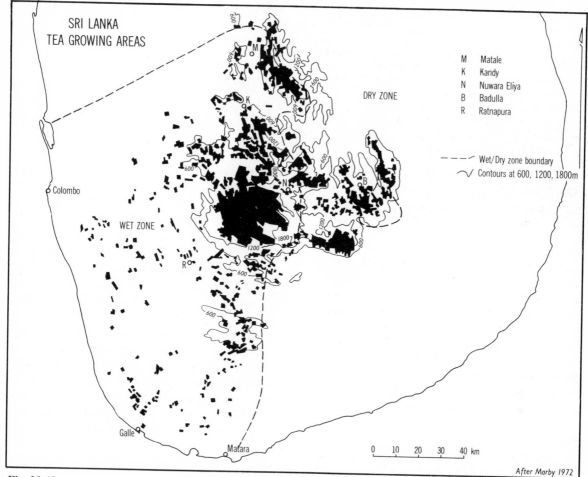

Fig. 20.12

compared with India, whose production is more concentrated in the summer monsoon. In order to compete in the world market it is essential for Sri Lanka to keep costs at a minimum. As pressures to increase wages are difficult to resist in the long run, greater efficiency must be achieved in other ways, important among them being the uprooting of heterogeneous old tea bushes and their replacement with high yielding clonal material guaranteeing uniformity.

Rubber

Rubber is more restricted in its distribution than is tea. It is confined to the wet zone below 400 m, and to areas with regular all year rainfall. Of the area in production in 1976, 89 per cent was in the block of six districts in the wet zone lowlands: Colombo, Kegalle, Kalutara, Ratnapura, Galle and Matara. As Table 20.5 shows, rubber holdings tend to be

much smaller than tea estates. Once established, rubber is an easier crop to manage than tea for the small-holder. Processing of latex into sheet can be done on a small scale, though the trend now will be to encourage small-holders to deliver latex to modern 'block rubber' plants where the quality of the finished product can be maintained and a better price passed to the producer than he could get for his home rolled and smoked sheet.

As with tea, it is important to improve efficiency in the industry at every level. Uneconomic rubber lands are being converted to other crops while replanting holdings with clonal material is assisted with subsidies, and about 60 per cent of the total planted area has been renewed. There is an urgent need to expand planting if Sri Lanka is to maintain its share of the natural rubber market which is likely to grow as the cost of petroleum-based synthetic rubber increases. Producers have been

Table 20.5 Size of rubber holdings, 1976

	Number	Total area	Per cent of total
Small-holdings <4.05 ha	154,445	87,721	33
Estates 4.05 – <40.5 ha	6,873	64,991	25
Estates 40.5 ha and over	827	112,529	42
TOTAL	162,145	265,241	100

Source: Sri Lanka Yearbook, 1977

perhaps over-secure with over half the country's production assured of a market under the barter agreement with China, exchanging rubber for rice.

Coconuts

Occupying an area second only to that under paddy, coconuts have a widespread distribution, being found in every district. Nearly half the area (48 per cent) is in the coconut triangle of Chilaw–Kurunegala–Matale, 29 per cent in the four coastal districts from Colombo to Matara, 13 per cent in the dry zone districts (excluding Puttalam) and 10 per cent in the rest – the wet zone interior below 500 m altitude.

Coconut oil and desiccated coconut are staple ingredients in Sri Lanka cuisine, and artefacts

95 A Tamil labourer tapping rubber. He holds a cutting knife to clean the incision in the bark and beneath it a bundle of dried latex from the previous day's cut. The white latex collects in a coconut shell cup to be poured into a bucket at the end of the tapping round. Near Monaragala.

made of coir fibre such as rope, mats and mattresses, and screens made of coconut fronds, are found in or around almost every home. The timber is used for many purposes, and the shells of coconuts are used to make charcoal. From the flowering stalks a sweet juice is extracted which ferments to become toddy, a popular beverage, which can also be distilled to make arrack. It is estimated that everyone in Sri Lanka consumes 100 nuts each year.

The coconut industry is less highly organised than that of either tea or rubber. The trees grow both in plantations and in many homestead gardens, the products are diverse and since both the fibrous coir of the husk and the coconut kernel are fairly imperishable, it is not essential to associate the processing industry closely with production.

A sample survey showed that 57 per cent of the coconut land was in holdings of over 10 ha, 22 per cent between 4.05 and 10 ha and the remaining 21 per cent less than 4.05 ha. Rarely do coconuts represent a farmer's sole source of income; 85 per cent of coconut land-holders also have paddy land. Most (69 per cent) of the holders of coconut land were owner-cultivators. These facts indicate the more 'democratic' character of the industry than tea or rubber where monocultural corporation-run estates are important.

While coconuts grow widely where temperatures and relative humidity are high and sunshine abundant, in dry areas they tend to give place to palmyra. The coconut triangle and parts of the Matara district, both in the wet zone–dry zone transition are regarded as having the optimum growing conditions. Once planted, coconuts require little attention. The palms begin to bear in 7 – 10 years, reaching their maximum production at 15 – 20 years, and continuing at a high level until after 60 years when yields decline. Fertiliser application increases yields.

As in South India, it is now appreciated that the land under the coconuts can be made productive without detriment to the palm trees. Improved pastures on which dairy cattle can be grazed are being encouraged as are a variety of cash crops including pineapples, cocoa, coffee, bananas and pepper, whose vines can use the coconut trunks.

Minor Export Crops

Under this heading are grouped several crops which, although occupying a relatively small area, include the spice cinnamon that first attracted the Portuguese to the island for trade, and coffee which was once the major plantation crop. These crops are now mainly small-holders' interests, though cardamoms are chiefly grown as a minor crop in forested corners of tea estates.

Cinnamon, which is native to Sri Lanka, is grown as a shrub 2 m high to be cut and peeled to collect the bark from which the flavouring oil is extracted. The crop is concentrated in Matara and Galle (together having 71 per cent of the area) with a further 23 per cent in the adjacent districts of Kalutara, Hambantota and Ratnapura. Cinnamon grows well on the interfluve uplands, requiring no shade, high insolation and about 2,500 mm of rainfall.

By contrast, cocoa does best under shade, especially when young, and is found as an under-crop to rubber, coconut, jak tree, etc. or with Dadap (widely used for the same purpose in tea estates) as cover. Ninety per cent of the cocoa area is in Matale and Kandy where the valleys provide the desirable levels of equable heat and high humidity. The cocoa beans are processed on the farm and bagged for despatch to middlemen who prepare the product for export.

Pepper is a vine which must have either living or dead tree trunks on which to climb, protection from winds which might blow it down, and shade from excessive sunshine. Like cocoa, it needs high humidity and heat, and abundant rainfall, 2,500–4,500 mm. It is often seen growing as a cash crop using as climbing support kapok, arecanut, or shade trees in tea or cocoa gardens. Seventy per cent of the recorded pepper area is in the adjoining districts of Kandy, Matale and Kegalle. The vines begin to fruit in two to three years, reaching a maximum at about eight years and declining after 15 years. The green berries are sun-dried on mats to produce black pepper.

Coffee, both *C. arabica* and *C. robusta* are grown in the wet zone and its transition to the dry zone. Sixty per cent of the area is in Kandy, Matale and Kegalle. *Coffea arabica*, being tolerant of cooler and less humid conditions than *C. robusta*, does well over 600 m and for neither is shade essential, though they are successfully grown as an under-crop to rubber or coconut.

Cardamoms grow naturally as low shade-loving plants in humid forest in the highland wet zone. As a commercial crop cardamom is generally planted in natural forest partly opened up by clearing undergrowth. It is a rewarding export crop but requires the kind of care in cultivation, harvesting and processing that is given to tea, if high quality is to be achieved. The capsule should be 'green cured' in hot air barns and rigorously graded.

Finally, citronella, almost wholly grown in western Hambantota District and in the adjacent part of Matara, merits mention as a source of an essential oil. Two species of *Cympobogon*, a perennial grass, are grown to be cut two or three times a year and distilled to extract the oil. Apart from weeding and maybe manuring, the crop is not a demanding one, growing on slopes and often poor soils. Cuttings are row planted and need replacing after five years. Production is of the order of 35 kg of oil per ha. Since the grass is hand cut and the extraction process is crude, the industry is labour intensive and is unlikely to survive greatly increased labour costs.

Overall, the economic survival of Sri Lanka's plantation industries depends very largely on increasing their efficiency and so their ability to compete in world markets.

96 Mature coconut plantation near Lunawila, Puttalam District. On some estates the palms are now intercropped with pineapples, bananas or other cash crops.

Chapter 21

Sri Lanka: Population Spread and Concentration

The contrast between wet and dry zones made so frequently in the previous chapter is repeated understandably in any view of the distribution of population. Of the estimated population of 13.7 million in 1976, 71 per cent were in the wet zone districts; in its simplest terms, more than two-thirds of the population are in one-third of the area. The overall density of population in the wet zone is 446 per km² compared with 89 per km² in the dry zone (and 212 per km² in the island as a whole). Figure 21.1 shows population densities by electorates at the 1971 Census.

The wet zone shows relatively high densities almost everywhere. With the exception of three hilly electorates where Ratnapura, Galle and Kalutara Districts meet, the 200 per km² isoline could almost be used to define the wet zone. Outside the wet zone only part of the Uva Basin, the environs of Batticaloa and the Jaffna peninsula have in excess of 200 persons per km².

Within the wet zone certain patterns stand out. From north of Negombo to Tangalla, east of Matara the coastline is marked by a practically continuous narrow belt of electorates with densities over 400 per km². Often this belt is as little as 5 – 15 km wide and consists of a ribbon of continuous settlement along the coastal road and railway. Much of it is effectively a suburban extension of the Colombo metropolis, and commuters travel regularly from as far away as Galle. Colombo's influence is seen also in the cluster of high density electorates inland of the city.

Another striking belt of high density links Colombo with Kandy along the main routes. Kandy itself is the focus of a cluster of six electorates with densities exceeding 800 per km², two of them, covering urban Kandy, with over 1,600 per

km². The rural areas surrounding this cluster are among the most diverse in their agricultural activities, combining valley floor paddy with smallholder and medium-scale mixed and specialised plantation cropping, intensive homestead gardens, and some dry cash cropping on steep hill slopes.

Although, with the exception of the Jaffna peninsula, the Uva Basin and the urbanised electorates of Batticaloa, the dry zone shows a relative sparsity of population, some noteworthy features are apparent. There is a large block of electorates in the north of the island with densities of less than 50 per km², including Vavuniya (26) and Mannar (31). The better peopled electorates flanking this block to the south have enjoyed the benefits of tank renovation and colonisation as have similarly those in the middle Mahaweli and Gal Oya Schemes between Kandy and Batticaloa. The southeast coast in Hambantota also includes irrigation development.

The effect that irrigation development and colonisation have had on dry zone settlement is impressive. Some of the areas with seemingly low densities today have experienced remarkable growth. Thus Vavuniya had an increase of 348 per cent between 1946 and 1976; Anuradhapura and Polonnaruwa 327 per cent, figures that compare with 106 per cent for Sri Lanka as a whole. Much of such growth is attributable to colonisation by migrants from elsewhere.

Although in the 1971 Census 22 per cent of the population was recorded as 'urban', the proportion is only 16 per cent – if one restricts the term to towns having over 20,000 inhabitants – a quite modest level compared with its northern neighbours India (20 per cent) and Pakistan (26 per cent) but higher than Bangladesh's 9 per cent.

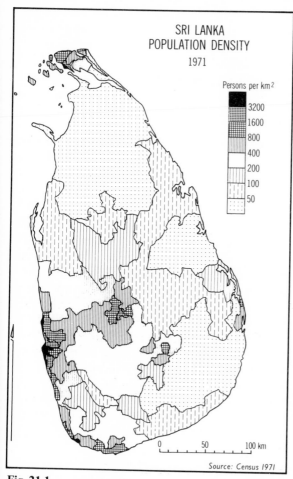

Fig. 21.1

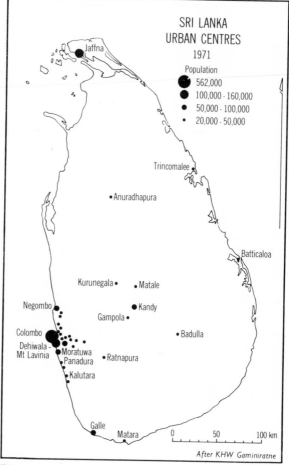

Fig. 21.2

Figure 21.2 shows how 18 of the 32 centres with more than 20,000 are in Colombo District. These account for 52 per cent of the urban population, Colombo with Dehiwala–Mt. Lavinia, continuous with it to the south, making up 25 per cent. However Colombo is defined it is clearly a 'primate' city. Colombo Municipal Council Area held 607,000 in 1976, Dehiwala–Mt. Lavinia 166,000. The next largest town was Jaffna with 117,000 followed by two more of Colombo's close satellites – Moratuwa (103,000) and Kotte (100,000) – and Kandy (101,000).

97 A crop of maize on a *chena* clearing, Vavuniya District. The forest has been burnt off. A pumpkin vine is growing up the dead trunk to the rear of the farmer.

An ESCAP* study concludes that in Sri Lanka urbanisation has not been associated with industrialisation, but rather with commercial activity generally and the trading functions of Colombo in particular. The colonisation schemes and other government investment in rural areas have taken up some of the pressures of population growth, while the compactness of the island and its easy communications perhaps reduce the urge to migrate permanently to the city while the social contacts with the rural ancestral home can be maintained.

Industry

Several of the industrial plants established since Independence are in rural areas in order to be close to raw materials: thus the two cement works, at Kankesanturai on the north Jaffna coast, and 8 km southeast of Puttalam; the paper mills (using paddy straw, wastepaper and imported pulp) at Valaichchenai north of Batticaloa, and near Embilipitiya in the Uda Walawe Scheme; the sugar mills at Kantalai southwest of Trincomalee, and Amparai (Gal Oya); the chemical plant alongside the salterns at Elephant Pass, the causeway to Jaffna from the south.

Sri Lanka is not rich in resources for manufacturing. Heavy rainfall in the hill country fortunately gives rise to adequate HEP potential. Installed capacity totals 402 MW, and a 132 kV system transfers power to Colombo, Galle, Puttalam, Trincomalee and Jaffna. Coal, petroleum, natural gas and the principal metaliferous ores are lacking. Graphite (plumbago) and gemstones, while bringing in foreign exchange, are in themselves no basis for industry. About 130,000 tonnes of salt annually are evaporated from seawater in the two dry coastal zones of Hambantota and from the northeast. Beach sands 50 km north of Trincomalee are sorted to produce ilmenite, rutile and zircon for export. At several places local clay and kaolin are used in ceramic industries as well as brick and tile factories.

Apart from the sugar and paper mills mentioned, agriculture provides the raw material for making rubber tyres, copra for coconut oil extraction,

coir for fibre industries, hides for leatherwork, milk for processing into powder, while forests yield timber for plywood and furniture trades. For many industries regarded as essential for a modern state raw materials have to be imported: petroleum for refining, steel for re-rolling and wire making, wheat for milling, cotton lint and yarn for textiles.

Most large scale industry is now State owned and run by corporations: Ceylon Cement, Paranthan Chemicals, Ceylon Mineral Sands, National Paper, Ceylon Ceramics, Ceylon State Hardware, Ceylon Steel, Ceylon Plywood, Sri Lanka Sugar, National Textiles, Ceylon Fisheries, State Graphite, Sri Lanka Petroleum etc. Another corporation is responsible for assisting small-scale industries, both in traditional crafts and modern manufacturing.

The small size of the Sri Lanka market and its low purchasing power add to the difficulties in establishing viable industries. A recent development, the Free Trade Zone, is aimed to attract foreign investors who seek a relatively low cost labour force to manufacture goods for overseas markets. An area between Colombo and Negombo has been designated for the FTZ where industrialists may import and export without paying duty on materials or products, and where a period of tax-free operation is guaranteed as an incentive.

Production levels in some major industrial corporations in 1978 are shown in Table 21.1.

Most of the manufacturing industry not linked to specific local raw materials is located in Colombo or the urban centres of that district.

Levels of Development

By way of summary it is helpful to consider the relative levels of development by districts as analysed by Samarasinghe who took into account urbanisation, industry, social welfare, commercial and traditional agriculture, vital demographic statistics and education.* The following regions were identified in order of developmental level:

1. Advanced: Colombo
2. Developing I: Kurunegala

*Economic and Social Commission for Asia and the Pacific: *Population of Sri Lanka*, 1976. Country monograph Series No. 4 (Bangkok)

*Samarasinghe, L.K.V. *Polorisation of Colombo in the Economic Geography of Ceylon*, 1973 (Unpublished Ph. D. thesis, Cambridge University)

3. Developing II: Anuradhapura
4. Slow Growing:
   (a) Kandy
   (b) Jaffna, Matara
   (c) Kalutara, Galle, Mannar, Puttalam
5. Less developed:
   (a) Vavuniya, Batticaloa, Polonnaruwa, Hambantota
   (b) Matale, Kegalle, Ratnapura, Trincomalee, Amparai
6. Backward: Nuwara Eliya, Monaragala, Badulla

An axis of development is seen northeast from Colombo through Kurunegala to Anuradhapura. Slow growth is seen to be related to the independent urbanised districts of Kandy and Jaffna, and the coastal urbanised ribbon south of Colombo to Galle and Matara and north to Puttalam. The less developed regions include much of the dry zone, but also some of the mid-country wet zone (Matale, Kegalle and Ratnapura). That Nuwara Eliya and Badulla rank as backward may seem somewhat surprising in view of their highly developed tea industry and market gardening, but in many aspects of social welfare the estate sector of the economy has lagged behind. The study was based on 1963 data, so the present ranking of districts may have changed to favour those where there has been considerable colonisation, such as Amparai (the Gal Oya Scheme).

Table 21.1   Industrial production, 1978

Product	Unit	Amount
Processed milk	Thousand litres	17,292
Sugar	Tonnes	24,780
Flour	Tonnes	61,788
Salt	Tonnes	152,784
Cotton yarn	Tonnes	5,736
Cotton cloth	Thousand metres	18,276
Shoes	Pairs	179,000
Paper and board	Tonnes	25,500
Caustic soda	Tonnes	1,860
Plywood	Thousand m^2	3,096
Tyres	Number	256,968
Petrol	Tonnes	120,624
Aviation fuel	Tonnes	35,088
Crockery	Tonnes	4,428
Cement	Tonnes	575,064
Ilmenite	Tonnes	37,260
Rolled steel	Tonnes	33,108
Graphite	Tonnes	10,697

Source: Central Bank of Ceylon *Bulletin*, Feb. 1979

98   Mechanisation is common in Sri Lanka, tractors with special attachments to the wheels as here, being used for working wet paddy lands.

Chapter 22

The Himalayan Kingdoms: Nepal

Introduction

The Kingdom of Nepal extends for 840 km along the southern flank of the Central Himalaya. Mount Everest (8,848 m) stands on its border with China, Kangchenjunga (8,579 m) on the border with Sikkim (Fig. 22.1). Some ranges exceeding 7,000 m

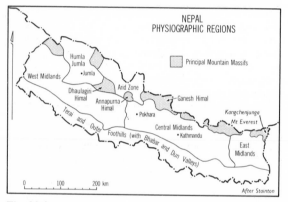

Fig. 22.2

stand well within Nepalese territory and the water parting, to which the frontier approximates, while generally over 6,000 m, lies often 50 km behind these ranges. The bulk of Nepal's 11.6 million people (1971) live in the Midlands, below 3,000 m, a hilly region with some broad valleys, the largest being that of Kathmandu. About 10 per cent of the population are in the High Mountain regions, 53 per cent in the Midlands and the remaining 37 per cent in the Terai districts south of the Mahabharat Lekh. The latter range, rising to over 2,700 m forms the rear continuous inner line of the Outer Himalaya. Towards the plains, discontinuous ridges of the Siwaliks at around 1,350 m separate minor intermontane *duns* and step down to the *bhabar* and *terai*. The *bhabar* immediately flanking the hills is a relatively narrow sloping belt of coarse alluvial gravels into which

drainage quickly disappears to re-emerge in the flatter *terai*, which beyond Nepal's border merges imperceptibly with the Ganga Plain.

For long a region of endemic malaria, the *terai* acted as a barrier to penetration from the plains just as the high Himalaya deterred intercourse with the plateau of Tibet. In addition to these natural obstacles to invasion and intercommunication, Nepal until after World War II maintained a policy of excluding visitors. A more open-door policy in recent decades has combined with the greater mobility offered tourists by air services, to convert Nepal into one of the world's most popular resorts for mountain-climbing and trekking, and at the same time to open it to trade. Brought so abruptly into contact with the outside world, the question today is how Nepal's 'feudal' society can adapt to the inevitable discovery of new economic pressures and political aspirations.

An attempt in 1959 to institute democratic government based on elections came to an abrupt halt when the leader of the winning Congress Party forming the new government was gaoled by the King. Nepal is a Kingdom ruled by its monarch assisted by a cabinet of a Prime Minister and seven Ministers who sit in the National Panchayat, a parliament of 135 members, which is the highest of a series of panchayats, the members of each being nominated by the next lower, down to the village level. Of the 135 members, 23 are the King's direct nominees. The King also has a State Council of 69 (including his own nominees) to represent various national interests.

Political parties are banned and press and radio are controlled. A recent study comments that 'a tradition of non-participation by most citizens who have always been regarded and thus have come to believe themselves to be, subjects of inherently superior rulers, has ... prevented demands for

99 A simple two storeyed farmstead with thatched roof near Kathmandu. The wet flood plain in the background is ridged to grow potatoes and other vegetables. Mustard is growing in the right foreground.

popular participation from becoming unmanageable'.* The nature of the country and its limited economic infrastructure make extremely difficult the reduction in the 'gross regional disparities' that must otherwise become the breeding ground for disaffection as the population become aware of their own condition compared with that of others.

The Economy

That 94 per cent of the occupied population is engaged in agriculture, forestry and fishing is an indication of the relative backwardness of the economy even compared with the other South Asian countries. Gross Domestic Product in 1976–

Table 22.1 Gross Domestic Product, 1976–77 (per cent of total, Rs 17,344 million)

Agriculture	62.3
Mining	0.04
Manufacturing	4.1
Construction	1.7
Transport communications	6.9
Cottage industry	6.2
Finance	1.6
Dwellings	4.9
Public administration and defence	2.3
Wholesale and retail trade	4.9
Public utilities	0.3
Services	4.8

*Upadhyaya D. P. and Abneva J. V. 'Problems of rapid population growth in relation to development', in their edited volume *'Population and development in Nepal'*, Kathmandu Univ. Press (1975) p. 15

Table 22.2 Exports, 1977–78 (per cent of total, Rs. 601 million)

Rice	23.1
Spices	5.2
Hides and skins	12.8
Jute, raw	28.3
Other agricultural products	7.5
Jute textiles	10.5
Carpets	4.0
Other manufactures	8.3

Table 22.3 Imports, 1977–78 (per cent of total, Rs. 1,111 million)

Food, drink, tobacco	6.5
Textiles, clothing	22.9
Petroleum products	17.6
Chemicals, fertilisers	9.6
Other intermediate goods	5.3
Machinery, equipment	11.7
Transport equipment	14.0
Others	12.6

77 was derived 62 per cent from agriculture. The full distribution is shown in Table 22.1.

Trade is mainly with India which also dominates in providing one-third of the foreign aid, followed by the USA (19 per cent) and China (13 per cent). Almost 40 per cent of the annual budget is met from aid grants and loans. Understandably, the unavoidably close presence of India makes the relationship difficult and engenders some resentment.

Major exports are rice, jute and jute goods, maize, bristle and cattle (Table 22.2). Imports are dominated by ready-made garments and carpets,

Table 22.4 Land-use, 1970–71

	Area (*thousand ha*)	Per cent of total
Forest	4,475	32
Perpetual snow	2,112	15
Waste, unreclaimable	2,566	18
Waste, reclaimable	1,860	13
Cultivated land*	1,980	14
Other uses	1,087	8
Total	14,080	100

*Note: The total cropped area, taking double cropping into account is 2,231,000 ha

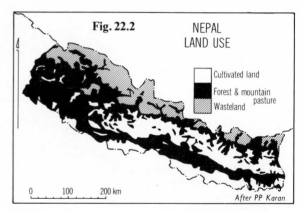

Fig. 22.2   NEPAL LAND USE

Cultivated land
Forest & mountain pasture
Wasteland

0   100   200 km

After PP Karan

vehicles, all kinds of constructional materials, machinery and buffaloes (Table 22.3). Tourism is an expanding source of foreign exchange: 156,000 visitors in 1978 brought in Rs 343 million.

Apart from its magnificent scenery, highly 'exportable' to tourists, Nepal's resources are principally its agricultural land, forests and water, for power and irrigation, though not necessarily solely for Nepalese use. Mineral wealth so far discovered is only modest. There is iron ore near Kathmandu which might support the production of 50,000 tonnes of pig iron annually. Mica is a minor export. Table 22.4 shows the major categories of land-use, though it is clear that almost half the area is snow or waste, and another third under forest.

Agriculture

Figure 22.2 shows the distribution of agricultural land and Figures 22.3–22.5 that of the principal crops, rice, maize and wheat. There is considerable regional disparity in the availability of land. The greatest pressure of population on land is in the high mountain valleys which have 4.9 per cent of the cultivated area to support almost 10 per cent of the people at an average of 0.47 ha per household (both agricultural and non-agricultural). Conditions in these most remote valleys are hard indeed. In the Midlands 30 per cent of the country's agricultural area supports 53 per cent of the population, and holdings average 0.56 ha per household. The *terai* fares better with 65 per cent of the area, 37 per cent of the population, and holdings averaging 1.63 ha.

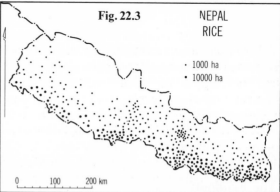

Fig. 22.3   NEPAL RICE

· 1000 ha
· 10000 ha

0   100   200 km

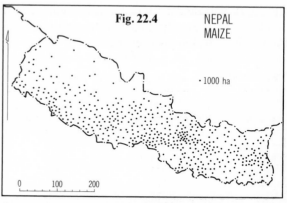

Fig. 22.4   NEPAL MAIZE

· 1000 ha

0   100   200

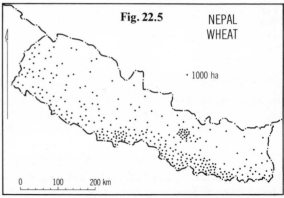

Fig. 22.5   NEPAL WHEAT

· 1000 ha

0   100   200 km

100 Women carrying loads in a village near Kathmandu while others rest under the trees, beside the sheep and goats.

These contrasts, accentuated by regional differences in environmental possibilities, account for the major demographic characteristics of Nepal, the migration of its peoples from the mountains and hills to the plains of the *terai*. At the 1971 Census more than half a million people were recorded as in-migrants to the *terai* districts from the mountains and hills. The continued migration of the Gurkha soldiers to serve in the Indian and British Armies is another response to the need to find work outside the hill country.

Table 22.5 shows the area under the major crops in 1978–79 and their production.

Table 22.5 Area and production of principal crops

	Area (thousand ha)	Production (thousand tonnes)
Rice	1,263	2,339
Maize	454	743
Wheat	374	454
Millets	123	133
Barley	26	22
Potato	51	268
Oilseeds	144	92
Sugar cane	23	379
Jute	45	66

Rice and maize are *kharif* crops, rain-fed by the summer monsoon or by irrigation from the numerous streams and rivers. Rice, the main food crop, produces best under tropical conditions at lower altitudes and is predominant in the *terai* plains and the Midland valleys, as the map shows. Maize flourishes on the terraced hill slopes, provided it can get rain, and so is comparatively and often absolutely more important in the hilly Midland districts and the eastern highland valleys. Potatoes are a crop on higher slopes. Jute is grown as an export crop in the eastern *terai*. Wheat and oilseeds (mustard) are the main *rabi* crops, grown widely in the dry season generally following paddy or maize on the same fields. Sugar cane and tobacco are also grown as cash crops mainly in the *terai*.

There is great disparity in levels of agricultural development between the *terai* and the remote mountain valleys. Quite apart from its easier terrain and its irrigation projects, the *terai's* accessibility to Indian markets is a major advantage. Consequently the *terai* farmer is a commercial entrepreneur to a degree undreamt of among the subsistence peasants of the mountains.

Nepal has vast water resources for power and irrigation, the latter far in excess of lands on which to use it. India on the other hand has land in the plains of Uttar Pradesh and Bihar where irrigation would be very beneficial during the dry *rabi* season particularly. India also has a great need for electricity. Under agreements with India, the waters of the Gandak and Kosi are being harnessed to the mutual benefit of the two countries. The Kosi multi-purpose project is the larger, based on a barrage near Hanumannagar, from which the eastern Kosi canal system already irrigates lands in both sides of the border. A western Kosi canal, flood protection embankment and power installations to generate 20 MW are in train in which Nepal will share the advantages. The Gandak scheme is similarly multi-purpose. There are schemes to develop power on the Trisul and Bagmati Rivers. Ultimately, Nepal is likely to have an abundance of hydro-electric power for sale to India which will probably have to provide the capital to develop it.

The development of agriculture, Nepal's main resource, will inevitably concentrate on the more accessible areas. The feudal character of the land-holding system is unlikely to change in a hurry. A Land Act in 1964 made some effort to improve the condition of tenants, but although ceilings were placed on ownership (17 ha in the *terai*, 4.11 ha in the hills, 2.67 ha in Kathmandu Valley) all members of a family could own this ceiling amount. Tenants pay 50 per cent of their product to the owner, and even if now more secure, they can hardly have much incentive to invest in increased productivity. Ceilings for tenant holdings are only 2.67 ha in the *terai*, 1.51 ha in the hills and 1.02 ha in Kathmandu Valley.

Population and Development

Figure 22.6 shows the density of population of districts at the 1971 Census*. The Kathmandu Valley, covering Kathmandu, Bhaktapur and Patan (or Lalitpur) Districts is the most closely settled part of Nepal, with over 320 people per km². This is a very small region however in relation to the total. The districts of the eastern *terai*, with over 160 per km² stand out clearly, as do parts of the Midlands with upwards of 80 per km². Much of the western *terai* along with the districts including the Mahabharat Lek, is moderately populated by

comparison. The Inner Himalaya, including the arid zone of Nepal in the rainshadow of the Dhaulagiri and Annapurna Massifs, is generally sparsely peopled. The districts Dolpa with 2, Manag with 4 and Mustang with 8 per km² form this arid zone, where precipitation is probably less than 750 mm annually (cf. Pokhara, 3,477 mm).

An important constraint upon national political development is the strong sense of community among the various ethnic groups whether of Mongolian or Northern Indian racial stock. Linguistically, the mountain dwellers tend to be Tibeto-Burman speakers, those of the Terai Indo-Aryan, with mixed groups between. Nepali, an Indo-Aryan language, is spoken by 52 per cent of the population. In religion, while Buddhism and Hinduism are both practised, the bulk of the people probably follow faiths incorporating elements of the two.

Among the groups with Tibetan affinities the Bhotiyas, Sherpas and Thakals are the most important. They have been immigrating for centuries, occupying land above 2,400 m and so not conflicting with the indigenous Mongoloid midlanders, the 'Ancient Nepalese' groups. The Newars dominate the latter in culture, crafts and literature. Others here are the Gurungs (many of whose young men find employment as soldiers in the Gurkha regiments), the Mangars, Thamangs, Sunwars, Rais and Limbus. Indo-Nepalese groups occupy the Midlands and *terai*. Thakurs are common in the West, and elsewhere Hindu caste-stratified communities of Brahmins, Chetris and

Fig. 22.6

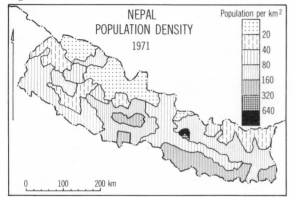

Fig. 22.7

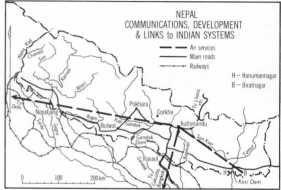

*Central Bureau of Statistics, National Planning Commission Secretariat: *The Analysis of the Population Statistics of Nepal*, 1977

101 Terraced fields on the edge of the Kathmandu Valley carry rice or maize in the wet season, wheat in the dry season.

Kshatriyas (to which the Gurkha people belong). In the Indian border districts Indian immigrants are numerous as farmers and successful traders.

The rates of literacy and school enrolments are very low. In the urban population (only 4 per cent of the total) 62 per cent of males and 28 per cent of females of 10 years and over were literate in 1971, and the corresponding figures for school attendance were 60 per cent males, 36 per cent females. In rural areas 23 per cent of males were literate, and less than 3 per cent of females, while 23 per cent males and 5 per cent of the females went to school.

Figure 22.7, by the sheer sparsity of its data, demonstrates the very modest amount of economic development that has taken place. Apart from the several roads from the *terai* into India, there are only three or four major routes usable by motor traffic: those from Raxaul (India) to Kathmandu, from Kodan (on the China border) to Kathmandu, the road through the Midlands from Kathmandu as far as Pokhara, and one from the latter to the Indian border at Bhairawa. Expansion of the in-

ternal road system is essential if regional disparities in wealth are not further to increase, though it is very difficult to see how the present growth and dominance of the Kathmandu Valley and the developing districts of the *terai* can be resisted in order to give the backward areas a chance to 'catch up'.

Modern industrialisation is still at a rudimentary stage. Processing of agricultural products is carried out in several towns in the *terai*, notably Biratnagar in the east which has jute presses for compacting raw jute fibre, jute mills, rice and vegetable oil mills, a plywood and bobbin factory, cotton textile manufacturing and a button factory. Birganj, on the road from Kathmandu to India, has a match factory, rice, oil, sugar and cotton mills and a plant established with USSR aid to make agricultural implements. Bhairawa on the road out from Pokhara has a sugar mill and associated distillery; Nepalganj in the western Terai makes matches.

In the Kathmandu Valley there are industrial estates to stimulate modern enterprise but much fine craft work is still done. Leather and shoe industries and the manufacture of cigarettes, bricks and tiles have been set up.

Industrial production in 1977–78 is summarised in Table 22.6.

Total sugar production during the year 1977–78 was 26,502 tonnes, some of it from imported Indian cane. Nepal can satisfy only 26 per cent of its demand for tea, but expansion towards self-sufficiency by 1984–85 is planned.

Altogether, industrialisation is not an easy process in Nepal. The local market is poor and highly dispersed and difficult to protect from penetration by low cost Indian goods sold by energetic merchants from over the border.

Table 22.6 Industrial production, 1977–78

Jute goods (tonnes)	16,347
Sugar	26,502
Cigarettes (million)	1,634
Matches (gross)	677,000
Liquor, distilled (l)	687,000
Leather shoes (pairs)	59,031
Tea (kg)	405,000
Beer (l)	788,000
Cotton textiles (thousand m)	3,889
Cement (tonnes)	38,080

Source: Economic Survey, 1978–79

Chapter 23

The Himalayan Kingdoms: Bhutan

Approximately 300 by 150 km in extent, the little Kingdom of Bhutan, now confined to hilly and mountainous country, used formerly to extend into the *terai*, or the *duars* as the submontane belt is called here in the Brahmaputra Valley. Unlike Nepal the grain of the country runs north to south. From peaks exceeding 7,000 m along the border with Chinese Tibet, ranges slope to about 2,400 m near the Indian border with intervening valley floors at little more than 200 m (Fig. 23.1).

Bhutan is a backward country, still feudal and tribal in its political organisation. Following the pattern set by the British, the Indian government formally controls Bhutan's foreign policy and informally its defence (although the country has been a member of the United Nations since 1971) and heavily subsidises the national budget to the extent of 95 per cent of the total. The Head of State is the hereditary King, the Druk Gyalpo, who rules with a council of ministers, administration

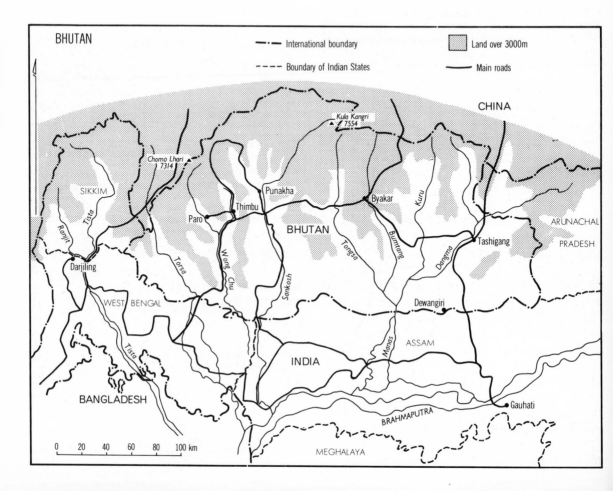

being through a hierarchical system down to the village headman. An assembly, the Tsongdu, of 150 members (25 per cent of them the Druk Gyalpo's nominees) is by the village headman.

Mahayana Buddhism is the state religion, through which Bhutan formerly had strong traditional links with Tibet. Trade in rice and blankets in return for wool used to follow these cultural ties.

The population totals about 1.2 million, 95 per cent of whom are illiterate and 25 per cent immigrant Nepalese. Farming and pastoralism are the main sources of livelihood. In the mountains, transhumance is practised between winter and summer homesteads. The range of crops grown is much as in Nepal: rice is by far the most important food staple followed by wheat, maize and potatoes. Barley, buckwheat and millets are minor crops. A little jute is grown (adjacent to the Indian jute belt). About 300 tonnes of cardamoms

annually form a major earner of foreign exchange, along with postage stamps, and recently tourism, the latter at very high cost. Timber, liquor and canned fruits are also exported.

Traditional crafts include working in wood and bamboo and weaving in wool. Minor modern industries are the making of soap and candles from local animal raw materials, of carpets, textiles and matches. A cement works at Pugli is designed to produce 1,000 tonnes daily, and a hydro-electric station with 336 MW capacity is under construction.

Clearly, modernisation has begun, but it has far to go. Road building is a first priority. The capital Thimbu, and the former summer capital Paro are connected by road to the lowlands in India, as is similarly, but separately, Tashigang in the east.

102 The Bhutanese are culturally close to the Tibetans, as their dress suggests. Here the aristocracy are practising their national sport, archery. (Courtesy R. Hancock).

Chapter 24

The South Asian City

It is proper that in a study of the 'essential' geography of South Asia the rural and agricultural activities of the people should predominate. This should not however blind us to the fact that South Asia is a region of great cities, many of them of considerable antiquity.

In this chapter, six important cities are examined: Lahore, in Pakistan, is studied as approximating very closely to what might be mentally constructed as the model of the South Asian city. India's greatest urban agglomerations, Bombay and Calcutta, provide us with an insight into the huge scale urban development can achieve in two quite different settings. Dacca, capital of Bangladesh, exemplifies the old district town elevated to metropolitan status by having 'greatness thrust upon it'. Sri Lanka's primate city, Colombo, so far outstrips the other centres of the island in its urban qualities as to make them look mere towns. Finally, Pakistan's newly planned capital Islamabad, still evolving alongside its foster-parent Rawalpindi, is an example of new town development in South Asia.

Lahore*

In all its diverse ingredients Lahore provides a classic example of the South Asian city (see Fig. 24.1)†

Its character and importance cannot be appreciated without some knowledge of its past. The Old City of Lahore stands on a terrace bluff of the

*This section is heavily indebted to Muhammed Mushtaq Chaudhury, 'Lahore: a Geographical Study', University of London Ph.D. thesis, 1965. Recent data is courtesy of Lahore Development Authority. Figure 24.3 is based on an original courtesy of Prof. Samuel V. Noe
† The present author in *India: Resources and Development*, Heinemann Educational Books, London 1978 elaborated a 'model' of the Indian city which could equally apply to Lahore

River Ravi, a part of the left-bank cover floodplain, with the fickle Ravi washing and cutting into its northwestern corner as it flows on its braided meandering course towards the southwest. If present-day planners bemoan the threat that the Ravi presents and have had to protect Lahore by

Fig. 24.1

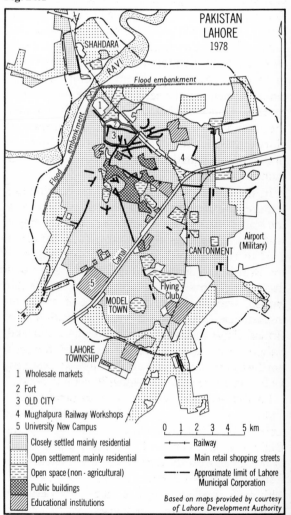

1 Wholesale markets
2 Fort
3 OLD CITY
4 Mughalpura Railway Workshops
5 University New Campus

Closely settled mainly residential
Open settlement mainly residential
Open space (non - agricultural)
Public buildings
Educational institutions

Railway
Main retail shopping streets
Approximate limit of Lahore Municipal Corporation

0 1 2 3 4 5 km

Based on maps provided by courtesy of Lahore Development Authority

massive bunds along its northern and western flanks, the site of the Fort at the extreme northwest corner of the city suggests that the defensive possibilities of the site facing northwest were well appreciated in the past. It was from the northwest that invaders repeatedly entered the subcontinent, travelling down the Grand Trunk Road from the Khyber Pass and Peshawar to Lahore, and then heading for Delhi and the Ganges plain.

In the twelfth century, Lahore became the capital of the Ghazni Empire that stretched westwards beyond the Indus to its mother country in eastern Afghanistan. As this empire expanded eastwards, the capital of its ruling sultans was moved to Delhi, leaving Lahore a regional capital. The Moghuls were next to invade, and Babar laid the city waste before adopting it as the Moghul capital in 1526, a position it shared from time to time with Delhi, Agra (and briefly Fatepur Sikri). Under Babar, Akbar, Jehangir and Shahjahan, Lahore lived out its golden age, acquiring much of its magnificent architecture. Akbar built the Fort in 1566, to which Jehangir and Shahjahan added embellishments in the early half of the seventeenth century. Under Shahjahan, Jehangir's Tomb and the Shalimar Gardens were built, but the crowning glory of the Moghuls came towards the last quarter of the century with the Badshahi Masjid or Mosque built by Aurangzeb.

In the declining years of the Moghul Empire, Lahore was once again exposed to invasion from the northwest by the Afghans seeking to struggle with the Maharattas for control of Delhi. From 1767 to 1840 when they in turn were dislodged by the British, the Sikhs ruled in Lahore, then but a desolate shadow of its former glory. Under the British, Lahore regained something of its earlier importance. Once more it outshone Delhi for the British chose Calcutta as their Indian capital, and Lahore became the cultural leader of the rich northwestern provinces until displaced again by Delhi which became the Imperial capital in 1912.

Lahore became the fulcrum of British political and economic strategy in the Indus basin. With the arrival of the railway from Calcutta, Bombay and Delhi via Amritsar in 1862 and from Karachi in 1865, Lahore's strategic position as the rear base from the Northwest Frontier region was assured. Although rivalled and overtaken by Delhi in imperial rank, Lahore remained capital of the

103 Veiled women shopping in the Old City, Lahore. The metal pots are sold by weight. (Courtesy Govt. of Pakistan).

Punjab, the most prosperous and best-run province of British India. Partition in 1947 temporarily shook the Punjab, leaving Lahore too dangerously exposed close to the Indian border to become capital of Pakistan, though for a while, between 1956 and 1970, West Pakistan was administered as 'one unit' with Lahore as its capital. Today, Lahore continues as provincial capital of the Punjab but it still maintains its status as the intellectual and cultural centre of Pakistan.

The Lahore Development Authority estimates the present population at 2.63 million (1977). In 1951, the first census after Independence recorded that 45.5 per cent of Lahore's population of 849,000 were refugees who numbered 386,000. It is probable that they replaced at least as many Sikhs and Hindus who fled to India. Between 1951 and 1961 about half the increase was due to migration (mainly from within Pakistan) and the proportion of the increase accountable to migration has if anything increased between 1961 and 1972.

Lahore suffers many of the constraints characteristic of a city standing on a promontory projecting into the ocean. The physical threat of the Ravi prevents any urban expansion northwards into the wedge of left-bank terrace left to Pakistan. Eastwards, the Indian border post is only 25 km from the city centre so the hinterland in that direction is practically nil. Growth has perforce to go southwards parallel to the Ravi and the frontier, but at a strategic distance from both.

The Urban Regions of Lahore

Figure 24.2 shows in simplified fashion the major regions discernible in the morphology of Lahore today:

1. The historic core, the Old City;
2. An intermediate zone south and southeast of the core;
3. The Cantonment in the southeastern sector;
4. The suburban zone surrounding the core and intermediate zone;
5. The arterial industrial ribbons;
6. The 'urban' wedges and fringe.

1. *The Old City*

This is the most distinctive area of Lahore (Fig. 24.3). Formerly a walled city dominated by the fort at its northwestern corner and overlooking the Ravi (now an abandoned channel at this point), the line of the walls is now marked by gardens and broad streets. Covering about 2.6 km² the Old City contains some third of a million inhabitants living at extremely high density. One quarter, Waksowali, is estimated to have 194,224 per km², that is 786 people per acre or 503,040 per square mile. To achieve such density the minimum space is given for movement among the tiny plots which often carry four-storey buildings, occupied at ground level by a shop or workshop, with family living quarters above, topped by a flat roof for summer sleeping and a latrine. Some efforts have been made to open up sections of the Old City but it retains its essential character as a pedestrian enclave, only its wider 'streets' being accessible to slow moving bullock- or horse-drawn carts, tongas and auto-rickshaws. Away from such lanes, only head porterage penetrates the alleys. Mushtaq classifies the streets as (a) 'bazars', where some motor traffic can penetrate from one of the 13 city gates, lined with shops and 5–7 m wide at most; (b) 'streets', which are about 2 m wide, sinuous and dark; and with (c) 'lanes', which are 1–1.3 m wide leading off them to house plots. Open drains run down the side of the streets, which themselves quickly become fouled with rubbish despite regular sweeping. Some of the lanes as well as the bazar streets are occupied by specialised retail quarters, each trade clustering together. The Old City confronts the town planner, schooled in western philosophies of urban life and speedy and efficient

transport flow, with a living fragment of the classic pre-industrial city. Until he attunes himself to the traditions of the place and realises that all is not squalor within, and finds the corners of great wealth and industry among its alleys, he may well think that the only solution is to raze it to the ground and build anew a modern CBD in glass, steel and concrete with parking lots and wide streets agog with perilous traffic.

There is no doubt that its drains, its light, its water supply – all its 'amenities' – can be much improved, but it is most improbable that the living organs that constitute the Old City would stand surgery and transplantation. To this observer the answer seems to be to leap the many evolutionary stages that have shaped the western city and to come in one gentle shuffle, as it were, to the city of pedestrian precincts so applauded by the avant-garde in planning.

2. *The Intermediate Zone*

This zone lies south and southeast of the Core. The British administration in the nineteenth century established its offices in the western part of this zone, into which some of the commercial and retail functions for the expanding Lahore spilled out from the Old City into Anarkali. Banks, Law Courts, the GPO, the Punjab University (Old Campus) and the Museum are concentrated in this

Fig. 24.2

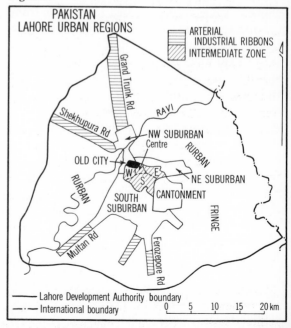

Lahore Development Authority boundary
International boundary

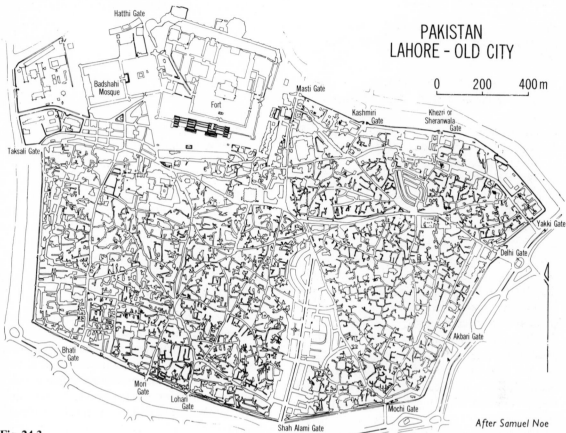

PAKISTAN
LAHORE – OLD CITY

0   200   400 m

Hatthi Gate

Badshahi Mosque

Fort

Masti Gate

Kashmiri Gate

Khezri or Sheranwala Gate

Taksali Gate

Yakki Gate

Delhi Gate

Bhati Gate

Akbari Gate

Mori Gate

Lohari Gate

Mochi Gate

Shah Alami Gate

After Samuel Noe

Fig. 24.3

part. The centre of the intermediate zone is more closely settled with residential retailing and small industrial workplaces. Foundries, hardware shops, markets for wool, metals and fruit make this a very busy quarter in which the roads, fortunately, are reasonably wide. To the east is the distinctive area of the railway stations (passenger and goods), the railway workshops, and the residential quarters of its staff. The southern part of the zone contains the Civil Lines, the well laid out residential quarter for the British administrators, with cheek-by-jowl, sharing the security and prestige of the imperial rulers, the huge residences of the Indian princes – Bahawalpur House, Kashmir House, Patiala House, and Chamba House. Government offices now occupy them. The Upper Mall provided high class shopping facilities and a link to the administrative centre in the west of the zone; exclusive colleges catered for the élite, and botanical gardens for their recreation. Altogether, density was low and remains so, though the

process of infilling and intensification of land-use is now visible.

3. *The Cantonment*
The Cantonment in the southeastern quadrant of Lahore is the military reflection of the administrative Civil Lines, and a functional centre. From the 1850s it was developed to house the army, its troops in barracks with parade grounds and rifle ranges, hospitals and bazars, the officers and their families in widely spaced bungalows in gardens. A Government Dairy Farm, Military Cattle Farm and Grass Farm provide food and fodder for man and beast. Independence has changed the occupants, but neither the settlement pattern nor the way of life.

4. *The Suburban Zone*
This zone contains a range of residential areas which vary in density of settlement inversely with socio-economic status. Cramped for space closer to the centre, industry has found a foothold here

104 A modern middle class street in Karachi.

and there, but had been overwhelmed by residential sprawl before much in the way of an industrial region could develop.

In the northwest an area of very mixed and generally poor development occupies the badly drained ground of the former bed of the Ravi and its sand bars. It extends beyond the Ravi in Shahdara. Flood risks make it a 'less desirable' residential area on both sides of the river and is thus relegated to poor low class dwellings. The strategic economic position of the left-bank portion close to the Old City and the bustle of the western parts of the intermediate zone make it important as a wholesale market for fodder vegetables and livestock.

The mirror image of this area to the north and east of the Old city and intermediate zone is similarly low-lying and only protected from flooding by the bund. Parts of the Ravi's cut-off billabongs still hold stagnating water, and occasionally (as in 1955) excessively high floods may outflank the defences. The whole area has something of a 'beyond the tracks' character about it. Although the Engineering University has been established here, development has been a mixture of industry and housing clusters for the working class population, separated from Lahore by the 6 m embankment of the railway. In the east of this sector, between the Grand Trunk Road leading to Shalimar Garden and the Lahore Branch of the Upper Bari Doab canal, is more mixed development characterised by crowded hutments. Promixity to the Indian border has no doubt inhibited more profitable use of this area which lies beyond the Lahore Municipal Corporation's boundary.

To the south of the intermediate zone, flanked by the Ravi Bund to the west and Cantonment to the east, suburban growth has had unfettered opportunity to sprawl. To western eyes, backed by a consciousness of high land values, such sprawl seems at first sight to be an excessively lavish use of resources. Furthermore, it tends to put people at a considerable distance from the job opportunities of the inner city areas and the industrial ribbons to be discussed below. This south suburban sector contains several planned, better-class suburbs, some like Model Town dating from before Independence and using, as do indeed the later Gulberg suburbs, plans reminiscent of British garden cities. At Kot Lakhpat, beyond the Municipal boundary, Lahore Township is another example of a planned, integrated residential suburb. Travelling through these suburbs, it is often hard to believe that one is in Pakistan, and that one is seeing the homes of the urbanised and westernised élite, infinitely small in relation to the population as a whole, but wielding great political and economic power – a fact that helps to explain the glaring contrasts in housing standards within the society.

Not all the south suburban zone is high-class residential. Within Gulberg, space at an appropriately higher density is provided for the menials who serve the luxury residences. Some government departments, like Posts and Telegraphs, have built staff colonies in the southwest, the University has its New Campus (designed by Doxiades) in the south, and there are several colonies for lower paid government servants and others. One cannot, however, escape the sense of occupational 'caste' in the residential pattern.

5. *The Arterial Industrial Ribbons*

The justification for strong planning laws and their firm application is too often seen in the disasters that result in their absence. Despite the abundant examples from western experience of laissez-faire development in the inter-war period, industrial growth around Lahore has been allowed to take place along several of the major highways that bring traffic to the city, in particular from the north along the Grand Trunk Road from Gujranwala, and from the west along the Sheikhupura Road. For many kilometres right up to the limits of the Lahore Development Authority's jurisdiction and beyond, these roads are lined intermittently with industrial sites to which, as a rule, the labour force has to be transported by 'company bus' from the city 20 km and more distant. There is a tendency for similar ribbon development along the Multan and Ferozepore Roads, southwest and southwards from the city. The opportunity to lay out a consolidated industrial sector nearer to the homes of potential workers seems to have passed.

6. *The 'Urban' Wedges and Fringes*

Finally, between these ribbons and the other roads that radiate from the city, beaded with clusters of settlements and various kinds of service and commercial activity, remain wedges of mainly agricultural land dotted with villages, in form typical of any Punjab rural settlement, but in function poised between town and country. The farmers grow some vegetables for the Lahore market, but increasingly urban sprawl is devouring the traditional market gardening areas, or they are giving way to fodder crops, bulkier and less able than vegetables to stand the cost of carriage from further away. Day and night, bullock and buffalo carts and rehras ply the radial roads to bring cut fodder into the city to feed its milk herds and draught animals. The urban villages have become semi-urban in their employment base, the workers either cycling to work or riding in the numerous small buses that serve the outer fringe of the city's labour catchment. Some villages have already lost all their lands to become 'urban' villages, mud houses, farmyards and all, overwhelmed in the tide of urban expansion, but adapting to the situation by capitalising on their ability to supply fresh milk to the citizens, albeit becoming themselves dependent on distant supplies of fodder.

Housing in Lahore

The rapid growth of population in Lahore creates a constant demand for housing. The influx of the rural poor, the dispossessed and the redundant from the march of modernisation, has led to much squatter settlement, often in neglected corners, or on unviable strips of land along drains and railways. LDA policy now is to accept their presence as inevitable and to help the dwellers in these *jhuggis* or *kachha abaddis* to make the best of their environment by providing water and drainage. They have even been granted rights of occupance where they are on government land. Many are located where building projects first attracted them as labourers, and there they have remained. There are some 120 *jhuggi* settlements housing about 80,000 people in Lahore.

105 Anarkali Bazar in Lahore leads to the crowded Old City. Note the concentration of cloth shops side by side.
(Courtesy Govt. of Pakistan).

More formal housing is undertaken by the Lahore Development Authority and by private enterprise. By 1976–77, the LDA had built 6,500 residential flats and 3,500 'quarters' (single-storey small home units); 1,000 flats were built in the public sector in that year alone, and 3,000 more in the private sector. The LDA acquires land, provides it with urban services and either builds homes for sale or sells land for private development. Its function is to act as a catalyst in the housing business rather than to become a super-landlord itself.

Retail Trade

The bazars of the Old City have already been mentioned. Figure 24.1 shows the main shopping areas. Apart from the concentrations in Anarkali and the adjacent Upper Mall and Gwalmandi areas, the pattern of retailing tends to be linear along Multan and Ferozepore Roads within the south suburban sector, and in small shopping and market centres in the several Gulberg suburbs, Model Town, etc. In every shopping area, informal commerce in the shape of itinerant peddlars and pavement hawkers seems to occupy as much of the roadway as it dares. The open stalls of the Old City and the markets gradually give way to the glass fronted shops of the suburban areas, more familiar to the western visitor, but not designed for the casual, haggling commerce of the bazars.

Transport

A major problem facing the planner of Lahore in the last quarter of the twentieth century is the persistence therein of traditional transport modes competing for road space with modern motorised vehicles. The number of vehicles in 1976 registered in Lahore is set out in Table 24.1, with the 1964 data for comparison.

Some major city streets have been banned to animal drawn traffic, but away from these confusion breeds confusion as tongas, rickshaws, buses and buffaloes try to sort themselves out at crossroads. In addition to vehicles there are the animals themselves: donkeys with saddle sacks of bricks and sand proceeding on their lawful occasions, the strung out camel train loaded with firewood or fodder and the stately half-tonne buffalo cows going down from their dairy plot to the canal to drink, or herds of prime goats on

Table 24.1 Lahore, registered vehicles, 1964–76

	1964	1976
Motorised		
Motor cycles/scooters	11,548	52,283
Motor cars	9,274	22,832
Jeeps	1,201	1,109
Buses	2,298	4,331
Taxis and auto-rickshaws	2,120	9,521
Trucks and delivery vans	3,509	5,578
Tractors, etc.	8 59	4,720
Animal drawn		
Tongas	3,974	4,041
Rehras	3,728	5,400
Bullock carts		1,200
Hackney carriages (human-hand carts)		9,383
Others		5,000

Note: The categories of non-mechanised vehicles are not strictly comparable between the years. Bicycles are thought now to number one for every other household – say 250,000

the way to market and ultimately the butcher. Amongst it all, unlike the developed western city, people in their thousands walk and jostle under head bundles and baskets, and cyclists wend their way among the crowds. And the more the planners strive to open up the roads, the more they come, as the enormous increase in vehicles between 1964 and 1976 indicates, and the more they will come if living standards rise to bring a motor cycle into every home where a push bike now carries the breadwinner to work.

Urban Farms

One further feature that distinguishes Lahore in its pre-industrial phase from the industrial city of the developed world is the continued presence within its limits of great numbers of dairy cattle, particularly buffaloes. While they ensure a fresh (if not an undiluted or an unpolluted) supply of milk within the city, they put a great load on the transport system to maintain them in fodder. The herds of ruminating buffaloes may be seen along the canal drains easements, on almost every vacant lot, and even in the heart of the Old City. Their dung, a precious byproduct, is plastered in neat, round cakes to dry on the walls and to be used or sold as fuel for the kitchens of the poor.

Lahore as a Model of the South Asian City

The several morphological elements present in Lahore which recur in so many South Asian cities justifying the use of this city as a 'model' may now be summarised.

(a) The fort, guarding the Medieval pedestrian city within its walls; retail markets are within the city, markets for livestock, fodder and firewood lie around the walls.

(b) The mosque of the Muslim Moghul rulers, or in some cities a major Hindu temple, stands close to the old city nucleus.

(c) The British Cantonment laid out in the nineteenth century at a healthy and strategic distance from the old city has its own structure: segregated housing for military officers, troops and followers, its dairy farm, etc. Often as a distinct sub-region within the Cantonment but on the flank nearest the indigenous city, the Civil Lines housed the British administrators, not far from their revenue offices, courts and jail. Military and Civil had their own sometimes separate (in the larger cities) retail shopping 'Sadr' bazar. Today, these elements are little changed except that the military and civilian élites who occupy them are nationals of the now independent countries.

(d) Schools, colleges, and maybe a university ultimately, provided education for the local élite but were initially established by the British to train junior civil servants for their administration.

(e) The coming of the railways introduced new elements: stations to serve the old city and cantonment, maybe workshops, and always a housing colony for staff who were often recruited from the mixed blood 'Anglo-Indian' community.

(f) Industry (other than local crafts which tended to be located in the old city) was initially near the railway, but since Independence it has tended to spread out along trunk roads, with or without housing being specifically provided for the employees.

(g) Suburban growth, generally planned by the municipal authorities, has tended to be lavish in the use of land where the rich and middle class are being accommodated. Segregation by economic status is usual and may extend to segregation by caste or religious community among the lower classes.

(h) Squatter settlements, transient and semi-permanent, mushroom where unused space exists.

(i) Relics of rural life – dairy herds, for example – and often of village communities may become embedded in the sprawling city.

Bombay

Bombay and Calcutta are in several important respects very different. As a single urban unit Greater Bombay is the larger, having 5,970,575 inhabitants against 3,148,746 for the Municipal Corporation of Calcutta, but while Bombay has the character of a huge city with suburbs, the urban agglomeration that contains Calcutta is a straggling conurbation in the proper meaning of the term, with a total population of 7,031,382, contained in some 74 constituent urban units.

The setting of Bombay is shown in Figure 24.4. Its site is constrained by the sea, expansion now only being possible eastwards onto the mainland towards the foot of the Western Ghats. The sunken coastline accounts for the numerous indentations, one of which made Bombay harbour so attractive to British traders seeking shelter from the southwest monsoon. The coast itself is sometimes rocky where outliers and spurs of the Deccan lavas occur, but in sheltered sections mangrove swamps and mudflats are typical. Urban development concentrated first at the southern tip of Bombay Island, a narrow promontory 14 km long and at most 4 km wide, itself comprising three linked islets, separated from the larger Salsette Island to the north by Mahim Bay and the mangrove estuaries and flats of the Mahim and Sion Rivers. Docks were excavated the length of the eastern side of the island. The railway lines from Delhi and Gujarat along the coast, and from Peninsular India, down off the Deccan Plateau, converged to run along the spine of the island to termini in the south. Urban expansion, particularly after Independence, could only take place outside Bombay Island, on Salsette. In the inter-censal decade (1961–71) the population of Salsette's suburbs grew by 110 per cent while that of Bombay Island increased by only 11 per cent.*

---

*John E. Brush, 'Elite Residential Colonies', (mimeographed paper, publication pending)

At present, 53 per cent of Great Bombay's population live on Bombay Island, 27 per cent in the western half of Salsette and 20 per cent in the eastern half.

Twenty-two kilometres north of the southern extremity of Bombay, Salsette Island is separated from the mainland by Bassein Creek in the west and its continuation as Thana Creek on the east. Until 1973, all landward communication with Bombay had to cross these creeks at the northern end of Salsette, but recently the Vashi Bridge across the lower end of Thana Creek has shortened by 12 km the distance from central Bombay to Pune. It has also given impetus to modern industrial development in the Trans-Thana Creek Industrial Belt which provides the first substantial element of what will in time become New Bombay, a twin city of two million people facing Bombay across the harbour. Its industries are strongly oriented towards petrochemicals.

The population density of Bombay is shown in

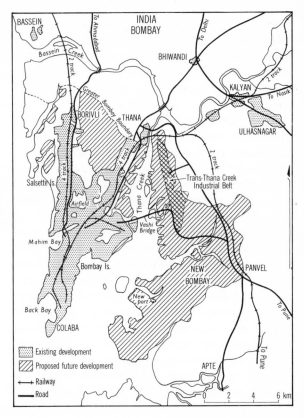

Fig. 24.4

106   Downtown Hyderabad where dozing 'sacred' cows are an added obstacle to the mixed traffic of push bikes, cycles, rickshaws, cars, buses and pedestrians. Two minarets of the Char Minar gate-way can be seen: Note the concentration of jewellers shops.

Figure 24.5. The core of concentration is clearly focused in the wedge fronting onto Back Bay where densities exceeding 70,000 per km^2 occur in an area almost 4 km from north to south and 1.5 km wide. Within this area three wards have densities over 250,000 per km^2, the peak reaching 371,176 for a population of 63,100 occupying 0.17 km^2, giving each human being 2.7 m^2 of land surface, including roads. A second area of extremely high density lies just south of Dadar in the city's main textile factory belt. Most of the wards with over 40,000 per km^2 are contiguous to those in the top quintile just described. Outside Bombay Island, densities remain high for some distance along the northern and northeastern communication corridors, where suburban railway suburbs are strung like beads along the line.* Outliers of concentration occur in Kanhari ward, served by Borival Station in the north, and at Mulund where Greater Bombay merges with Thana Municipality in the northeast, but in general population density decreases with distance from Bombay's CBD and away from the elongated arteries of communication. Colaba, Fort and Esplanade wards at the southern extremity of the island are notable for their lower densities, adjacent to some of the highest densities at the centre. Colaba and Fort were the areas of British administration and military barracks, and the Esplanade ward contains many business houses, railway and port terminal facilities, leaving little space for residential habitation. At the other end of Back Bay, Malabar Hill has a moderate density by Bombay standards (29,153 per km^2), in this the most sought after address for the city's élite.

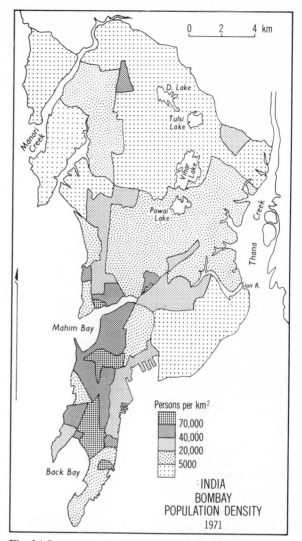

Fig. 24.5

Manufacturing engages over 47 per cent of the workers, over half (53 per cent) of them on Bombay Island, mainly in the northern half where the wards with over 40 per cent of their workers in manufacturing, account for 29 per cent of Bombay's total (Fig. 24.6). On Salsette Island, manufacturing is tightly concentrated along the northwest communications corridor towards Thana.

Trade and commerce are specially important in the vicinity of the docks and the two railway termini, near which is the central business district (Fig. 24.7). Outlying concentrations of workers in

commerce are found in the high class suburbs at Mahim at the northern end of Bombay Island, and at Santacruz, Kandivil and Borival in Salsette.

A characteristic of the South Asian industrial city is the numerical imbalance between the sexes, particularly in the working age groups. In Bombay at the 1971 Census, the ratio of females per 1000 males throughout the age range 20–59 was never better than 691 and fell to 592 between 40 and 49 years. These ratios are much improved on those in the 1961 Census when between 35 and 44 years there were only 471 females for 1,000 males. Clearly, many males migrate to the big cities without their families, returning home for seasonal festivals and to retire.

*C. D. Deshpande, *Suburbs of Greater Bombay*, Centre for Urban Research, Department of Geography, Osmania University, 1973

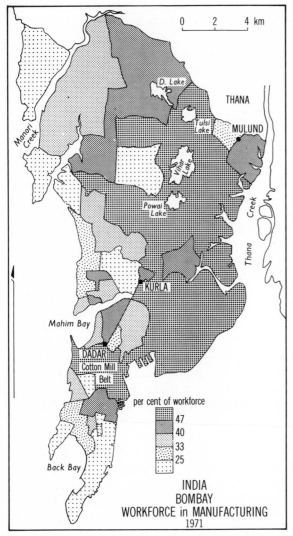

Fig. 24.6

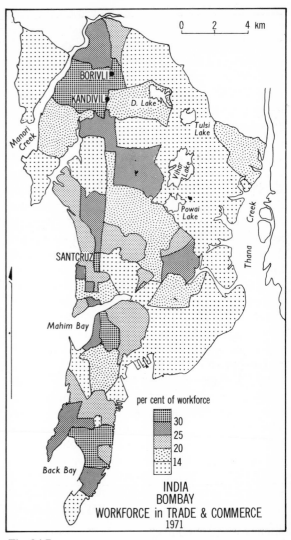

Fig. 24.7

Calcutta

The Hooghlyside conurbation or, in the words of
the Census, the Calcutta Urban Agglomeration,
corresponding approximately with the area within
the jurisdiction of the Calcutta Metropolitan
Planning Board, is strung out for more than 65 km
along both banks of the river Hooghly (see Fig.
24.8). Bansberia and Kalyani mark the northern
limits well upstream of the twin cities of Calcutta
and Howrah, linked by Howrah Bridge. Downstream the conurbation continues for another
30 km. In its general form the conurbation is most
unusual. For considerable distances it extends
back from the river as a built-up zone barely 2 km

wide, perched on the natural levee of the Hooghly
as a narrow dry-point site for settlement between
the river and its backswamp depression, low-lying
and flood-prone as is characteristic of a deltaic
environment. Situation rather than site has been
responsible for Calcutta's development however.
English and French merchants found this reach of
the Hooghly navigable by their merchant ships,
which could here take on cargoes brought down
river from the great cities of the Ganga Plain, the
centres of administration and craftsmanship like
Delhi, Agra, Allahabad and Banaras (Varanasi).
The English established factories at Fort William,
Calcutta (1691) following the Dutch lead at Chin-
sura (1653) and in competition with the French

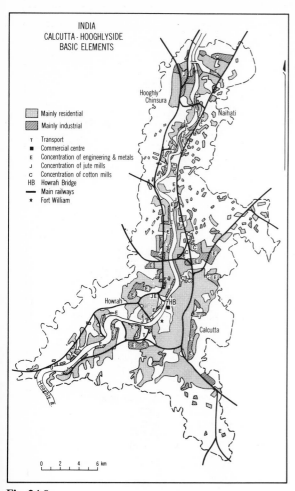

INDIA
CALCUTTA-HOOGHLYSIDE
BASIC ELEMENTS

Mainly residential
Mainly industrial
T   Transport
■   Commercial centre
E   Concentration of engineering & metals
J   Concentration of jute mills
C   Concentration of cotton mills
HB   Howrah Bridge
─   Main railways
★   Fort William

0 2 4 6 km

Fig. 24.8

Chandanagore (Chandanagar, 1690–92). So were laid the foundations of India's mercantile capital. With the eclipse of the French, the British East India Company's base at Calcutta became locally dominant, and here the British built their capital when the Empire of India replaced the administration of the Company. This function was lost to Delhi in 1912, but Calcutta continued as capital of Bengal, and for long as the principal mercantile and industrial metropolis. Railways had replaced river boats and roads as the chief means of transport down the Ganga valley, though to the east river-steamers carried cargoes of tea and jute from Assam and the more distant parts of the Ganga–

Brahmaputra delta, now in Bangladesh. The railways had their termini on either side of the Hooghly, Howrah in particular owing its growth in large part to its location at the end of lines converging from northwest and central India on the river bank opposite Calcutta. Railways and the opening of the Suez Canal in 1869 gave Calcutta's chief rival Bombay advantages of proximity to Britain from northwestern India, and reduced Calcutta's hinterland in this direction. On the other hand railways tied to Hooghlyside the development of the Damodar as an industrial region and source of coal, to their mutual benefit. On the east bank of the Hooghly, railways connected Calcutta with North Bengal and Darjiling. Partition severed East and parts of North Bengal from their traditional market for jute, and from the centre of Bengali culture in Calcutta, leaving the latter in a somewhat exposed position close to the East Pakistan Border. Despite these accumulated disadvantages, Calcutta and the conurbation have managed to hold their own commercially and industrially. At the time of Independence, Calcutta became the destination of many thousands of Hindu refugees from East Pakistan. Such movement recurred periodically as friction increased between India and Pakistan.

The war of independence in Bangladesh again released a flood of homeless refugees who pressed on the outskirts of Calcutta. Quite apart from these victims of specific political disturbance great numbers of workless poor have drifted to Hooghlyside in search of livelihood. The condition of the urban poor in Calcutta beggars description. Perhaps

107   Downtown Dacca: The Motijheel commercial area with its modern skyscrapers. (Courtesy Govt. of Bangladesh).

half the population has come from outside, many to settle in 'bustees', slums of make-shift shelters in which they cluster in groups with similar language, dialect, caste or birthplace. Just over half (53 per cent) of the population of Calcutta Municipality was migrant in 1961.

Sex ratios between ages 20 and 59 are never better than 517 and fall to 436 in the 40–49 group (1971). It is a sad commentary on the importance of children as breadwinners in the families of the poor that an unbalanced sex ratio of 890 girls to 1,000 boys appears even in the age group 0–14, and 680 in the group 15–19, suggesting that the young boys come to town with father, leaving mother and the girls at home. The corresponding figures for Bombay are 931 and 765, which again reflects on the even more dismal state of Calcutta's poor.

Calcutta has been described as an 'immature' city. People have poured in, and the local inhabitants have multiplied fast, but few of the necessi-

Fig. 24.9

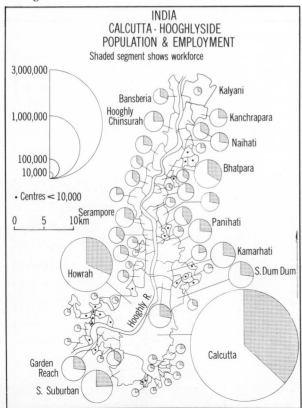

Fig. 24.10

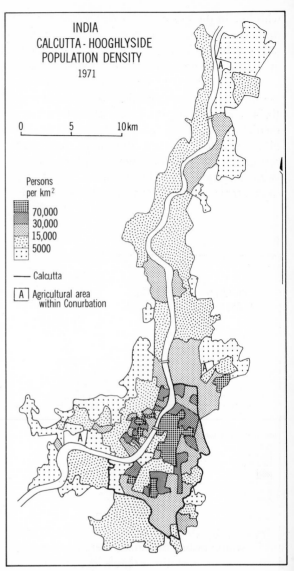

ties of life have been created to serve them. Employment opportunities increase too slowly to absorb them. Many of the conurbation's difficulties are common to other big Indian cities – water supply, drainage, sanitation, housing – but Calcutta's physiographic site (the 'city in the swamp') aggravates its problems of social hygiene and economic development. The efforts by the authorities to provide permanent shelter seem quite incapable of keeping pace with the inflow and increase of population, and policy today is first to provide the most rudimentary needs to those who live in the bustees: a protected water supply, drainage to prevent domestic waste, faeces and heavy rainfall from forming a seasonal morass, and latrines to control endemic enteric disease.

About 5 million of the conurbation's 7 million people are in Calcutta itself (3.15 million), Howrah (0.74 million) and the administrative areas immediately adjoining them (see Fig. 24.9). Many of the smaller units are little more than swollen residential rural suburbs with relatively low densities ranging up to 15,000 per Km², but often less than 5,000 per km² because of the non-urban land included within them. (Fig. 24.10). Howrah's relatively low overall density of 12,000 per km² is deceptive since the Municipal Committee area contains considerable areas of swamp.

Outside Calcutta proper there are few areas with densities exceeding 15,000 per km²; only Dum Dum (157,000 per km²) exceeds 30,000 per km².

Calcutta's is a different story.

More than one-fifth of its 101 wards have densities exceeding 100,000 per km². Indeed, two reach the incredible densities of 276,467 per km²

Fig. 24.11

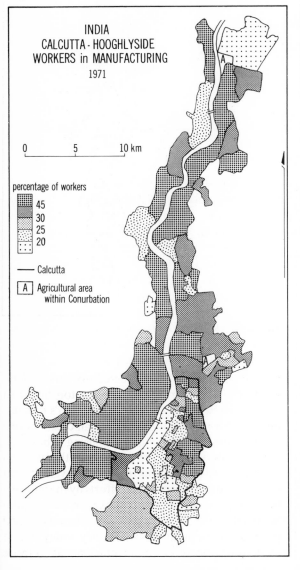

Fig. 24.12

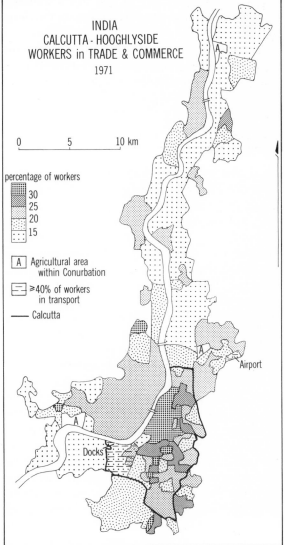

for a total of 41,500 people, and 228,000 for 22,800 people, a little less than in Bombay's peak ward, but extremely high in the context of Calcutta's more horizontal bustee development. The areas of highest density are concentrated close to the Howrah Bridge in north central Calcutta which contains the CBD. There are two lesser nuclei in the south.

In occupational structure Calcutta differs somewhat from the rest of its conurbation. It has the major share of trade and commerce, in which it serves the remainder of the region, while the lesser centres are more strongly industrial (see Fig. 24.11 and 24.12). The eastern wards of Calcutta have a high percentage of industrial workers, but levels are generally in two lower quintiles over the rest of the city. Extensively in the riverside towns over 45 per cent of the workers are in manufacturing. Transport engages over 40 per cent of the workforce living close to Kidderpore docks and the Dum Dum airport.

The industrial structure of Bombay and Calcutta are discussed in Chapter 8.

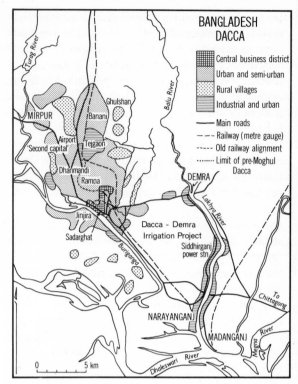

Fig. 24.13

Dacca

Dacca has long been unrivalled as the regional capital of what is now Bangladesh. Geographical centrality, reinforced by the fortunate combination of physiographic features favourable to both land and water communications with a populous and highly productive hinterland, has ensured its status. The basic physiographic element in the site, the prong of relatively high ground that extends southwards from the Madhupur Tract to the Buriganga River, is flanked by low flood lands of the Turag River to the west and the Balu River to the east (Fig. 24.13). The prong of flood-free terrace averages *c.* 6 km in width, and it has strongly influenced the direction of Dacca's growth, which has been generally northwards from the old nucleus of the pre-Moghul river port on the Buriganga levee. It may be premature to speak of a Dacca–Narayanganj conurbation, for the two urban areas are still but tenuously linked by a strip of discontinuous built-up area along the road and railway that clings to the Buriganga north bank. As yet Narayanganj and this strip of go-downs seem to look to their rivers rather than to their land-wise connections. However, such discussion is largely pointless, for whatever the physical appearances, Narayanganj with 255,000 in 1974 is close enough to Dacca (1,730,000) in distance and in time – *c.* 12 km separates their railway stations – to be regarded as part of an urban continuum now exceeding two million inhabitants. Its jute mills and presses may trace their antecedents to times when the economic viewpoint of Narayanganj was more clearly separate from that of Dacca, when the former stood for the raw jute collecting and exporting trade, of which the latter embodied British imperial administration of the region. Today, however, the Lakhya River banks at Narayanganj provide sites for power stations, boat yards and jute and cotton textile mills serving the country's internal demands in general and Dacca's in particular.

Earliest Dacca may date from the seventh century AD. From the thirteenth century it was a centre of Muslim rule, and was chosen as the Moghuls' capital in the early seventeenth century when its pre-eminence in trade attracted Portuguese and other European merchants. The eighteenth and nineteenth centuries saw Dacca decline in importance as Calcutta forged ahead as the British capital of Imperial India. The early twentieth century brought a brief renaissance of Dacca's significance as an administrative centre, when it was capital of the short-lived province of Eastern Bengal and Assam from 1905 to 1912. By this time a railway link with Chittagong had been established.

Figure 24.13 shows in a simplified way the major elements in Dacca's urban growth. Moghul Dacca stretched along the Buriganga for about 6 km with several forts sited close to the river – then the town's *raison d'être*. This belt is now the most congested area of Dacca and contains the older section of the central business district alongside the river port at Sadarghat. Characteristically, the railway has been re-aligned east of the city to avoid several level crossings within the growing city which had become the location of chronic frustrating delays. Development of Dacca as a British provincial capital led to the layout of stately administrative buildings and comfortable European bungalows in large gardens in the Ramna area, in the bend of the old railway line. This suburb remains one of high class residences, though more modern development has extended to the west in Dhanmandi and north in Gulshan Model Town. Government administration has outgrown its quarters in Ramna and is to be largely relocated in the northwest in Sher-e-Bangla Nagar.

Industry in Dacca before 1947 was closely tied to the banks of the Buriganga and to Naryanganj.

Independence brought new vigour to the city, now capital of a province of Pakistan, freed from subservience to India's Calcutta. While expansion in the jute industry took place along the Buriganga and the Lakhya rivers – for water transport is still essential to that trade – new manufacturing plants were set up in an industrial estate alongside the railway and roads to Tejgaon north of the city.

It is of interest to note how the main business area has migrated from the vicinity of Sadarghat to the administrative district east of Ramna. Dacca's CBD, or for that matter any of its retail trading centres should not be thought of as replicas of shopping areas in western cities. There are virtually no large stores, but rather a vast number of rival shops, cheek by jowl, so that all grocery shops are close together, and similarly cloth shops, variety shops, book shops and so on. It is only in the offices of banks and other business corporations and government departments that the CBD resembles more closely its western counterparts.

Reference has been made to the well-defined high class residential areas on non-flooding land. Towards the other end of the social scale, low class housing is crowded into the old city area along the Buriganga and is left with the low-lying lands on the east and west flanks of the terrace prong. The absolute nadir of squalor is suffered by the squatters, many of them refugees, who crowd into 'bustee' encampments of make-shift shelters wherever vacant land can be occupied without immediate eviction. Vacant building blocks

108 Suburban Dacca showing a squatter settlement in the foreground with middle class flats on the left and high class detached residences on the right.

109 Colombo harbour and the Fort commercial and administrative centre of the city. The clocktower is an old lighthouse. Note the motor traffic, in contrast to the more mixed traffic of other South Asian countries.

expand in area and population, and the most probable direction of urban extension is northwards to form a linear city to link with industrial settlement at Tungi where the metre gauge railway forks to Mymensingh and Chittagong. Narayanganj is likely also to expand along both banks of the Lakhya, a development encouraged by the new branch railway from Narsingdi which enables traffic to bypass Dacca's congested yards. The persistence of river communications none the less seems assured.

Colombo*

The urban area of Colombo, with 1·346 million people in 1971, was likely to reach 1.5 million by 1979. The Colombo Municipal Council area had 562,000 in 1971, but the effective city is much more extensive, continuing southwards without a break into Dehiwala–Mt. Lavinia (154,000), and inland in a number of quite populous suburbs.

Colombo has more in common with Bombay and Calcutta, essentially mercantile port cities developed by the British, than with Lahore, Dacca and even Rawalpindi, which trace their importance back to Moghul times and periods prior to European contact. As in Calcutta, Colombo's Fort was first built by Europeans, here the Portuguese, in the sixteenth century to defend their commercial interests in the area of the city now occupied by the CBD immediately adjacent to the harbour. Under the Dutch in the seventeenth and eighteenth centuries and the British from

adjacent to the modern CBD are typical examples of squatter settlement sites, but the scourge is widespread throughout the more open parts of the city. Cycle rickshaw drivers and their mechanics, and street-stall vendors of *pan* and cigarettes sleep in rough shelters on the roadside.

A type of residential area rare in modern western cities (but represented in the workers' tenements of mid-nineteenth-century Britain, for example) is found in association with the large jute mills which build for their employees cramped colonies which often take on the character of men's dormitories.

An indication of the conditions in which the poorer classes live in Dacca, and for that matter in most South Asian cities, may be had from the fact that in Lalbagh, part of the Old City, only 5 per cent of the houses had electricity and 13 per cent had water in 1961. In the squatter settlements there are practically no services whatsoever; the residents have to draw water from standpipes in the road and many have access to no latrine. To judge from the experience of expanding metropolitan cities in Asia the problem of squatter settlement is likely to increase rather than otherwise in the probably long years of transition to development, while the surplus of people on the land continues to grow at a rate far faster than that of the growth in alternative jobs. Meanwhile Dacca will

* Acknowledgement is made of two research theses upon which the author has drawn for valuable background to fieldwork:
B.L. Panditharatna's University of London Ph.D. thesis (1960) on *Colombo*
S.K. de Silva's University College, Swansea M.A. thesis (1973) on *Socio-spatial Patterns of the City of Colombo; a Factorial Ecology*

the nineteenth century, Colombo expanded to dominate the commerce and administration of the island colony. It now stands unchallenged in its primacy.

The three maps in Figure 24.14 show some of the main features of Colombo, physical, demographic and functional. The rocky outcrop forming the promontory on which stood the Fort, an area still so named, gave some shelter from the southwest monsoon on an otherwise exposed coastline. Here Muslim traders had established a settlement before the arrival of the Portuguese. The immediate coastal belt consists largely of a coastal sand plain backed by a discontinuous line of lagoons, still apparent in the Beira Lake and north of the Kelani Ganga. A cut linking the Beira Lake to the harbour continues to provide access by barges to warehouses around the lake. Another canal northwards from the Kelani Ganga formed a protected waterway as far north as Puttalam Lagoon.

Low ground in the floodplain of the Kelani Ganga and its tributaries and around the coastal lagoons has effectively limited urban growth inland, encouraging it to spread north and particularly south along the coastal sand plain, and the patches of 'mantled plain' that stand above them. The latter are remnants of a much dissected surface increasingly extensive inland, deeply weathered and carrying a generally lateritic soil cover. The low ground, ill-drained and very prone to flooding, provided some protection for the early foreign mercantile settlement of Fort and nearby Pettah, and extending on to the mantled plain northwards to the Kelani Ganga. Portuguese and Dutch interests lay in the coastal lowlands where spices could be obtained, but the British penetrated the interior, building railways to Kandy and into the hill country beyond as they developed plantations of coffee and, later, tea. Colombo expanded greatly under the impetus of trade, and as a key coaling station in the British Imperial system, conveniently sited between the Suez Canal and Singapore. After the opening of Suez, the harbour was protected from the southwest monsoon by moles.

The map of present day functional regions reflects the historical factors in Colombo's growth. Government and financial institutions are concentrated in Fort and close by, though with the expansion since Independence many government offices have had to be housed in former large residences and commercial developments scattered through the high class Cinnamon Gardens area and adjacent suburbs.

Commerce, wholesale handling of export commodities, and some related industries cluster round Beira Lake which is still linked to the harbour by barges, though with improved wharf facilities much cargo is moved to the dockside by road. Some industries like flour milling, tobacco and tea packing are located close to the harbour, but many of the modern factories have found sites on low lands unattractive to housing, on the fringes of residential development.

Retailing centres most densely on Pettah, the traditional focus of Muslim traders and Tamil craftsmen. Modern shops, in the style of departmental stores were established in Fort to serve the British plantation and administrative population. Now they linger on as somewhat pathetic relics. Here, and in the suburban retail centres strung along the Galle Road and at various road junctions, the shops are closer to western norms than to those found in other South Asian cities.

The map of gross population density indicates the highest concentration in Kochchikade just east of Pettah, rather than in Fort (dominated by office blocks) or Pettah itself, given over to retailing in small shops. East of Pettah the low status Tamil and Muslim areas are densely settled, with lower density northwards into lower middle class Tamil areas, and beyond these again, in the bend of the Kelani Ganga, low status housing mixed with industry and market gardening. Gross densities south of Fort and Pettah are reduced by the considerable areas of open space in the Galle Face and Beira Lake, but net residential densities in tenements exceed 500 persons per hectare in Kollupitiya. Cinnamon Gardens with only 47 per ha (gross density) is Colombo's high class residential area, under invasion, however, from institutional functions, e.g. the University, Meteorological and other Government departments, and various embassies. Southwards, areas of moderate densities of 50 – 100 per ha occupy the coastal sand plain, mainly high status residential, with lower densities inland as more of the land is low-lying and unsuited to housing, and the urban area gives way ultimately to a 'rurban' fringe, where rural

COLOMBO
LANDFORMS

COLOMBO
POPULATION DENSITY: 1971

Fig. 24.14

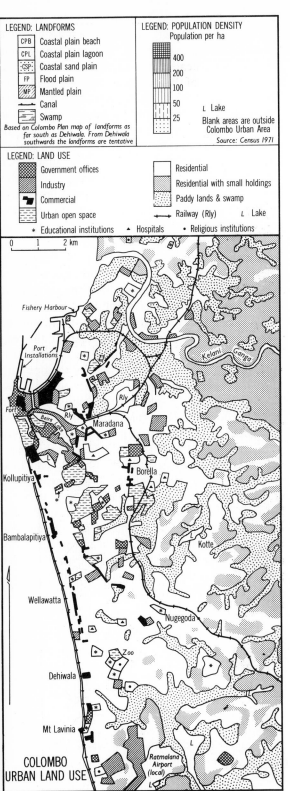

LEGEND: LANDFORMS

CPB	Coastal plain beach
CPL	Coastal plain lagoon
CSP	Coastal sand plain
FP	Flood plain
MP	Mantled plain
	Canal
	Swamp

Based on Colombo Plan map of landforms as far south as Dehiwala. From Dehiwala southwards the landforms are tentative

LEGEND: POPULATION DENSITY
Population per ha

400
200
100
50
25

L Lake

Blank areas are outside
Colombo Urban Area
Source: Census 1971

LEGEND: LAND USE

	Government offices
	Industry
	Commercial
	Urban open space
*	Educational institutions
	Residential
	Residential with small holdings
	Paddy lands & swamp
	Railway (Rly)
▲	Hospitals
•	Religious institutions

L Lake

Fishery Harbour
Port Installations
Fort
Beira
Rly
Maradana
Kollupitiya
Borella
Bambalapitiya
Kotte
Wellawatta
Nugegoda
Zoo
Dehiwala
Mt Lavinia
Ratmalana Airport (local)
Kelani Ganga

COLOMBO
URBAN LAND USE

homestead gardens become more common than strictly urban residences, and the population tends to be Sinhalese speaking, Buddhist and middle class.

Islamabad

Largely on account of its importance as Pakistan's military headquarters, with the appropriate ordinance factories, training establishments and regimental depots, Rawalpindi, after Independence, was the fourth largest city in the country with 237,000 inhabitants (including 95,000 – 40 per cent – refugees). It had become the regional centre for not only its own district and the others in the Potwar plateau, but also for the valleys leading north into the hills past Taxila to Abbotabad and Manshera, for the oilfields of the plateau, and for Azad (Free) Kashmir. Peshawar was too far from the strategically important areas to compete, and furthermore it was not in the Punjab. In 1959 under the military dictatorship of General (President) Ayub Khan, the capital was transferred from Karachi, thought to be exposed too much to exotic cultures and too removed from what was felt to be the heart of Pakistan national identity – Punjab, the Army and the North. Rawalpindi became the foster-parent for a new capital to be built at Islamabad to the plans of the Greek designer Doxiades. By the 1972 census Islamabad had reached a population of 77,318 and Rawalpindi 615,374. Figure 24.15 shows Rawalpindi and Islamabad as they are at present, the one an old district town onto which the British grafted large military installations which came completely to dominate its character and functions, the other brash and new and barely yet an independent city. The twice daily chariot race between the mini-buses that link the two cities, carrying commuting clerks from the relative cheapness of 'Pindi to work in the huge Secretariat buildings, are clear evidence of their interdependence. The plan for Islamabad envisages, somewhat cavalierly perhaps, the ultimate incorporation of Rawalpindi, almost as an ancient relic, into the spreading capital. The Punjab Provincial Government, still responsible for Rawalpindi, may have other ideas.

Rawalpindi evidences in its form the several characteristics of the dualism seen in other cities that gained favour under British rule. These have

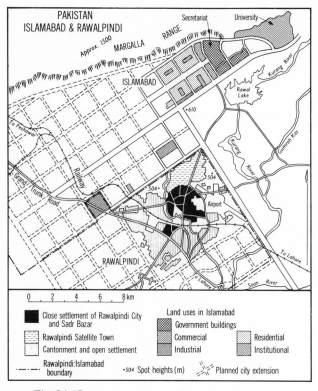

Fig. 24.15

been discussed above: the traditional city and exotic cantonment, unplanned bazars in the old city, tidy rectilinear regimentation for the civil lines and the military. Islamabad is exotic in a quite different sense. (One may comment somewhat ruefully in parentheses, that at least the British lived in the cantonments they designed: it is sometimes hard to imagine for whom the linear form of Islamabad was conceived as being the home.) In its grand design Islamabad will ultimately stretch almost 20 km along the foot of the splendid Margala Hills with the Government Secretariat and the University at the extreme northeastern corner. Foreign embassies have begun to cluster near the Secretariat and some five blocks of residential quarters, neatly graded according to the hierarchical status of their occupants in the civil service, represent the first completed in 38 planned for the areas north of the Murree Highway. A further 52 are projected for the areas south, excluding Rawalpindi and the airport left like an island, three parts surrounded. On the fourth side, in the southeast third of the master plan, a national park 15 km square is envisaged, in which Lake Rawal has already been completed to supply water to the city. In the linear scheme, commercial and industrial zones, and a continuous belt of open space parallel the residential blocks. The latter, each 0.6 km square, are already two deep, and will become four deep when the capital reaches its full extent to the southwest, and consequently the green belts will be enjoyed more by the passing commuter than by the residents 3, 4 or 6 kilometres distant. Islamabad is the linear city, conceived originally to cope with urban expansion in a highly mobile society, translated prematurely into a community who can barely afford the paisa for a bus ride and very few of whom have motorised transport of any kind. For the élites in the upper echelons of the Secretariat and for the foreign embassy staff, Islamabad may be a tolerably comfortable and increasingly green and beautiful city in which to live, but it is a far greater conceptual distance from the peasant ploughing his fields behind a pair of bullocks, than Canberra, Brasilia, New Delhi or other planned national capitals are from their respective citizens. In a way it epitomises a recurrent and significant problem for Pakistan: for whom is the country to be built?

110   Islamabad, Pakistan's national capital is dominated by the white blocks of the Secretariat which house government offices. The Margalla Range rises behind.

Index